THE CHEMISTRY AND
PHYSICS OF HIGH ENERGY
REACTIONS

THE CHEMISTRY AND PHYSICS OF HIGH ENERGY REACTIONS

ERNEST J. HENLEY

Associate Dean and Professor of
Chemical Engineering
University of Houston
Houston, Texas

EVERETT R. JOHNSON

Associate Dean of Engineering
University of Maryland
College Park, Maryland

Washington, D.C., University Press
6411 Chillum Place, N.W.
Washington, D.C.

Library of Congress Catalog Card Number 69-19832
Printed in the United States of America
McGregor & Werner, Inc.

Prefa

Until Lea's book "Actions of Radiation on Living Cells" appeared in 1947 no publication of a comprehensive systematization of the physical principles attending radiation effects on complex systems had been attempted. Prior to the effort expended in the Manhattan project, work had been confined largely to gases and to a more limited extent aqueous system.

Primarily as a result of the national effort in the peaceful uses of atomic energy, the field of radiation chemistry developed rapidly in the post-war years. ACS Symposiums were organized, the Radiation Research Society was founded (1951), and the first Faraday Discussion of Radiation Chemistry was published (1952). Electron generators and kilocurie cobalt 60 radiation sources were starting to become generally available. By 1953 a Gordon Conference on radiation chemistry was formed, and a common nomenclature as well as a few common notions were universally accepted.

It was our objective, as authors, to write a book based solely on the common notions and the trustworthy experiments which constitute the base upon which our present knowledge of radiation chemistry rests. In what may, at first, appear to be a sacrifice in continuity, we have inserted numerous example problems into the book. This was done in the hope that these examples would introduce an element of clarity, and will help emphasize the quantitative nature of the physical principles.

We have been extremely frugal in literature citations, a fact which we hope will not cost us unduly in friendships. Our objective, however, was to produce a coherent textbook, and not a well-indexed compedium of the literature. By producing a book which can be used as a text we hope to stimulate pedagological activity and to provide an easy entree for newcomers to the field of radiation chemistry.

Much of this book is based on unpublished work supported by the U. S. Atomic Energy Commission under contract AT(30-1)-3395. We are grateful for the technical guidance and support offered by J. N. Inglima, G. K. Ellis and other members of the Division of Technical Information of the Atomic Energy Commission. Thanks largely to their efforts we had the benefit of technical reviews by A. Charlesby, N. Barr, H. Schwarz, D. Richman, J. Silverman, V. Stannett, G. Odian, J. Wethington, T. Elleman, H. Carmichael, and a number of other specialists in radiation chemistry.

Ernest J. Henley
Everett Johnson

Contents

UNITS, RADIATIONS, RADIOACTIVITY, AND GENERAL NOMENCLATURE

1-1 BASIC UNITS

Work in this text will be based on the centimeter-gram-second (CGS) system* of measurements. Thus, electrical measurements will be in terms of electrostatic (esu) or electromagnetic (emu) units. The electrostatic force between two charges a distance ℓ apart is:

$$F = \frac{e_1 e_2}{\ell^2 K} \tag{1-1}$$

or for two like charges:

$$F = \frac{e^2}{\ell^2 K} \tag{1-2}$$

where the value of K depends on the medium; by definition the value of K is unity in a vacuum. The dimensions of force in the CGS system are:

$$F = m\,\ell\,t^{-2} \tag{1-3}$$

The dimensions of charge therefore are:

$$\frac{e^2}{\ell^2 K} = m\,\ell\,t^{-2}$$

$$e = m^{1/2}\ell^{3/2}t^{-1} \tag{1-4}$$

---

*The units recommended by the International Union of Pure and Applied Chemistry (IUPAC) are known as the International System of Units; however, this system has not been universally adopted. The CGS system, used in most of the current literature, will be used in this text.

Radiation chemists commonly employ the unit, electron volt (ev), which is the energy acquired by an electron with unit charge (4.803×10^{-10} esu) moving under 1 volt potential (1/300 esu). The electron volt is $4.803 \times 10^{-10}/299$, or 1.602×10^{-12} erg. Another common unit is the volt-coulomb or Joule, which is the work done by a flow of 1 coulomb of charge under 1 volt potential. This is equal to 10^7 ergs. Multiplying 1.602×10^{-12} erg by 6.02257×10^{23} gives 9.6487×10^{11} erg or 9.6487×10^4 Joules of kinetic energy for one gram atom of electrons after acceleration through one volt.

The unit of power is the watt which is one Joule/second. This is a unit frequently used when expressing the rate of energy absorption. Other basic units associated with heat and power are the calorie, kilocalorie, Btu, watt, and kilowatt. The relationships between these units is summarized in Table 1-1.

1-2 QUANTUM AND MASS-ENERGY RELATIONS

Calculations of energy based on the quantum theory involve the frequency of electromagnetic radiation, a defined quality represented by the Greek letter ν.

$$\nu = \frac{\text{speed of light, cm/sec}}{\text{wavelength, cm}} = \frac{c}{\lambda} \qquad (1\text{-}5)$$

A more commonly employed term is the wave number, the reciprocal of the wavelength in centimeters:

$$\lambda^{-1} = \text{frequency/speed of light} = \text{cm}^{-1}$$

Quantum theory introduces a proportionality between frequency and energy,

$$E = h\nu \qquad (1\text{-}6)$$

where h is Planck's constant, a fundamental constant of nature. The energy of the radiation may be calculated if its wavelength is known, and conversely, the wavelength may be determined if the energy is known. All electromagnetic radiation has associated with it quanta, the energy of which is given by Eq. (1-6).

Photons (electromagnetic radiation) are propagated through space as waves and therefore have associated with them a frequency of vibration, a velocity of propagation, and a wavelength. Photons also have momentum and are capable of transferring momentum; this capability can only be detected readily with high energy photons.

The kinetic energy of a particle (of relatively low velocity), such as a proton or an electron, is obtained from classical

Table 1-1. CONVERSION FACTORS FOR COMMON UNITS

	joule/ g-mole	cal/g-mole	cm^3/atom/ g-mole	kw-hr/ g-mole	Btu/lb mole	cm^{-1}/ molecule	ev/molecule
1 joule/g-mole =	1	2.390057×10^{-1}	9.86923	2.77778×10^{-7}	0.429923	8.35940×10^{-2}	1.036409×10^{-5}
1 cal/g-mole =	4.18400	1	41.2929	1.162222×10^{-6}	1.798796	3.49757×10^{-1}	4.33634×10^{-5}
1 cm^3/atom/g-mole =	0.1013250	2.42173×10^{-2}	1	2.81458×10^{-8}	4.35619×10^{-2}	8.47016×10^{-3}	1.050141×10^{-6}
1 kw-hr/g-mole =	3,600,000	860,421	3.55292×10^{7}	1	1,547,721	300,938	37.3107
1 Btu/lb mole =	2.32600	5.55927×10^{-1}	22.9558	6.46111×10^{-7}	1	1.944396×10^{-1}	2.41069×10^{-5}
1 cm^{-1}/molecule -	11.96258	2.85912	118.0614	3.32294×10^{-6}	5.14299	1	1.239812×10^{-4}
1 ev/molecule =	96,487.0	23060.9	952,252	2.68019	41482.0	8065.73	1

considerations and is $1/2\, m\overline{V}^2$. However, if the particle velocity approaches that of light, the mass of the particle changes, according to relativity theory, to

$$m = \frac{m_o}{[1 - (\overline{V}^2/c^2)]^{1/2}} \tag{1-7}$$

where m_o is the rest mass of the particle and $\overline{V}$ is velocity. Relativity theory also introduces a relation between mass and energy,

$$E = mc^2 \tag{1-8}$$

Substituting Eq. (1-7) into Eq. (1-8), the total energy of a mass m moving with a velocity $\overline{V}$ is

$$E_T = \frac{m_o c^2}{[1 - (\overline{V}^2/c^2)]^{1/2}} \tag{1-9}$$

For a particle such as an electron or proton, it is often necessary to have a knowledge of its velocity because the rate of energy deposition in a medium is directly related to the particle's velocity and its charge.

EXAMPLE 1-1: Calculate the velocity of a 25 Mev proton. What is the energy of an electron that has this velocity?

SOLUTION: When the energy equivalent of the rest mass of the particle is considerably greater than the energy of the particle, nonrelativistic mechanics applies. The rest mass energy, in electron volts, for any particle is

$$E = m_o c^2 = \frac{\text{atom-wt}}{\text{Avogadro's number}} \times c^2 \times \frac{1}{1.602 \times 10^{-12} \frac{\text{erg}}{\text{ev}}}$$

For the proton,

$$E = \frac{1.008\, g}{g\text{-atom}} \times \frac{1}{6.023 \times 10^{23} \frac{\text{atoms}}{g\text{-atom}}} \times 2.99 \times 10^{10} \frac{\text{cm}}{\text{sec}}^2 \times \frac{1}{1.602 \times 10^{-12} \frac{\text{erg}}{\text{ev}}}$$

$$E = 1\,008\, g \times \frac{\text{cm}^2}{\text{sec}^2} \times 931 \times 10^6 \frac{\text{ev}}{\text{erg}}$$

$$E \cong 931 \times 10^6\ \text{ev}$$

Since this is far in excess of the given energy of the particle, nonrelativistic mechanics applies, and

$$E = \frac{1}{2} m \overline{V}^2$$

$$25 \times 10^6 \text{ ev} = \frac{1}{2} m_p \overline{V}^2$$

$$\overline{V}^2 = 50 \times 10^6 \text{ ev} \times 1.6 \times 10^{-12} \frac{\text{ergs}}{\text{ev}} \times \frac{1}{1.67 \times 10^{-24} \text{ g}}$$

The dimensions of the erg in the CGS system are ml^2t^{-2}, and the velocity of a 25 Mev proton is, in centimeters per second,

$$\overline{V} = \sqrt{50 \times 10^{18} \frac{\text{cm}^2}{\text{sec}^2}} \cong 7 \times 10^9 \frac{\text{cm}}{\text{sec}}$$

The energy of an electron with the same velocity is

$$E = \frac{1}{2} m_e \overline{V}^2 = \frac{1}{2} \times 9.11 \times 10^{-28} \text{ g} \times \left(7 \times 10^9 \frac{\text{cm}}{\text{sec}}\right)^2$$

$$E = 225 \times 10^{-10} \text{ erg} \times \frac{\text{ev}}{1.6 \times 10^{-12} \text{ erg}}$$

$$E \cong 14,000 \text{ ev}$$

1-3 RADIOLOGICAL UNITS

Many units have been devised to characterize the absorption of ionizing radiation. In recent years, however, there has been a general acceptance of the recommendations of the International Commission on Radiological Units and Measurements (ICRU). The ICRU recommends that the use of certain units be restricted as follows:

The special unit of the absorbed dose is the rad.

$$1 \text{ rad} = 100 \text{ ergs/g} = \frac{1}{100} \text{ joules/kg}$$

or

$$1 \text{ rad} = \frac{100 \text{ ergs}}{g} \times \frac{\text{ev}}{1.602 \times 10^{-12} \text{ ergs}}$$

$$= 6.24 \times 10^{13} \frac{\text{ev}}{g} \tag{1-10}$$

The absorbed dose rate is the quotient of the rad divided by a unit of time, e.g. rad/day, rad/sec, etc. The absorbed dose is generally sought by the chemist or engineer since it is a direct measure of the energy transferred to the material under study. This dose is determined by the composition of the absorbing material and radiation spectrum.

The special unit of exposure dose is the roentgen (r). Exposure dose may be related to the absorbed dose under special conditions. One roentgen of exposure occurs when the sum of electrical charges on all the ions of one sign produced in air by all the electrons liberated by photons and completely stopped in a volume element of air whose mass is 0.001293 g is equal to 1 esu of charge.

$$1\,r \;=\; 2.58 \times 10^{-4} \text{ coulombs/kg} \qquad\qquad (1\text{-}11)$$

This is equivalent to the older definition in which 1 r is equal to 1 esu of charge per 1 cubic centimeter of dry air at standard temperature and pressure (STP). One cubic centimeter of dry air weighs 0.001293 g. The roentgen is defined only on the basis that the source is electromagnetic radiation (photons). The earlier definition limited the source to X- or gamma radiation; however, the latest ICRU recommendation is to include all photons, except bremsstrahlung arising from secondary electrons.

If the energy required to form an ion pair, W, is known and if the mass-energy absorption coefficients for air and the material in question are known, then the absorbed dose may be determined. These are the special conditions referred to previously.

EXAMPLE 1-2: Calculate the absorbed dose in air in rads assuming an exposure dose of 1 r.

SOLUTION:

$$1r = \frac{esu}{0.001293\ g} \times 2.082 \times 10^9\ \frac{electrons}{esu} \times W\ \frac{ev}{ion\ (or\ electron)} \times 1.602 \times 10^{-12}\ \frac{ergs}{ev} \times \frac{rad}{100\ ergs/g}$$

where W is the energy required to form an ion pair in air. From this

$$1\,r = 0.0258\ W \text{ rad}$$

If $W = 33.73$ is used, then 1 r = 0.869 rad (in air) per unit of time.

The roentgen equivalent man, rem, is equal to the dose in rads multiplied by modifying factors, the most important of which is the quality factor (qf). The quality factor is the ratio of absorbed doses required for different radiations to produce the same biological effect. (The quality factor is designated as *relative biological effectiveness*, abbreviated RBE.)

The term *rep*, roentgen equivalent physical, is no longer in use. This is the absorbed dose in ergs deposited in tissue by the absorption of 1 *r*.

The basic differences between the units of exposure and absorbed dose are not often appreciated. As will be seen in Chap. 2, it is not always a simple matter to calculate absorbed dose from the exposure.

1-4 RADIOACTIVITY

Radioactivity occurs as a result of the disintegration of an unstable nucleus. The unit of radioactivity is the curie, which is 3.7×10 disintegrations per second. Radioactive sources are described in terms of specific activity or unit concentration.

For any nucleus there is a certain proton-neutron ratio range beyond which the nucleus is unstable. The unstable nuclide may undergo one or more types of decay to attain stability.

There are only a few naturally occurring nuclides that undergo radioactive decay. These decaying nuclides emit either alpha or beta particles, both of which may be accompanied by gamma emission. Artificially produced radioactive nuclides emit positrons and gamma radiation, whereas such nuclear reactions as fission,(γ, n), (α, n), and (n, p) produce protons and neutrons.

The earliest known nuclear emanation is the alpha particle, which is a doubly charged helium atom. The alpha particles emitted by a particular nuclide may be monoenergetic or have a small number of discrete energies. A nuclide that emits alpha particles with different energies will also emit gamma rays whose energies can, as a rule, be correlated with the energy differences of the emitted alpha particles.

Gamma rays are high energy electromagnetic radiation emitted by nuclei. Gamma emission is a mechanism that an excited nucleus may use to return to the ground state. The energy range of gamma rays is from about 40 kev to about 4 Mev.

Another source of electromagnetic radiation is *bremsstrahlung*, which is any electromagnetic radiation produced by a charged particle that is accelerated or decelerated in an external coulomb field or a screened coulomb field. Bremsstrahlung, however, is usually thought of as the continuous energetic photon spectra, referred to as X-rays, produced when high energy electrons are decelerated in the coulomb field of nuclei.

When a metal target, such as gold, is bombarded by high energy electrons, X-rays are produced whose maximum energy is equal to that of the electron source. The X-ray spectrum is continuous, extending from the electron energy to near zero. The term 250 *kv-peak* (*kvp*) *X-rays* means that the source of electrons used to make the X-rays was 250 kv. The bulk of the photon energies emitted from an X-ray tube is very much lower than that of the energies of the bombarding electrons. Low energy X-rays are referred to as "soft" X-rays, and the high energy X-rays, as "hard."

It must not be inferred that all energy of a fast electron is converted to bremsstrahlung. Some of the energy is consumed to produce the characteristic X-ray spectrum of the target material, and some is consumed by other processes. The efficiency of the conversion of kinetic energy to bremsstrahlung depends on the energy of the electron and increases with increasing electron energy and the atomic number of the target.

Beta particles are electrons and, in general, are emitted by nuclei with neutron-proton ratios greater than the ratio that corresponds to the stability region. Beta emission occurs with a continuous energy distribution extending from zero up to the maximum energy. Accompanying beta emission is a second particle, the neutrino, which has no charge and a mass less than 0.05 of the electron mass. The cross section, or probability, for neutrino reactions is so small, however, that they are of no concern in radiation chemistry.

Positrons are positively charged particles with the same mass as electrons and are considered to be positively charged beta particles. Those nuclei with neutron-proton ratios less than the ratio required for stability decay by positron emission or by K capture. K capture occurs when the nucleus captures an electron from the K shell. An electron from the L or M shells could be captured; however, since K electrons are, on the average, closest to the nucleus, capture occurs with greater probability from this level than from the others.

K electron capture is accompanied by X-ray emission that occurs as a result of filling the electron vacancy by electron transitions from the outer orbits. The entire X-ray spectrum is observed; however, the K lines are the most prominent. Emission of Auger electrons often accompanies K capture. Auger electrons are emitted when an X-ray ejects an electron from one of the orbits, for example, L shell. The ejected electron would have an energy equal to the difference of the energy of the X-ray and the binding energy of the electron. Auger electrons are also formed by gamma rays emitted by excited nuclei.

Examples of these various processes are:

    a. Alpha emission

$$^{238}_{92}U \longrightarrow {}^{4}_{2}He + {}^{234}_{90}Th \tag{1-12}$$

    b. Beta emission

$$^{234}_{90}Th \longrightarrow e^{-} + {}^{234}_{91}Pa \tag{1-13}$$

    c. Positron emission

$$^{13}_{7}N \longrightarrow e^{+} + {}^{13}_{6}C \tag{1-14}$$

    d. K capture

$$^{64}_{29}Cu + e^{-} \longrightarrow {}^{64}_{28}Ni + (0.571 \text{ Mev X-ray}) \tag{1-15}$$

1-5 NUCLEAR REACTIONS

When a particular nuclide undergoes a nuclear reaction, the reaction, like a chemical reaction, is always accompanied by an absorption or emission of energy. The notation employed for nuclear reactions is

$$^{14}_{7}N + {}^{4}_{2}He \longrightarrow {}^{17}_{8}O + {}^{1}_{1}H + Q \tag{1-16}$$

where Q is the energy of the reaction. The Q for the reaction is obtained by determining the difference in the masses of the reactants and products. The energy is determined by substitution of the mass difference into Eq. (1-16).

The absorption or emission of a nuclear particle imparts kinetic energy to the nucleus. The amount of this energy varies with the particle and the nature of the nuclear reaction. Very often this energy is sufficient to break a chemical bond. The recoil atoms so produced are called "hot" atoms. These are atoms that possess considerable excess kinetic energy. For example, exposure of CH_3I to slow neutrons produces hot ^{128}I atoms, which can undergo reaction with other CH_3I molecules to produce HI and CH_2I_2.

A special case of a hot-atom reaction is the Szilard-Chalmers reaction, which occurs when an atom, as a result of thermal-neutron capture, undergoes the (n, γ) reaction and recoils with sufficient energy to break a chemical bond.

1-6 RADIOACTIVE DECAY

The decay of a radioactive nuclide is often complex. However, the mode of decay, the emanations, and the half-lives for most nuclides have been determined, and this information may be obtained by referring to a chart of the nuclides.[1,2] The decay schemes for ^{60}Co and ^{137}Cs are shown in Fig. 1.

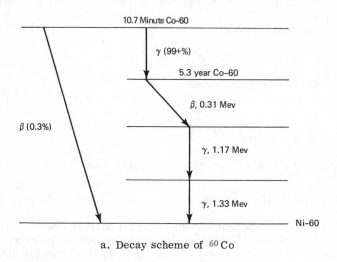

a. Decay scheme of ^{60}Co

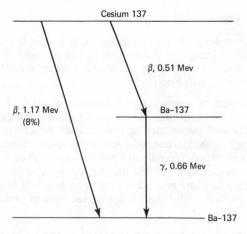

b. Decay scheme of ^{137}Cs

Fig. 1-1. Decay schemes.

Exposure of almost any material to neutron radiation will induce radioactivity. All elements undergo the nuclear reaction called activation reaction, which is an (n, γ) reaction of thermal neutrons with the nucleus. Nuclei may also capture fast neutrons. The cross sections for the two processes usually differ considerably.

The cross section is a measure of the probability for a process to occur and has the dimensions of an area. The unit for nuclear cross sections is the barn, which is equal to 10^{-24} cm^2. The cross section for fast neutron reactions is usually less than 10^{-24} cm^2; however, for slow-neutron reactions it may be as high as 10^5 or 10^6 barns. Cross sections are usually given for particular processes. For example, a total cross section may be given for the absorption of 10 Mev neutrons or a cross section may be given for the capture of slow neutrons by a particular nuclide. The total cross section for a neutron reaction refers to attenuation of a beam of neutrons by all processes, which include absorption and scattering. If the intensity of a beam of neutrons is attenuated in passing through a target material, the attenuation is given by

$$-dn = nN\sigma dx \qquad (1\text{-}17)$$

where $-dn$ = attenuation in the thickness
  n = number of incident particles
  N = number of target nuclei per cubic centimeter
  σ = cross section, which in this case is the total cross section

The number of incident particles is the flux (flux density), which is the number of particles or photons entering a sphere of unit cross-sectional area at that point in unit time. The units of flux are particles per square centimeter per second. The intensity of radiation is the energy entering a small sphere at the point of interest per unit time per unit cross-sectional area of the sphere. Units of intensity are ergs per square centimeter-second or watts per square centimeter.

From a statistical study of radioactive decay, it has been determined that the average rate of radioactive decay is proportional to the number of radioactive atoms, N, present,

$$-\frac{dN}{dt} = \lambda N \qquad (1\text{-}18)$$

where λ is the decay constant analogous to the first-order rate constant.

Radioisotopes are conveniently characterized by their half-lives, the time required for one half of the radioactive atoms originally present to decay. Integration of Eq. (1-18) between the limits $t = 0$, $N = N_o$ and $t = t_{1/2}$, $N = 1/2N_o$ gives

$$ln\ 2 = \lambda t_{1/2} \tag{1-19}$$

$$t_{1/2} = \frac{0.693}{\lambda}$$

It frequently happens that one isotope decays to another isotope, one which is also unstable and which, in turn, decays to produce an unstable or stable nuclide. For multiple decay of one isotope N_1, which decays to produce another unstable nuclide N_2, which then decays to stable nuclide N_3, the amount of N_2 present at any time is found by integrating Eq. (1-20).

$$\frac{dN_2}{dt} = \lambda_1 N_1 - \lambda_2 N_2 \tag{1-20}$$

where $\lambda_1 N_1$ is the rate of formation of N_2 and $\lambda_2 N_2$ is the rate of decay of N_2. Substituting $N_{o1}e^{-\lambda_1 t}$ for N_1 and integrating between the limits $N_2 = 0$ when $t = 0$ and $N_2 = N_2$ at $t = t$ in Eq. (1-20), we obtain

$$N_2 = \frac{1}{\lambda_2 - \lambda_1}\ N_{o1}\ \left(e^{-\lambda_1 t} - e^{-\lambda_2 t}\right) \tag{1-21}$$

The relative amounts of the two radioactive nuclides will depend upon their relative half lives.

For $\lambda_2 \gg \lambda_1$ at large t, Eq. (1-21) reduces to

$$N_2 = \frac{\lambda_1}{\lambda_2}\ N_o 1 e^{-\lambda_1 t} \tag{1-22}$$

as $\quad t \longrightarrow \infty$

$$N_2\ \lambda_2 = N_1\ \lambda_1 \tag{1-23}$$

This is the case of *secular equilibrium*. When secular equilibrium is attained, the rate of decay of the parent and the daughter are the same. This is frequently of importance in radiation chemistry. For example, a curie of pure ^{90}Sr which decays by beta emission with a half life of 28 years to ^{90}Y, also a beta emitter but with a half life of only 2-1/2 days, will also contain in a time equal to four half lives of ^{90}Y about 0.94 curies of ^{90}Y.

From a knowledge of the composition and cross sections, the radioactive nuclides that will be formed when a sample is exposed to a neutron flux may be anticipated, and, if the system is not too complex, the ultimate concentrations may be determined. The concentration of a particular radioactive nuclide may be determined from its cross section, decay constant, and neutron flux density and concentration. The rate of formation is given by the product of the cross section σ, the neutron flux density ϕ, and the concentration N. The rate of decay is given by Eq. (1-18). The net rate of formation is

$$\frac{dN}{dt} = \sigma\phi N_o - \lambda N = R - \lambda N \qquad (1\text{-}24)$$

For a polyatomic substance, Eq. (1-24) would be used to calculate the net activity for each nuclide. If the active nuclide decays to another radioactive nuclide, then Eq. (1-20) would have to be used also.

EXAMPLE 1-3: Calculate the net activity of a sample of cobalt that is exposed to a slow neutron flux of 10^{12} neutrons per cm^2 for a period of six months. The cross section of ^{59}Co is 21.7 barns, and the half life of ^{60}Co is 5.26 years.

SOLUTION:*

$$\frac{dN}{dt} = \sigma\phi N_o - \lambda N$$

Integrating between $t = 0$, $N = 0$ and $t = t$, $N = N$

$$\int_{N=0}^{N=N} \frac{dN}{R - \lambda N} = \int_{t=0}^{t=t} dt$$

$$t = -\frac{1}{\lambda} \ln \frac{R - \lambda N}{R}$$

Solving for N

$$N = \frac{\sigma\phi N_o}{\lambda}(1 - e^{-\lambda t}) = 21.7 \times 10^{-24}\, cm^2 \times \frac{10^{12}}{cm^2\text{-}sec} \times \frac{8.9\, g}{cm^3} \times \frac{1\, g\text{-}mol}{59\, g} \times \frac{6.02 \times 10^{23}\, molecules}{g\text{-}mol}(1 - e^{-0.693t/5.26})$$

$$N = 8.82 \times 10^{19}\, atoms/cm^3$$

---

*The formation of the 10 min isomer is neglected since more than 99% undergoes an isomeric transition to the 5.26 year isomer.

The number of curies corresponding to this number of ^{60}Co atoms per cubic centimeter is obtained as follows:

$$\text{Rate of disintegration} = -\frac{dN}{dt} = \lambda N$$

Using Eq. (1-19) to obtain λ

$$\lambda = \frac{0.693}{5.26 \text{ (years)} \times 365 \times 24 \times 3600} = \frac{4.2 \times 10^{-9}}{\text{sec}}$$

$$-\frac{dN}{dt} = \frac{4.2 \times 10^{-9}}{\text{sec}} \times 8.82 \times 10^{19} \frac{\text{atoms}}{\text{cm}^3} \times \frac{1 \text{ cm}^3}{9 g}$$

$$= 4.11 \times 10^{10} \frac{\text{atoms}}{\text{sec}}$$

The number of curies is

$$\frac{4.11 \times 10^{10}}{3.7 \times 10^{10}} \cong 1.10 \frac{\text{curies}}{g} \times \text{number of grams}$$

The value 1.10 curies per gram is the specific activity.

PROBLEMS

1-1 Using the value of the charge on an electron, show that 1 ev = 1.6×10^{-12} erg.

1-2 What are the average wavelengths of the 1.33 and 1.17 Mev gamma photons emitted by ^{60}Co?

1-3 A proton has a kinetic energy of 50 Mev. What is the velocity?

1-4 An electron is traveling at a velocity of 0.95 c. Calculate its kinetic energy with and without relativity corrections.

1-5 The half life of ^{60}Co is 5.26 years. What is its decay constant? If there were a 10,000 curie source on January 1, 1965, how many curies would there be today? What is the fractional decay of ^{60}Co per month?

1-6 The activity level of an isotope having a half life of 2 min is established by counting over an interval of 5 min. By what factor must the average count rate be multiplied to obtain the initial activity?

1-7 A block of silver 3 cm thick with a density of 2.7 g/cm^3 placed in a neutron beam reduces the neutron count by a factor of 50. What is the total cross section of silver for the neutrons?

1-8 A gold foil 0.02 cm thick and 1 cm^2 in cross section is exposed to a neutron flux of 10^{12} neutrons/cm^2/sec. The gold has a density of 19.3 g/cm^3 and a thermal neutron absorption cross section of 98.7 barns. What is the total number of curies of the radioactive ^{198}Au available in 1 hr, 1 day, 1 week, and 1 year? The half life of ^{198}Au is 2.69 days.

REFERENCES

1. D. J. Hughes and R. B. Schwartz, Neutron Cross Sections, *USAEC Report*, BNL-325 (2nd ed.), Brookhaven National Laboratory, July 1, 1958.

2. D. T. Goldman and J. Roesser, Chart of the Nuclides, 9th edition, General Electric Co., Schenectady, N.Y.

2

INTERACTION OF
RADIATION WITH MATTER

The radiations of principal concern to radiation chemists are charged particles (electrons, protons, alpha particles, fission fragments, etc.), photons (X-rays and gamma rays), and neutrons. Each of these interacts with matter in a different manner. For example, charged particles have a definite maximum range in air, but neutrons and electromagnetic radiation do not. The various interactions are discussed in this chapter.

2-1 CHARGED PARTICLES

Particles interact with matter either by scattering or by nuclear capture. Scattering is usually thought of as the interaction between a particle (or particles) and matter in which the particle maintains its identity. There are basically two types of scattering, elastic and inelastic. In elastic scattering the projectile particle does not lose energy regardless of the scattering angle. In inelastic scattering* the projectile particle loses energy. There are primarily two processes to be considered in inelastic scattering: (1) collisions resulting in atomic displacement and (2) collisions leading primarily to excitation and ionization.

Under certain conditions, where scattering is through a large angle, the particle is decelerated and a quantum of electromagnetic radiation, known as bremsstrahlung, emitted. Although all charged particles can lose energy by bremsstrahlung emission and inelastic collision, the relative importance of these energy loss processes is different for electrons than for heavy charged particles (protons, alpha particles, deuterons, etc.). Bremsstrahlung emission as an energy loss process is important for electron beams in the energy range of interest to radiation chemists; it becomes important for alpha particles only when the alpha-particle energies are in the billion electron volt range.

The foregoing interactions are characteristic not only of the incident particles but also of the high energy electrons ejected in

---

*Strictly speaking, all scattering by charged particles is inelastic except that between free particles (excluding bremsstrahlung emission).

ionization processes.   Such high energy secondary electrons are
called delta rays.

2-1.1 Heavy Charged Particles

2-1.1a *Energy Loss in Collisions with Bound Electrons.* A charged
particle moving through matter loses energy by electromagnetic
interaction with the electrons composing the material, i.e. bound
electrons. The interaction produces excitation and ionization, the
energy for these processes being taken from the kinetic energy of
the incident particle. The total distance traveled by a charged
particle before its kinetic energy is reduced to zero is known as
the *range* of the particle.

An approximate expression for the rate of energy loss per unit
path ($-dE/dx$) is derived* in the following paragraphs. Figure 2-1
is a schematic diagram of the interaction of a charged particle of
mass M, charge Ze (where Z is atomic number and e is the ele-
mentary electric charge), and velocity $\bar{V}$ with an electron at rest
of mass m_o at a distance r from the path of the incident particle.

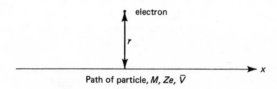

Fig. 2-1. Schematic diagram of the interaction
of a charged particle of mass M , charge Ze ,
and velocity $\bar{V}$ with an electron at rest of mass
m_o at a distance r from the path of the incident
particle. The particle is assumed to spend a
time ($2r/\bar{V}$) in the field of the electron.

It is assumed that the electron is free and is not displaced during the collision; thus the force acting on the electron can be calculated at its initial location.

---

*This is essentially the derivation given by Bohr, as reported in "Nuclear
Physics, A Course Given by Enrico Fermi at the University of Chicago," by
J. Orear, A. W. Rosenfeld, and R. A. Schulter (comp.), p. 27, The University
of Chicago Press, Chicago, 1950.

The electrostatic force acting on the electron, by Coulomb's law, is

$$F = \frac{Ze^2}{r^2} \tag{2-1}$$

The momentum, p, transferred to the electron perpendicular to the path of the particle is

$$p = \text{(electrostatic force)} \times \text{(duration of collision)}$$

$$= \left(\frac{Ze^2}{r^2}\right)\left(\frac{2r}{\overline{V}}\right) \tag{2-2}$$

The energy acquired by the electron is

$$\frac{p^2}{2m_o} = \frac{2Z^2e^4}{m_o \overline{V}^2 r^2} \tag{2-3}$$

Conversely, each collision the particle undergoes results in a *loss of energy* equivalent to that stated by Eq. (2-3). Therefore the energy lost per unit path length of the particle can be calculated by determining the number of collisions per unit path. To do this, one must first determine the probability of collision.

The probability of a collision occurring between the distance r and $r + dr$ is proportional to the area available for collision at radius r, $2\pi r\, dr$. This area represents a fraction of the total area, A,

$$A = \pi r^2 \tag{2-4}$$

The probability of a collision is simply

$$\frac{2\pi r\, dr}{\pi r^2} = \frac{2r\, dr}{r^2} \tag{2-5}$$

If N is the number of electrons per cubic centimeter, then the number of collisions per unit path length is the number of electrons per unit path of the particle, $\pi r^2 N\, dx$, times the probability of a collision

$$\text{Number of collisions} = (\pi r^2 N\, dx)\left(\frac{2r\, dr}{r^2}\right)$$

$$= 2\pi N r\, dr(dx) \tag{2-6}$$

The energy lost per unit path length to the electrons is obtained by multiplying Eq. (2-3) by Eq. (2-6).

$$- \frac{dE}{dx} = \frac{4\pi Z^2 e^4 N}{m_o \overline{V}^2} \frac{dr}{r} \tag{2-7}$$

The integration is carried out between the limits r_{max} and r_{min}, the maximum and minimum distances for collision:

$$- \frac{dE}{dx} = \frac{4\pi Z^2 e^4 N}{m_o \overline{V}^2} \ln \frac{r_{max}}{r_{min}} \tag{2-8}$$

Thus Eq. (2-8) gives the general expression for the energy loss of a charged particle. Bohr developed expressions for r_{max} and r_{min}; however, this was done using classical considerations with the concept of quantized energy levels for the atoms. The result of these considerations was unsatisfactory since the calculation of r_{max} and r_{min} entails arguments involving the wave properties of matter.

The minimum collision distance r_{min} is half the de Broglie wavelength, $\lambda = h/2m_o \overline{V} = r_{min}$. The maximum collision distance is proportional to the speed of the incident particle $\overline{V}$ and inversely proportional to the excitation potential I, the proportionality factor being Plank's constant, h; $r_{max} = h\overline{V}/I$. Thus

$$\frac{r_{max}}{r_{min}} = \frac{(h\overline{V}/I)}{(h/2m_o \overline{V})} = \frac{2m_o \overline{V}^2}{I} \tag{2-9}$$

Substitution of Eq. (2-9) into Eq. (2-8) gives

$$- \frac{dE}{dx} = \frac{4\pi Z^2 e^4 N}{m_o \overline{V}^2} \ln \frac{2m_o \overline{V}^2}{I} \tag{2-10}$$

The excitation potential, I, is the geometric mean of all the excitation and ionization potentials of the atom or molecule in question.

The exact quantum mechanical treatment of Bethe and Ashkin[1], which takes into account relativistic effects, leads to an expression analogous to Eq. (2-10)

$$- \frac{dE}{dx} = \frac{4\pi Z^2 e^4 N}{m_o \overline{V}^2} \left[\ln \frac{2m_o \overline{V}^2}{I(1 - \beta^2)} - \beta^2 \right] \tag{2-11}$$

where $\beta = \overline{V}/c$. The factor 2 in the numerator of the logarithmic term applies to heavy particles (alpha particles). It is replaced by unity for electrons (see Sec. 2-1.2).

Equation (2-10) predicts the major features of Fig. 2-2. We note that dE/dx (in terms of ion pairs) increases as $\overline{V}$ decreases.

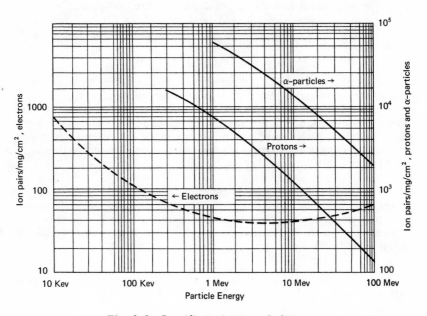

Fig. 2-2. Specific ionization of electrons, protons, and alpha particles in air.

All factors in Eqs. (2-10) and (2-11) can be readily established except I, the excitation potential. In general, I is determined experimentally: the amount of energy which is lost in a given absorber is measured and I is chosen to make the calculated loss equal the measured loss. Table 2-1 lists values of I for various materials.

Several approximations regarding energy loss can be made on the basis of Eqs. (2-10) and (2-11). For instance, Z and $\overline{V}$ are the only terms that depend on the incident particle. Two particles of equal charge will thus have energy losses inversely proportional to the square of their velocities, and two different particles traveling

Table 2-1.* SELECTED VALUES OF
MEAN EXCITATION POTENTIALS I

Substance	I
Hydrogen (liquid)	20.7
Hydrogen (gas)	14.8
Lithium	38
Beryllium	67
Carbon (graphite)	78.4
Nitrogen (liquid)	85.1
Air	85
Oxygen (liquid)	98.3
Aluminum	164
Chlorine	170
Iron	264
Copper	306
Silver	462
Tin	517
Tungsten	750
Lead	812
Uranium	945

*National Bur. of Standards Handbook
85, March 31, 1964, "Physical Aspects
of Irradiation."

at the same velocity will have ranges inversely proportional to
their charges. Furthermore, since the logarithmic term is only a
weak function of I and $\overline{V}$, we may write as an approximate expression for the rate of energy loss

$$ - \frac{dE}{dx} = \frac{4\pi Z^2 e^4 N}{m_o \overline{V}^2} \tag{2-12} $$

EXAMPLE 2-1: The mean energy-loss rate of 3 Mev protons in air
   is 12.5×10^{-2} Mev/cm. What is the approximate energy-loss
   rate of 3 Mev alpha particles in air?

SOLUTION: Using the subscript 1 for protons and 2 for alphas,
   according to Eq. (2-12),

$$ - \frac{dE_1/dx_1}{dE_2/dx_2} = \frac{4\pi Z_{11}^2 e^4 N_1}{m_o \overline{V}_1^2} \frac{m_o \overline{V}_2^2}{4\pi Z_{12}^2 e^4 N_2} = \frac{Z_{11}^2 N_1 \overline{V}_2^2}{Z_{12}^2 N_2 \overline{V}_1^2} $$

where $Z_{11} = 1$ and $Z_{12} = 2$.

It is now necessary to obtain the relative velocity $\bar{V}_2^2 / \bar{V}_1^2$. Since $E = m\bar{V}^2$, $E_1 = 3$ Mev, $E_2 = 3$ Mev, $m_1 = 1$, and $m_2 = 4$,

$$E_1 = 3 = 1\bar{V}_1^2$$

$$\bar{V}_1^2 = 3$$

$$E_2 = 3 = 4\bar{V}_2^2$$

$$\bar{V}_1^2 = 0.75$$

Thus

$$-dE_2/dx_2 = (12.5 \times 10^{-2})\ \frac{(4)(3)}{(1)(0.75)} = 2\ \text{Mev/cm}$$

2-1.1b *Range of Charged Particles.* The range of a particle, R, is defined as

$$R = \int_o^{E_o} \frac{dE}{-dE/dx} \tag{2-13}$$

where E_o is the initial energy of the particle. The integration is carried out along the entire path.

If in Eq. (2-13) the expression resulting from the differentiation of $E = m\bar{V}^2/2$, i.e. $m\bar{V}d\bar{V}$, is substituted for dE and if Eq. (2-10) is substituted for $-dE/dx$, the range becomes

$$R = \frac{m\,m_o}{4\pi Z^2 e^4 N} \int_{V_o}^o \frac{\bar{V}^3 d\bar{V}}{ln\,(2m_o\bar{V}^2/I)} \tag{2-14}$$

Equation (2-14) is difficult to use in this form. It is most useful, however, for obtaining the range of a particle by comparison with the known range of another particle of the same velocity traversing the same media. For example, if the different particles are designated by the subscripts 1 and 2 (noting that the integral is the same for two particles of the same velocity), the ratio is simply

$$\frac{R_1}{R_2} = \frac{m_1}{m_2}\,\frac{Z_{12}^2}{Z_{11}^2} \tag{2-15}$$

and the unknown range can be easily determined. This expression is useful for energies greater than about 0.2 Mev.

To use Eq. (2-15), it is necessary to know the range of a reference particle in a reference material. The most common reference particles are alpha particles, and the most common reference material is air. Figure 2-3 for example gives the range of alpha particles in air as a function of energy.[2]

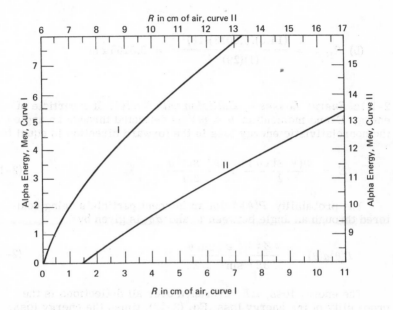

Fig. 2-3. Range vs. energy for alpha particles
in dry air (at 15°C, 760 mm Hg).

For different absorbing media the range becomes a function of the material properties. Here, an empirical relation based on the Bragg-Kleeman rule can be used to obtain comparative ranges in different absorbers:

$$\frac{R_1}{R_2} \cong \frac{\rho_2 (M_1)^{1/2}}{\rho_1 (M_2)^{1/2}} \tag{2-16}$$

where R_1 and R_2 are the ranges of the same particle in two different absorbers, and ρ_1 and ρ_2 are the absorber densities, and M_1 and M_2 are the molecular weights of the absorbers.

EXAMPLE 2-2: The range in air of a 3 Mev proton is about 14.5 cm. (a) What is the range in air of an alpha particle having the same velocity? (b) What is the range of the 3 Mev proton in water?

SOLUTION:

(a) $R_2 = \dfrac{R_1 m_2 Z_{11}^2}{m_1 Z_{12}^2} = \dfrac{14.5 \times 4 \times 1}{1 \times 4} = 14.5$ cm

(b) $R_{H_2O} = \dfrac{(14.5)(0.0013)(18)^{1/2}}{(1)(29)^{1/2}} = 0.0155$ cm

2-1.1c *Energy Losses by Collision with Nuclei.* If a particle of energy E and momentum $p = m\bar{V}$ is deflected through an angle θ, the nonrelativistic energy loss in the forward direction is equal to

$$E = \frac{m(\bar{V} \sin \theta)^2}{2} = \frac{p^2 \sin^2 \theta}{2m} \qquad (2\text{-}17)$$

The probability $P(\theta)d(\theta)$ of an incident particle's being scattered through an angle between θ and $d\theta$ is given by*

$$P(\theta)d(\theta) = \frac{\pi Z_1^2 Z_2^2 e^4 \sin \theta}{8E^2 \sin^4 \theta/2} \qquad (2\text{-}18)$$

The energy loss, $\Delta\bar{E}$, averaged over all deflections is the probability of the energy loss, Eq. (2-18), times the energy loss, Eq. (2-17)

$$\Delta\bar{E} = \int \Delta E(\theta) P(\theta) d\theta$$

$$= \frac{p^2}{2m} \frac{\pi Z_1^2 Z_2^2 e^4}{8E^2} \int \frac{\sin^3 \theta}{\sin^4 \dfrac{\theta}{2}} d\theta \qquad (2\text{-}19)$$

Equation (2-19) is integrated with the upper limit of $\theta = \pi$, which is the maximum angle when the incident particle is deflected 180°. The lower limit will be designated by θ_{min} for purposes of integration.

Integrating Eq. (2-19) between these limits gives

$$-\Delta E = \frac{p^2}{2m} \frac{\pi Z_1^2 Z_2^2 e^4}{E^2} \, 2 \left[ln \left(\frac{2}{\theta_{min}} \right) + \frac{\theta_{min}^2}{4} - 1 \right] \qquad (2\text{-}20)$$

*The derivation of Eq. (2-18) may be found in most texts on nuclear physics.

The minimum angle, θ_{min}, is related to the closest distance to which a particle of velocity $\bar{V}$ can approach a nucleus of charge Z_2. Experimental and theoretical evidence indicates that this distance is a function of the size and charge of the nucleus as well as of the velocity and charge of the incident particle. In general, the distance approximates the size of the nucleus (2×10^{-12} cm), and the angle θ_{min} for light elements is about 10^{-6} radians. The term $\theta_{min}^2/4$ and the -1 in the brackets of Eq. (2-20) may be neglected in comparison to the $\ln 2/\theta_{min}$ term.

$$- \Delta E = \frac{p^2}{2m} \; \frac{\pi Z_1^2 Z_2^2 e^4}{E^2} \; 2 \left[\ln \left(\frac{2}{\theta_{min}} \right) \right] \tag{2-20a}$$

The energy loss due to scattering over an interval dx is obtained by multiplying the right-hand side of Eq. (2-20a) by $N_1 \, dx$, where N_1 is the number of particles per cubic centimeter and E is substituted for $p^2/2m$ to give

$$- \frac{dE}{dx} = \frac{2 \pi Z_1^2 Z_2^2 e^4 N_1}{E} \; \ln (2/\theta_{min}) \tag{2-20b}$$

EXAMPLE 2-3: Compare the ratio of energy loss by collision with nuclei (scattering) and energy loss by collision with bound electrons for a 4 Mev alpha particle traveling through carbon with that of a fission fragment, such as ^{90}Sr.

SOLUTION: The ratio of scattering losses to collision losses, dE_s/dE_c, is the ratio of Eq. (2-20b) to Eq. (2-10).

$$\frac{- \dfrac{dE_s}{dx}}{- \dfrac{dE_c}{dx}} = \frac{\dfrac{2 \pi Z_1^2 Z_2^2 e^4 N_1}{E} \; \ln \left(\dfrac{2}{\theta_{min}} \right)}{\dfrac{4 \pi Z_1^2 e^4 N}{m_o \bar{V}^2} \; \ln \left(\dfrac{2 m_o \bar{V}^2}{I} \right)}$$

Substituting the following values: $\theta_{min} = 8 \times 10^{-5}$, $Z_1 = 2$, $I \cong 80$, $\bar{V} = 1.40 \times 10^9$ cm/sec, $m_o = 9.11 \times 10^{-28}$ g, $Z_2 = 6$, $N = 3.01 \times 10^{23}$ electrons/g, $N_1 = 0.5 \times 10^{-23}$ nuclei/g, $E = 4$, and $2 m_o \bar{V}^2 = (2)(9.11 \times 10^{-28})(1.40 \times 10^9)^2 (6.24 \times 10^5) = 22.3 \times 10^{-4}$ Mev, and cancelling the Z_1, π, and e^4 terms, gives

$$\frac{dE_s}{dE_c} = \frac{(2)(6)^2 (0.5)(10^{-23})/4 \; \ln (2/8 \times 10^{-5})}{(4)(3.01)(10^{-23})/(11.15 \times 10^{-4}) \ln (2230/80)}$$

$$= 2.5 \times 10^{-3}$$

It is seen that the scattering loss by collision with nuclei is less than 1% of the collision loss with electrons.

If the incident particle is a strontium ion, the following values may be substituted: $\theta_{min} = 1.7 \times 10^{-3}$, $Z_2 = 6$, $I \cong 80$, $m_o = 9.11 \times 10^{-28}$ g, $\bar{V} = 2.93 \times 10^8$ cm/sec, $Z_{1s} = 39$, $Z_{1c} = 5$, and $2m_o \bar{V}^2 = (2)(9.11 \times 10^{-28})(2.93 \times 10^8)^2(6.24 \times 10^5) = 9.75 \times 10^{-5}$ Mev

$$\frac{dE_s}{dE_c} = \frac{(2)(39)^2(6)^2(0.5)(10^{-23})/4 \, ln \, (2/1.7 \times 10^{-3})}{4(10)^2(3.01)(10^{-23})/(4.88 \times 10^{-5}) \, ln \, (97.5/80)}$$

$$= 0.085$$

The scattering loss is now an appreciable fraction, 8.5%, of the total energy loss. The choice of $Z = 5$ for the fission fragment charge (the ^{90}Sr) was somewhat arbitrary since the effective charge on the ^{90}Sr will vary from 20 to 0 depending on its fractional range.

2-1.2 Electrons

Electrons interact with matter in a manner analogous to heavy particles. They lose energy by inelastic scattering, elastic scattering, and emission of bremsstrahlung. There are significant differences, however, in the energy loss parameters between electrons and heavy charged particles. These are due almost entirely to the small mass of the electron. At high energies the energy loss is primarily by bremsstrahlung; at electron energies below those at which bremsstrahlung emission occurs, inelastic collisions with electrons of the absorber are the dominant process.

2-1.2a *Energy Losses in Collisions with Electrons*. Equation (2-10), the energy loss equation for heavy particle-electron interactions, is applicable also to electron-electron interactions if it is modified to take into account the reduced mass of the system and the fact that after the collision it is impossible to differentiate between the impinging and the impinged electrons. If all the energy of the impinging electrons were transferred to the impinged electron, for instance, no change could be detected. This results in an $(e/2)^{1/2}$ correction in the logarithmic term, e being the base of natural logarithms:

$$-\frac{dE}{dx} = \frac{4\pi Z_1^2 e^4 N}{m_o \bar{V}^2} \, ln \, \left(\frac{2m\bar{V}^2}{I}\right) \sqrt{\frac{e}{2}} \qquad (2-21)$$

For electron energies greater than 0.5 Mev, relativistic corrections must be made. The resulting formula is

$$- \frac{dE}{dx} = \frac{2\pi Z_1^2 e^4 N}{m_o V^2} \left\{ ln \ \frac{m_o V^2 E}{2I^2(1-\beta)^2} \right.$$

$$- \left[2(1-\beta^2)^{1/2} - (1+\beta) \right] ln \ 2 + 1 - \beta^2$$

$$\left. + 1/8 \left[1 - (1-\beta^2)^{1/2} \right]^2 \right\} \tag{2-22}$$

This equation fails to take into account two phenomena of importance at high energies: (1) polarization in condensed media (the Fermi density effect) and (2) bremsstrahlung.

Values of $-dE/dx$ calculated using Eq. (2-22) are shown in Fig. 2-4 (collision loss curves). Comparison of Eq. (2-21) with Eq. (2-22) shows that the relativistic correction results in an increase of dE/dx at the high energies. This accounts for the minimum in the curve at 1 to 2 Mev.

2-1.2b *Energy Loss by Radiation (Bremsstrahlung)*. When a particle of charge Z_1 and mass m passes close to a nucleus of charge Z_2, a coulomb force proportional to $Z_1 Z_2$ is established, and the particle will be decelerated. According to classical physics, the particle will radiate electromagnetic energy at a rate proportional to its energy loss.

The detailed treatment of energy loss by radiation must be carried out quantum mechanically and is beyond the scope of this text. A useful approximation, however, is Eq. (2-23), which gives the ratio of the loss of energy by radiation to that by collision:

$$\frac{(-dE/dx)_{rad}}{(-dE/dx)_{col}} \approx \frac{EZ_2}{800} \tag{2-23}$$

where E is in Mev and Z_2 is the atomic number of the absorber. Energy loss by bremsstrahlung emission is only significant for electrons of high energy and for high-Z absorbers (Fig. 2-4).

2-1.2c *Range*. Unlike the heavy particles, which undergo no large deflections as they pass through matter, electrons follow erratic paths. Those that escape large individual energy losses travel a long distance; others undergo numerous large deflections. In Fig. 2-5 is shown a typical number vs. distance curve for electrons (the number of particles left in the beam at any point is plotted against the distance from the source). This may be compared with a similar curve for heavy particles (Fig. 2-6). The extrapolated range, R_p, is obtained by extrapolation of the linear portion of the curve; the maximum range, R_o, is determined by the intersection of the "tail" with the background.

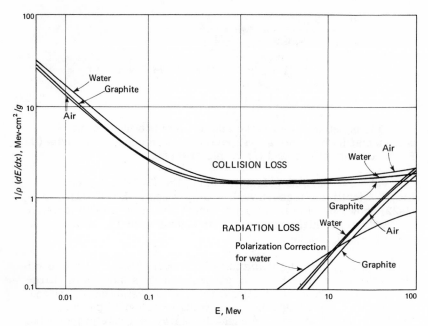

Fig. 2-4. Rates of energy loss of electrons in matter

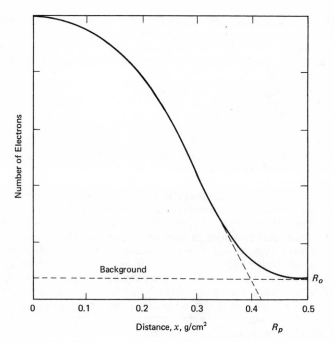

Fig. 2-5. Rates of energy loss of electrons in matter.

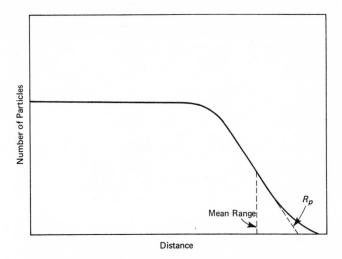

Fig. 2-6. Number-distance curve for heavy particles.

If the electron beam is not monoenergetic, then a curve of log N vs. distance becomes almost a straight line. The number-distance curve then is obtained by the superposition of a large number of linear curves of different slopes, each corresponding to a different initial energy.

Electron ranges in grams per square centimeter are described with good precision by an empirical formula of the form

$$R = AE - B \qquad\qquad (2\text{-}24)$$

where A and B are empirical constants whose values depend on the energy of the electron and the atomic number of the absorber.

For light elements and electrons whose energy E is $0.8 < E < 3$ Mev

$A = 0.5$

$E = 0.5$ to 3 Mev

$B = 0.16$

2-1.2d *Secondary Electrons.* Secondary electrons are the electrons ejected in the passage of the primary electrons through matter. Figure 2-7 shows the approximate energy distributions of secondary electrons produced by energetic primaries. It indicates that only about 2% of the electrons, the so-called "delta" electrons, possess relatively high energies, i.e. about 150 ev. The distribution

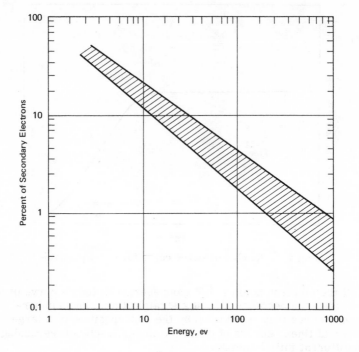

Fig. 2-7. Distribution of energies for secondary electrons
produced by particulate and photon radiation.

of secondary electron energies shown in Fig. 2-7 is typical for
particles as well as photons; distribution is largely independent of
primary beam energy. The maximum secondary electron energy
E_{max} is, however, a function of the incident particle energy. For
heavy particles $E_{max} = 4E_1(m_o/m_1)$, where the subscript 1 identi-
fies the primary particle.

The low energy electrons possessing less than 150 ev travel
only a short distance, about 10 Å in a condensed medium and about
5000 Å in gases. Thus, the energy of the low energy secondary
electrons is dissipated over a small volume, and little clusters of
ionizations and excitations are formed. These clusters are called
spurs. Those secondary electrons with energies greater than
150 ev, the delta electrons, have sufficient energy to escape the im-
mediate surroundings in which they were formed and behave like
low energy primary electrons.

Quantitative considerations based on the number and geometric
distribution of secondary electrons, and attendant energy dissipation,
have resulted in the formulation of a generalized picture that can

be most clearly visualized when we consider both ends of the energy spectrum of the incident particles that are of primary concern to radiation chemists. The low energy secondary electrons dissipate their energy over a small volume called a spur. The distance between spurs depends on the rate of energy deposition. Thus a particle with an energy that results in a high rate of energy deposition will produce densely ionized cylindrical columns, but a particle with a low rate of energy deposition will produce isolated clusters of ions (excited molecules, etc.) stretched like beads in a string along its path. Figure 2-8 is a schematic diagram of the presumed distribution of spurs along the track of a fast electron and of an alpha particle. Note that the scale for the fast electron is about one one-thousandth that of the alpha particle. Table 2-2, which is based on estimates made by Lea[3] gives the proportion of ion clusters containing 1, 2, 3, 4, or more ion pairs.

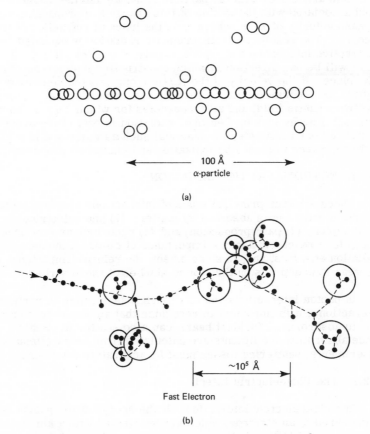

Fig. 2-8. Distribution of spurs and primary events along particle tracks. (a) Alpha particle, (b) Fast electron.

Table 2-2. FREQUENCY OF ION CLUSTERS CONTAINING VARIOUS NUMBERS OF ION PAIRS

Number of ion pairs per cluster	1	2	3	4	>4	Total
Proportion of clusters of that dimension	43	22	12	10	13	100

2-1.2e *Energy Loss by Cerenkov Radiation.* Another source of energy loss is Cerenkov radiation. Cerenkov radiation is visible light emitted whenever a charged particle passes through a transparent medium with a velocity greater than the velocity of light in the medium.

When a charged particle having a velocity approaching that of light passes into a transparent dielectric, such as water, the electric field associated with the particle's charge and the magnetic field associated with the motion of this charge are propagated with a phase velocity of c/η, where η is the index of refraction of the medium. The resulting electromagnetic radiation is canceled by destructive interference if $\beta\eta < 1$ (where $\beta = \overline{V}/c$). If $\beta\eta > 1$, there will be one direction in which constructive interference can take place. If the velocity of the particle exceeds the velocity of light in the medium (c/η), the particle can move ahead of its own electromagnetic field, and all frequencies for which $\beta\eta > 1$ can be emitted. Energy loss by Cerenkov radiation is only of the order of 1000 ev per centimeter for material such as water and is negligible compared to losses by ionization and excitation processes.

2-2 ELECTROMAGNETIC RADIATION

There are four principal types of interactions by which electromagnetic radiation is absorbed by matter: (1) photoelectric, (2) Compton, (3) pair production, and (4) photonuclear reactions. These four reactions assume importance at different incident radiation energies, and, to some extent, the relative importance of the reactions depends on the atomic number of the absorber.

In photon interactions and to a much lesser extent in particle interactions, it is important to recognize that an absorber, in addition to absorbing an incident beam, can also scatter it. Hence, since absorption coefficients are calculated from beam attenuation experiments, scattering losses must be accurately determined.

2-2.1 The Photoelectric Effect

In a photoelectric interaction, all the energy of the photon is transferred to an electron, which is then ejected with a kinetic energy, E, equal to the photon energy, $h\nu$, less the electron binding energy, ϕ.

$$E = h\nu - \phi \qquad\qquad (2\text{-}25)$$

The photoelectric absorption process cannot occur with a free electron because of momentum conservation. Total absorption of the photon can take place, however, if the electron is initially bound in an atom; momentum may then be conserved by recoil of the atom. The most tightly bound electrons, such as those in the K shell, have the greatest probability of absorbing a photon.

The cross section, τ, for photoelectric interactions is zero for photon energies lower than the electron binding energy. It rises to a high value at photon energies equal to the binding energy and then falls off. This is demonstrated by the curves marked τ/ρ in Figs. 2-9 and 2-10, which show attenuation coefficients as a function of energy for air and lead. For lead, at energies below 13 kev, the photoelectric interaction is with the more loosely bound L electrons. As the energy approaches 88 kev, the K-shell electron energy, these electrons are ejected.

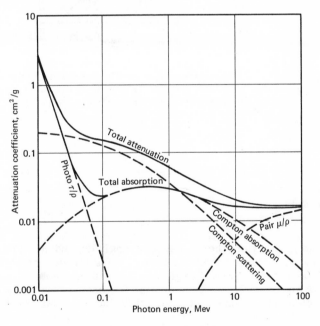

Fig. 2-9. Mass attenuation coefficients
for air as a function of photon energy

As a general rule, when the incident photon energy becomes greater than the binding energy of the K electrons, roughly 80% of the interactions are with K electrons. The total photoelectric cross section per atom is given approximately by

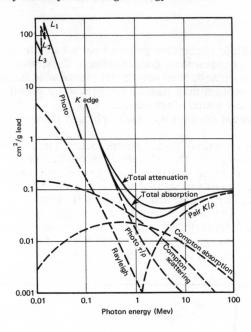

Fig. 2-10. Mass attenuation coefficients for lead as a function of photon energy. (From R. D. Evans, "The Atomic Nucleus," McGraw-Hill Book Co., New York, N. Y., 1955.)

$$_a\tau \approx \frac{kZ^4}{(h\nu)^3}$$

(2-26)

where k is a constant.

The interaction, therefore, is strongly dependent on photon energy and on absorber atomic number, being largest for high Z materials at low energies. Large increases in the photoelectric coefficients occur at the electron binding (resonance) energies. For the heavy elements as much as an eightfold increase has been observed.

Electromagnetic radiation (X-rays) is emitted as the outer electrons fall into the unoccupied orbitals left by the ejected photoelectron. The resulting electromagnetic pulse will have an energy spectrum roughly equivalent to the X-ray spectral emission of the material.

The angular distribution of the photoelectrons depends on the photon energy. At low energies the electrons are ejected predominantly at right angles to the direction of the incoming photon, but at high energies the distribution is shifted to the forward direction.

The angular distribution of photoelectrons per unit angle, Ω, may be calculated from

$$\frac{dN}{d\,\Omega} = \frac{\sin^2 \theta}{(1 - \beta\cos\,\theta)^4} \qquad (2\text{-}27)$$

where θ is the angle between the photon and the photoelectron, N is the number of photoelectrons, and β is the ratio of velocity of electrons to velocity of light. At high energies, where $\beta \rightarrow 1$, a relativistic formula must be used.

The linear attenuation coefficient in cm^{-1} is given by $\tau = {}_a\tau N$, where N is the number of atoms per cubic centimeter and ${}_a\tau$ is the cross section in centimeters per atom. The mass attenuation coefficient is τ/ρ. For photoelectric processes there is no practical distinction between the linear attenuation coefficient and the linear absorption coefficient* since the X-rays emitted as a result of ejection are assumed to be absorbed in a distance comparable to the range of the photoelectron.

2-2.2 The Compton Effect

A Compton interaction is an elastic collision between a photon and a loosely bound or unbound electron. In the process the electron is set in motion, and the energy of the photon is reduced. A schematic diagram of this process is shown in Fig. 2-11.

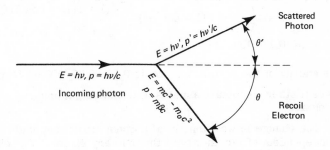

Fig. 2-11. Schematic diagram of the collision
of a photon with a free electron.

*See Sec. 2-2.5 for a more complete discussion of terms.

In the collision both energy and momentum must be conserved. Since $m_o c^2$ is the rest mass of the electron, the energy balance is

$$h\nu = h\nu' + mc^2 - m_o c^2 \qquad (2\text{-}28)$$

where $m = m_o (1 - \beta^2)^{-1/2}$.

Conservation of momentum demands that

$$\frac{h\nu}{c} = \frac{h\nu'}{c} \cos \theta' + m_o c \cos \theta \qquad (2\text{-}29)$$

$$h\nu' \sin \theta' = m_o c \sin \theta \qquad (2\text{-}30)$$

These equations may be algebraically arranged to give the change in photon wavelength on collision, $\Delta\lambda$,

$$\Delta\lambda = \frac{c}{\Delta\nu} = \frac{h}{m_o c} (1 - \cos \theta') \qquad (2\text{-}31)$$

The energy of the scattered photon is

$$h\nu' = \frac{h\nu}{1 + (h\nu/m_o c^2)(1 - \cos \theta')} \qquad (2\text{-}32)$$

EXAMPLE 2-4: A 0.51 Mev gamma ray is scattered through 180°. What are the energies of the scattered photon and recoil electron?

SOLUTION: Substituting in Eq. (2-32) gives for the photon

$$h\nu' = \frac{h\nu}{1 + \left(\dfrac{h\nu}{m_o c^2}\right)(1 - \cos \theta')} = \frac{0.51}{(1 + 1)(1 - \cos 180°)}$$

$$= 0.17 \text{ Mev}$$

The energy of the recoil electron is $0.51 - 0.17 = 0.34$ Mev.

Several other important aspects of Compton gamma-ray scattering are:

(1) The change in wavelength, at a given scattering angle θ, is independent of the energy of the primary photon. The change in scattered photon energy increases with increasing energy.

(2) The energy of a photon scattered back at the maximum angle (180°) approaches a limiting value 0.25 Mev as $h\nu$ increases.

(3) A photon scattered through a large angle loses more energy than one scattered through a small angle.

(4) Low energy photons are scattered with only a moderate energy change, but high energy photons suffer a very large change. At large photon energies the electrons acquire a larger fraction of the energy.

2-2.2a *Compton Cross Sections*. The cross section for Compton scatter is given by the Klein-Nishina formula, which predicts the cross section per electron:

$$_e\sigma = 2\pi r_o^2 \left\{ \frac{1+\alpha}{\alpha^2} \left[\frac{2(1+\alpha)}{1+2} - \frac{1}{\alpha} \ln(1+2\alpha) \right] \right.$$

$$\left. + \frac{1}{2\alpha} \ln(1+2\alpha) - \frac{1+3\alpha}{(1+2\alpha)^2} \right\} \frac{cm^2}{electron} \qquad (2\text{-}33)$$

where $\alpha = h\nu/m_o c^2$, r_o is the classical electron radius.

The total energy removed from the incident beam by Compton collisions is measured by $_e\sigma$, as given by the Klein-Nishina formula above; the average scattered energy is measured by $_e\sigma_s$

$$_e\sigma_s = \frac{2\pi e^4}{m_o^2 c^4} \left[\frac{1}{\alpha^3} \ln(1+2\alpha) + \frac{2(1+\alpha)(2\alpha^2 - 2\alpha - 1)}{\alpha^2(1+2\alpha)} \right.$$

$$\left. + \frac{8\alpha^2}{3(1+2\alpha)^3} \right] \frac{cm^2}{electron} \qquad (2\text{-}34)$$

From the conservation of energy, the energy absorbed by the electron, $_e\sigma_a$, must be the difference between the total energy and that scattered:

$$_e\sigma_a = {}_e\sigma - {}_e\sigma_s \qquad (2\text{-}35)$$

The absorption coefficient is $_e\sigma_a$. The prefix e signifies it is per electron. For calculations involving the fractional transmission through an absorber, a total linear attenuation coefficient σ is more practical. Since there are N atoms each having Z electrons per cubic centimeter, the total linear coefficient is

$$\sigma = NZ_e\sigma \ cm^{-1} \qquad (2\text{-}36)$$

The mass attenuation coefficient is $(\sigma/\rho) \ cm^2/g$, where ρ is the density.

Figures 2-9 and 2-10 show the scattering, attenuation and absorption (mass) coefficients for air and lead, respectively. It may be noted in these figures that for Compton scattering:

(1) Both the scattering coefficient (σ_s/ρ) and the total Compton mass-attenuation coefficient (σ/ρ) fall off steadily with increasing energy.

(2) Up to 0.5 Mev, σ_a/ρ rises, or is relatively constant, and then falls.

(3) Compton scattering per electron is essentially independent of Z; hence, the mass absorption coefficient is practically constant and independent of the nature of the absorber.

In addition to giving the total absorption coefficients, the Klein-Nishina equation can be used to obtain the initial distribution of Compton electron energies. Table 2-3 shows the probability of photons with energies between 0 and 30 Mev ejecting an electron of a given energy.

2-2.3   Other Scattering Processes

Compton scattering is incoherent in the sense that the electrons are presumed free; hence there is a random phase relation between the incident and scattered radiation. There are, however, also bound electron interactions that give rise to a coherent scattering process known as Rayleigh scattering. In Rayleigh scattering, photons are scattered by bound atomic electrons under conditions such that the atom is neither ionized nor excited. The process occurs mostly at low energies and for high-Z materials and is of most significance in the interpretation of "narrow beam" attenuation coefficient measurements.

In Fig. 2-10, the curve σ_a/ρ is the total Compton absorption coefficient, including coherent scatter. Coherent scattering coefficients are largest in a region where the photoelectric coefficient is one or two orders of magnitude larger than Compton scattering coefficients; hence their effect on the total absorption coefficients is small.

Two other scattering processes, which involve the atoms as a whole, are called Thomson scattering and nuclear resonance scattering. These processes are barely detectable and will not be discussed here.

Table 2-3.   INITIAL DISTRIBUTION OF COMPTON ELECTRONS IN WATER*†

Photon Energy, Mev	Electron Energy, Mev														
	0.1	0.5	1.0	2.0	3.0	4.0	6.0	8.0	10.0	12.0	14.0	16.0	18.0	20.0	22.0
0-1	234	43.6													
1-2	40.8	38.8	39.4												
2-3	14.1	13.8	14.4	22.2											
3-4	7.06	7.01	7.06	8.76	15.8										
4-6	7.13	7.03	7.11	7.66	9.95	17.5									
6-8	3.58	3.55	3.55	3.66	3.96	4.70	12.4								
8-10	2.13	2.12	2.13	2.16	2.25	2.43	3.44	9.60							
10-12	1.42	1.41	1.42	1.44	1.47	1.53	1.83	2.73	7.86						
12-14	1.02	1.01	1.02	1.02	1.04	1.07	1.19	1.47	2.28	6.66					
14-16	0.760	0.760	0.760	0.768	0.774	0.789	0.846	0.968	1.23	1.96	5.77				
16-18	0.590	0.590	0.590	0.595	0.599	0.608	0.639	0.702	0.820	1.07	1.72	5.10			
18-20	0.472	0.472	0.472	0.475	0.479	0.484	0.502	0.538	0.599	0.713	0.940	1.54	4.56		
20-22	0.386	0.386	0.386	0.388	0.391	0.394	0.406	0.428	0.464	0.524	0.632	0.842	1.38	4.13	
22-24	0.321	0.321	0.321	0.323	0.324	0.327	0.335	0.350	0.372	0.408	0.466	0.567	0.759	1.27	3.77
24-26	0.273	0.273	0.273	0.274	0.274	0.276	0.281	0.291	0.306	0.329	0.364	0.420	0.513	0.699	1.16
26-28	0.234	0.234	0.234	0.234	0.235	0.236	0.240	0.247	0.257	0.272	0.295	0.329	0.381	0.473	0.645
28-30	0.203	0.203	0.203	0.203	0.203	0.204	0.207	0.212	0.220	0.230	0.245	0.268	0.299	0.352	0.436

*From D. Cormack and H.E. Johns, Brit. J. Radiol., 25:369 (1952).

†This table gives the number of electrons per Mev interval produced per cubic centimeter of water by 1 photon/cm^2 in the energy intervals shown in the first column. Multiply all table values by 10^{-3}. To use this table for material other than water containing N electrons/cm^3, multiply the table values by $N/(3.34 \times 10^{23})$.

2-2.4   Pair Production

In pair production, which has no analog in classical physics, a photon is absorbed and a pair of particles, a positron and an electron, appear in its place. The total energy of the photon that disappears equals the rest mass of the positron plus that of the electron plus their kinetic energies, E_p and E_e

$$E_p + E_e + 2m_o c^2 = h\nu \tag{2-36}$$

Pair production cannot take place if the incident photon energy is less than the rest mass of the particles; therefore, for pair production to occur, $h\nu > 2m_o c^2 = 1.02$ Mev. The process occurs only in the field of charged particles, principally in the field of the nucleus but also to some degree in the field of an electron. The positron, after losing its kinetic energy, is annihilated by combining with an electron with the subsequent emission, in opposite directions, of two 0.51 Mev gamma rays.

Several other minor effects associated with pair production, but which do not contribute significantly to energy transfer, are:

(1) Recoil of the nucleus.

(2) Annihilation of positrons while they still have some kinetic energy.

(3) Annihilation with the emission of three photons (triplet production).

The total pair-production attenuation coefficient is κ, and, like the Compton process it is composed of a true attenuation coefficient, κ_a, and a scattering coefficient, κ_s. The scattering coefficient is invariably small, and common practice is to set $\kappa = \kappa_a$. The mass attenuation coefficient for pair production is κ/ρ.

Table 2-4 lists the value of κ (in cm^{-1}) for lead at different photon energies. The value of κ for any other element may be obtained from the relation

$$\kappa = \kappa_{Pb} \frac{\rho}{11.35} \frac{207.2}{A} \left(\frac{Z}{82} \right)^2 \tag{2-38}$$

where A is the atomic weight, Z is the atomic number, and ρ is the density.

Table 2-4. PAIR PRODUCTION
ATTENUATION COEFFICIENTS
FOR LEAD

Photon energy, Mev	κ_{Pb}, cm^{-1} Pb
1.02	0.0
1.53	0.011
2.04	0.042
3.06	0.116
5.1	0.255
7.66	0.368
10.22	0.462
17.0	0.630
25.5	0.768
51.0	1.00
102.0	1.18
255.0	1.33
510.0	1.40

2-2.5 Mass-Energy Absorption Coefficients

There is a considerable amount of confusion concerning the nomenclature for the absorption of photons by matter. This comes
about largely through the use of the term "absorption coefficient,"
which is often used synonymously with attenuation coefficient. [4] The
attenuation coefficient is usually thought of as the number of interactions (without specifying energies) between photons and matter.
The absorption coefficient on the other hand usually refers to the
amount of energy dissipated by the secondary electrons produced as
a result of these interactions. Instead of "absorption coefficient"
either "mass-energy transfer coefficient" or "mass-energy absorption coefficient," are recommended terminology for the absorption
of photon energy by matter. The mass-energy absorption coefficient
is μ_{en}/ρ and is equal to $(\mu_k/\rho)(1 - G)$ where G is the proportion of
energy of secondary charged particles that is lost to bremsstrahlung
and μ_k/ρ is the mass-energy transfer coefficient. The mass-
energy transfer coefficient μ_k/ρ and the mass-energy absorption
coefficient μ_{en}/ρ do not differ appreciably unless the kinetic energies of the secondary particles are comparable with or larger than
their rest energy. For practical purposes therefore $\mu_{en}/\rho \cong \mu_k/\rho$.

The mass energy transfer coefficient for X or gamma rays of
incident energy $h\nu$ is defined as:

$$\frac{\mu_k}{\rho} = \frac{\tau_a}{\rho} + \frac{\sigma_a}{\rho} + \frac{\kappa_a}{\rho} \qquad (2\text{-}39)$$

where τ_a/ρ = photoelectric mass absorption coefficient = $\tau/\rho \, (1 - \delta/h\nu)$

τ/ρ = photoelectric mass attenuation coefficient

δ = average energy emitted as X-rays

σ_a/ρ = Compton mass absorption coefficient = $\sigma/\rho \, (E_e/h\nu)$

σ/ρ = Compton mass attenuation coefficient

E_e = average energy of the Compton electrons per scattered photon

κ_a/ρ = pair production mass-absorption coefficient =

$$\kappa/\rho \left(1 - \frac{2mc^2}{h\nu}\right)$$

κ/ρ = pair production mass-attenuation coefficient

mc^2 = rest energy of the electron

The mass attenuation coefficient μ/ρ refers to the *attenuation* of electromagnetic radiation and is defined as follows:

$$\frac{\mu}{\rho} = \frac{\tau}{\rho} + \frac{\sigma}{\rho} + \frac{\sigma_{coh}}{\rho} + \frac{\kappa}{\rho} \qquad (2\text{-}40)$$

where σ_{coh}/ρ = mass attenuation coefficient for coherent scatter. All other terms are defined previously.

Tables 2-5 and 2-6 give the total mass-energy absorption coefficient for a number of common elements plus water and air. These tables may be used directly for elements; for compounds or mixtures whose bulk density is ρ the mass-energy absorption coefficients are given by

$$\frac{\mu_{en}}{\rho} = \frac{\mu_1}{\rho_1} X_1 + \frac{\mu_2}{\rho_2} X_2 + \ldots \frac{\mu_n}{\rho_n} X_n \qquad (2\text{-}41)$$

where X_1, X_2 etc., are the fractions by weight of the various elements. For example, for 1 Mev photons incident on water from Table 2-6

$$\frac{\mu_{en}}{\rho} \ (\text{H}_2\text{O}) = \frac{2}{18} \ (0.0555) + \frac{16}{18} \ (0.0279) = 0.0310$$

2-2.6 Photonuclear Reactions

Photons of sufficiently high energies are capable of ejecting neutrons or protons from nuclei. The photon energy must exceed the binding energy* of the neutron or proton. For most materials, except beryllium and deuterium, the photon energies required for photonuclear reactions are of the order of 6 to 18 Mev. The

Table 2-5. MASS-ENERGY ABSORPTION COEFFICIENTS AT ENERGIES
BETWEEN 10 AND 100 KEV
(Values in cm^2/g)

Photon energy, kev	Element							
	H	C	N	O	Na	Mg	Al	P
10	0.0099	1.87	3.31	5.35	15.0	20.5	25.6	39.8
15	0.0111	0.494	0.882	1.45	4.30	5.93	7.48	11.8
20	0.0133	0.199	0.352	0.508	1.73	2.39	3.05	4.89
30	0.0186	0.0595	0.101	0.161	0.475	0.698	0.866	1.42
40	0.0231	0.0302	0.0456	0.0673	0.187	0.262	0.335	0.545
50	0.0271	0.0221	0.0400	0.0400	0.0969	0.135	0.170	0.272
60	0.0306	0.0201	0.0802	0.0302	0.0622	0.0821	0.102	0.162
80	0.0802	0.0200	0.0238	0.0238	0.0363	0.0448	0.0526	0.0760
100	0.0406	0.0214	0.0231	0.0231	0.0285	0.0331	0.0368	0.0495
	S	A	K	Ca	Fe	Cu	Water	Air
10	50.2	61.6	76.8	89.8	148.	160.	4.76	4.54
15	15.0	19.1	24.3	28.7	50.9	61.8	1.29	1.25
20	6.25	8.05	10.2	12.0	22.6	28.1	0.506	0.502
30	1.82	2.41	3.07	3.70	7.30	9.42	0.145	0.145
40	0.702	0.937	1.23	1.51	3.16	4.11	0.0624	0.0622
50	0.349	0.469	0.606	0.746	1.59	2.14	0.0386	0.0376
60	0.210	0.276	0.356	0.434	0.948	1.29	0.0302	0.0287
80	0.0952	0.123	0.156	0.188	0.413	0.563	0.0252	0.234
100	0.0600	0.0724	0.0889	0.109	0.229	0.300	0.0250	0.0231

National Bur. of Standards Handbook 85, March 31, 1964, "Physical Aspects of Irradiation."

---

*The binding energy is the energy equivalence of the difference between the mass of the free products and the mass of the bound system.

Table 2-6. MASS–ENERGY ABSORPTION COEFFICIENTS AT
ENERGIES ABOVE 100 KEV*
(Values in cm²/g)

Photon energy, Mev	H	C	N	O	Na	Mg	Al		P	S
0.10	0.0406	0.0213	0.0222	0.0231	0.0285	0.0331	0.0369		0.0494	0.0599
0.15	0.0481	0.0244	0.0247	0.0250	0.0256	0.0274	0.0281		0.0313	0.0349
0.20	0.0525	0.0264	0.0265	0.0268	0.0264	0.0276	0.0273		0.0289	0.0307
0.30	0.0570	0.0287	0.0287	0.0287	0.0277	0.0288	0.0281		0.0288	0.0300
0.40	0.0586	0.0295	0.0295	0.0296	0.0283	0.0294	0.0287		0.0290	0.0301
0.50	0.0593	0.0299	0.0299	0.0299	0.0286	0.0295	0.0288		0.0290	0.0301
0.60	0.0588	0.0296	0.0296	0.0296	0.0283	0.0292	0.0285		0.0286	0.0297
0.80	0.0573	0.0289	0.0288	0.0288	0.0276	0.0284	0.0278	(0.0279)	0.0278	0.0287
1.0	0.0555	0.0279	0.0279	0.0279	0.0267	0.0275	0.0268	(0.0270)	0.0269	0.0277
1.5	0.0508	0.0255	0.0255	0.0255	0.0243	0.0251	0.0245	(0.0247)	0.0246	0.0254
2.0	0.0464	0.0234	0.0235	0.0234	0.0225	0.0232	0.0227	(0.0229)	0.0228	0.0235
3.0	0.0398	0.0204	0.0205	0.0206	0.0199	0.0206	0.0202	(0.0205)	0.0204	0.0211
4.0	0.0351	0.0184	0.0185	0.0187	0.0183	0.0191	0.0188	(0.0192)	0.0191	0.0198
5.0	0.0316	0.0170	0.0172	0.0174	0.0173	0.0180	0.0178	(0.0184)	0.0183	0.0191
6.0	0.0288	0.0159	0.0162	0.0165	0.0166	0.0174	0.0172	(0.0179)	0.0178	0.0186
8.0	0.0249	0.0145	0.0149	0.0153	0.0157	0.0165	0.0165	(0.0173)	0.0173	0.0182
10.0	0.0222	0.0136	0.0141	0.0146	0.0152	0.0161	0.0162	(0.0172)	0.0172	0.0180

Photon energy, Mev	A	K	Ca	Fe		Cu	Water	Air†
0.10	0.0724	0.0889	0.109	0.219		0.302	0.0250	0.0231
0.15	0.0366	0.0431	0.0486	0.0803		0.105	0.0276	0.0249
0.20	0.0300	0.0337	0.0365	0.0486		0.0588	0.0297	0.0266
0.30	0.0277	0.0302	0.0317	0.0338		0.0365	0.0318	0.0287
0.40	0.0274	0.0298	0.0309	0.0306		0.0315	0.0328	0.0295
0.50	0.0273	0.0295	0.0304	0.0294	(0.0295)	0.0297	0.0332	0.0299
0.60	0.0270	0.0291	0.0300	0.0285	(0.0287)	0.0285	0.0328	0.0296
0.80	0.0259	0.0281	0.0288	0.0272	(0.0275)	0.0272	0.0320	0.0288
1.0	0.0250	0.0270	0.0277	0.0261	(0.0264)	0.0257	0.0310	0.0279
1.5	0.0229	0.0247	0.0253	0.0236	(0.0239)	0.0231	0.0283	0.0255
2.0	0.0212	0.0229	0.0235	0.0219	(0.0224)	0.0216	0.0260	0.0234
3.0	0.0192	0.0207	0.0213	0.0204	(0.0211)	0.0201	0.0227	0.0205
4.0	0.0182	0.0197	0.0204	0.0198	(0.0208)	0.0198	0.0205	0.0185
5.0	0.0177	0.0192	0.0199	0.0197	(0.0209)	0.0198	0.0190	0.0173
6.0	0.0173	0.0189	0.0197	0.0198	(0.0212)	0.0201	0.0179	0.0163
8.0	0.0170	0.0188	0.0195	0.0201	(0.0220)	0.0206	0.0164	0.0150
10.0	0.0171	0.0188	0.0198	0.0206	(0.0230)	0.0212	0.0154	0.0143

*Energy transfer coefficients without corrections for bremsstrahlung losses are given in parentheses.
†Air: 0.755 wt. % N, 0.232 wt. % O, and 0.013 wt. % Ar.

number of neutrons produced per photon incident on shielding material can be approximated by

$$n \cong 0.044 \sqrt{Z} \ W \qquad\qquad (2\text{-}42)$$

where n is the number of neutrons, W is the total photon energy in Mev, and Z is the atomic number.

The cross sections for photonuclear reactions are negligibly small compared to those for Compton processes and pair production. For practical purposes therefore this effect is of importance primarily in shielding considerations around high energy electron accelerators or for special applications.

Two photonuclear reactions of special interest are:

$$^{9}_{4}\text{Be} + \gamma \rightarrow \, ^{8}_{4}\text{Be} + n$$

and

$$^{2}_{1}\text{D} + \gamma \rightarrow \, ^{1}_{1}\text{H} + n$$

Commonly written $^9\text{Be}\,(\gamma, n)^8\text{Be}$ and $^2\text{D}\,(\gamma, n)^1\text{H}$, they are used to calibrate electron accelerators by measuring the peak bremsstrahlung energy when the electrons are stopped in a heavy metal target. The threshold energies for these photonuclear reactions are 1.666 ± 0.002 Mev and 2.226 ± 0.003 Mev, respectively. In Table 2-7 are summarized some threshold energies and cross sections. These cross sections may be compared with those for Compton scattering and pair production, which are also given in Table 2-7.

Table 2-7. PHOTODISINTEGRATION CROSS SECTIONS*

Element	Reaction	Threshold energy, Mev	Energy of peak cross section, Mev	Peak cross section, $10^{24}\text{cm}^2/\text{atom}$	Pair and Compton cross section, $10^{24}\text{cm}^2/\text{atom}$
^{12}C	(γ,n)	18.6	22.9	0.013	0.307
	(γ,n)	16.0	21.5	0.034	
^{14}N	(γ,n)	16.5	24.2	0.0028	0.379
^{16}O	(γ,n)	15.6	24.2	0.011	0.461
^{63}Cu	(γ,n)	10.9	18.1	0.10	3.56
^{65}Cu	(γ,n)	9.8	18.6	0.15	3.58
Pb (natural)	(γ,n)	7.9	13.7	0.81	18.8

*From R. Montalbetti, L. Katz, and J. Goldberg, Phys. Rev., 91:659 (1953).

2-2.7   Electromagnetic Radiation — General

Usually absorption coefficients are determined by placing an absorber in the path between a source and a detector. The probability of a photon's passing through a certain thickness of an absorber without suffering any kind of interaction (Compton, photoelectric, or pair production) is the product of the probabilities of survival for each type of interaction. After passing through an absorber of thickness x, a beam of high energy photons with initial intensity I_o will have a final intensity I given by

$$I = I_o e^{-\mu x} \tag{2-43}$$

where μ is the total linear attenuation coefficient ($\sigma_a + \sigma_s + \tau + \kappa$) and x is absorber thickness. This equation is analogous to the radioactive decay law and the Beer-Lambert law.

The total linear attenuation coefficient has the dimensions cm^{-1}, and, when divided by the density (ρ), it becomes the mass attenuation coefficient with dimensions $cm^2/gram$. The attenuation coefficient as described here is for narrow-beam conditions. Narrow-beam conditions are only attained under very special laboratory conditions; the usual condition encountered in shielding or radiation chemistry experiments is the broad-beam condition. Narrow-beam conditions exist when only that part of the primary beam which has not interacted with the absorber in any manner is detected. No photons that are incoherently or coherently scattered by a few degrees reach the detector. This is true also of all photons arising from photoelectric processes and pair encounters. Broad-beam attenuation is the condition encountered in the average radiation chemistry situation and in every practical problem in gamma ray shielding. Broad-beam (or poor geometry) conditions occur whenever a significant fraction of the scattered radiation reaches the detector. Some typical arrangements for broad-beam and narrow-beam conditions are shown in Fig. 2-12.

For situations where broad-beam geometry applies, Eq. (2-43) has to be modified by two additional factors. One of these is the geometry factor, which depends on source geometry, and the other is the buildup factor, which takes into account the secondary radiation produced in the absorber which reaches the detector.

For broad-beam conditions Eq. (2-43) must be modified to include a buildup factor:

$$I = I_o B e^{-\mu_o x} \tag{2-44}$$

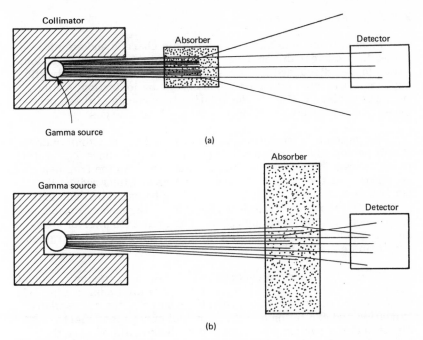

Fig. 2-12. Narrow- and broad-beam geometries. (a) Narrow beam. A "good geometry" experiment, the scattered radiation does not enter the detector. (b) Broad beam. A "bad geometry" experiment. Note that the scattered gamma rays strike the detector.

where B is the buildup factor. The buildup factor is the ratio of the observed transmission of radiation to the measured transmission of radiation under narrow-beam conditions. Buildup factors in various mediums have been calculated for the most representative source geometries.[4,5]

Buildup factors must be included in energy absorption considerations because, when electromagnetic radiation penetrates an absorber, secondary electrons are generated. In any small volume there will exist electrons that have been generated in the volume element plus electrons scattered into it. As the distance from the surface (interface) increases, the number of electrons that are scattered into a small volume element increases. At a point equal to the average range of the secondary electrons, the number of electrons scattered into a small volume element will reach a maximum. In terms of absorbed dose, the maximum absorbed dose will occur some distance from the surface.

48 The Chemistry and Physics of High Energy Reactions

2-2.8   Fission Fragments

Fission fragments have variable ionic charges and atomic rather than nuclear dimensions. Because of this the theory of ionization losses discussed for other charged particles is not strictly applicable. Fission fragments lose energy by ionization, excitation, and nuclear collision; the relative importance of these processes being different at different energies and charges.

Excitation and ionization losses in a medium of atomic number Z will be roughly proportional to $(Z_{av})^2 Z/m_o \bar{V}^2$ where Z_{av} refers to the average charge on the fission fragment. As the fragment penetrates matter, it will capture electrons and thus reduce its net charge and also its rate of energy loss by excitation and ionization. As the fission fragment slows down, the energy losses by elastic nuclear collisions increase. The final encounter of a fission fragment is a nuclear collision in which a relatively large energy transfer takes place.

Figure 2-13 shows an energy loss curve for a fission fragment compared with that of an alpha particle. The minimum in Fig. 2-13 occurs over the transition between the portion of the curve where ionization and excitation are the principal energy loss mechanisms, and the portion where elastic nuclear collisions are the principal mechanisms. The mass, charge, range in air, and initial energy for typical light and heavy fragments from U^{235} fission are given in Table 2-8.

2-3   NEUTRONS

Neutrons interact with matter primarily through reactions with nuclei. The principal energy loss mechanisms for neutrons are: (1) elastic scattering (billiard-ball collision), (2) inelastic scattering (capture scattering), and (3) nuclear reactions. Fast neutrons, when they undergo elastic collision, especially with light atoms (hydrogenous material), produce charged particles. Neutrons involved in nuclear reactions, except for fission, also produce charged particles, e.g., protons, alpha particles, and beta particles as well as photons. The various energy loss mechanisms occur with a certain probability which is related to the cross section for the particular process.

Generally speaking, the cross sections for nuclear reactions may be roughly divided into a scattering cross section (elastic and inelastic scattering) and an absorption cross section

$$\sigma_{total} = \sigma_s + \sigma_{abs}$$

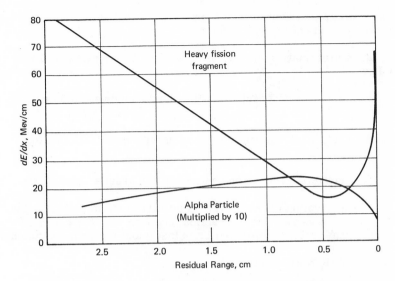

Fig. 2-13. Energy loss curve for fission fragments compared with that of an alpha particle multiplied by 10 for clarity. (From C. Goodman, "The Science and Engineering of Nuclear Power," Addison-Wesley Publishing Company, Inc., Reading, Mass., 1952.)

Table 2-8. CHARACTERISTICS OF AVERAGE FISSION*
FRAGMENTS FROM ^{235}U FISSION

	Light fragment	Heavy fragment
Mass	97	138
Initial charge	20	22
Energy, Mev	97	65
Mean range in air, cm	2.5	1.9
Velocity, cm/sec	1.4×19^9	0.93×10^9
Mev/mass	1.00	0.47
Energy of electron having same velocity, kev	0.50	0.26

*From M. Steinberg, in Advances in Nuclear Science and Engineering, E. J. Henley and H. Kouts (Eds.), Academic Press Inc., New York, 1962.

The neutron cross section depends on the velocity (kinetic energy) of the neutron and the nuclide in question. Neutron energies are divided roughly into the following energy regions:

1. Thermal: These are neutrons that are in thermal equilibrium and have a most probable velocity of 2200 meters/sec for

a Maxwellian distribution at a temperature of $20.44°\,C$. This corresponds to an energy of 0.025 ev.

2. Epithermal: neutrons with energies in the range of 0.1 to 300 ev.

3. Intermediate: neutrons with energies between 0.5 and 10 kev.

4. Fast: neutrons with energies in the range 10 kev up to 20 Mev.

5. Relativistic: neutrons with energies greater than 20 Mev.

The absorption cross section is usually given for a particular process, such as activation, reaction, and fission. The cross section for scattering is separated into elastic and inelastic scattering.

2-3.1 Elastic Scattering

An elastic collision is one in which the neutron does not penetrate the nuclear surface. It is a "billiard ball" type collision and can be analyzed in terms of classical mechanics. The recoil atoms receive energies from zero up to a maximum, E_m, in a head-on collision. The average loss in one collision, the logarithmic energy decrement, ξ, is given by

$$\xi = ln\,\frac{E}{E_o} = \frac{(A-1)^2}{2A}\,ln\left(\frac{A+1}{A-1}\right) - 1 \qquad (2\text{-}45)$$

After n collisions

$$ln\,\frac{E_n}{E_o} = n\left[\frac{(A-1)^2}{2A}\,ln\,\frac{(A+1)}{(A-1)} - 1\right] \qquad (2\text{-}46)$$

where A = atomic weight of struck atom

E_o = initial neutron energy

E = neutron energy after collision

E_n = neutron energy after n collisions

For materials with $A > 10$, Eq. (2-45) may be approximated by

$$ln\,\frac{E}{E_o} = \frac{2}{A+2/3} \qquad (2\text{-}47)$$

The energy loss per collision is seen to be independent of the initial energy of the neutron, a constant fraction of the initial energy being lost in each collision. The "lost" neutron energy appears as kinetic energy of the struck atom and must ultimately be dissipated by ionization and/or excitation. The logarithmic energy decrement is an important material parameter in that it measures the moderating ability of a given medium. For protons Eq. (2-46) reduces to $E_n = E_o e^{-n}$ in hydrogenous material. Neutrons of 2 to 3 Mev are reduced in about 20 collisions to thermal energies.

EXAMPLE 2.5: A 10 Mev neutron is "thermalized" by a graphite moderator in a nuclear reactor. How many collisions with carbon atoms does the neutron undergo before it reaches thermal (~ 0.025 ev) energies?

SOLUTION: According to Eq. (2-47)

$$\xi = \frac{2}{12 + 2/3} = 0.158$$

$$\text{Total collisions} = \frac{\text{Total energy reduction}}{\text{Loss per collision}} = \frac{ln\, E_o / E_n}{\xi}$$

$$= \frac{ln\left(\dfrac{10 \times 10^6}{0.025}\right)}{0.158} = 127$$

At low neutron energies, where the neutron wavelength is large compared with the radius of the scattering nucleus, the struck atom may not receive sufficient energy to free it from its neighbors. It thus behaves as a bound atom, the cross section being increased by a factor of about $(A + 1)^2 / A^2$. Figure 2-14 gives the total cross section (in barns) for hydrogen in the low energy region, where $\sigma_{\text{total}} = \sigma_s$. The constant value above 1 ev is characteristic of scatter processes in light elements. Below 1 ev the rise in cross section can be attributed to a transition from free atom to bound atom behavior.

At higher energies, where neutron wavelengths become comparable to interatomic dimensions, diffraction effects occur. These are known as shadow effects, and they cause oscillations in the otherwise smooth absorption curve.

2-3.2 Inelastic Scattering

At sufficiently high neutron energies, the neutrons and nuclei may form compound nuclei, which subsequently decompose. If the neutron energy is insufficient to raise the nucleus to an

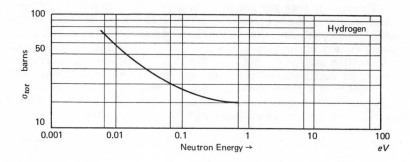

Fig. 2-14. Total cross section of hydrogen in the low energy region.

excited state, the process is equivalent to simple elastic scatter. If, on the other hand, the nucleus is raised to an excited state, it reemits the neutron plus one or more gammas.

At energies below several Mev, the cross section for inelastic scatter is small compared to that for elastic scatter, even for heavy elements. This is borne out by Table 2-9, which gives experimentally determined cross sections for inelastic scatter at various energies and for various absorbers.

2-3.3 Absorption

As used here, the term absorption covers a multitude of processes wherein a neutron is captured by the nucleus. The fate of the compound nucleus is determined by the relative probability of the various modes of nuclear disintegration.

Cross sections for neutron capture tend to be somewhat complicated, the major simplification being the so-called $1/\overline{V}$ law. This rough approximation is usually valid only at low neutron energies for the isotopes of heavy elements; however, for many isotopes of light elements, the $1/\overline{V}$ law may extend to neutron energies up to about 100 kev. The $1/\overline{V}$ law states that the probability of a neutron's causing a nuclear reaction is proportional to the time it spends in the vicinity of the nucleus. This time, as would be expected, is inversely proportional to the neutron velocity $\overline{V}$

$$\sigma_{abs} \propto \frac{1}{\overline{V}} \tag{2-48}$$

The major deterrent to a quantitative formulation for neutron absorption coefficients is the large increase in neutron capture in

Table 2-9. INELASTIC SCATTERING CROSS SECTIONS*

Material	Cross section for monoenergetic neutrons, barns			
	2.5 Mev	3.3 Mev	4.1 Mev	14 Mev
Carbon				0.63
Sodium	0.53		0.57	
Magnesium	0.77		0.78	1.08
Aluminum	0.96	0.81	0.78	1.13
Phosphorus	0.7			1.13
Sulfur	0.54			1.15
Chlorine	0.6		0.90	
Calcium	0.4			1.36
Chromium	1.4			
Iron	1.16	1.51	1.58	1.29
Cobalt	1.40			
Nickel	0.83	1.35		1.38
Copper	1.58	1.67	1.68	1.35
Zinc	2.18	2.18	1.58	1.37
Selenium	1.88			1.40
Molybdenum	1.9			
Silver	2.13			
Cadmium	2.15	2.35	2.3	1.83
Tin	1.65	1.73	2.11	1.81
Antimony	2.00	2.11	2.13	1.90
Tellurium	2.0			1.97
Iodine	1.96			1.88
Barium	0.8	1.3	2.2	
Tungsten	2.6			2.35
Mercury	2.6	2.99	3.36	2.65
Lead	1.69		1.72	2.42
Bismuth	0.62	0.62	1.14	2.44

*From M. V. Pasechnik, "Inelastic Scattering of Fast Neutrons by Atomic Nuclei," in Proceedings of the International Conference on the Peaceful Uses of Atomic Energy, Geneva, 1955, Vol. 2, p. 3, United Nations, New York, 1956 (with modification).

the vicinity of the so-called "nuclear resonance" energies. Figure 2-15, for instance, gives the total and capture cross sections for aluminum. The total cross section was obtained from transmission measurements and thus includes both scatter and radiative capture. The capture cross section was obtained by measuring the induced radioactivity.

2-3.4   Fission

Fission is a unique type of capture process in which a nucleus captures a neutron and then disintegrates, emitting two or more

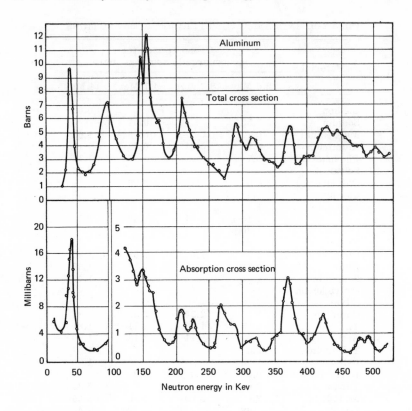

Fig. 2-15. Total and absorption cross sections of aluminum for neutrons in the intermediate-energy region. [From R. L. Henicel and H. H. Barschall, *Phys. Rev.*, 80:145 (1950).]

neutrons in the process. The most important fission reaction involves ^{235}U and is approximated by Eq. (2-49)

$$^{235}_{92}\text{U} + n \rightarrow ^{95}_{42}\text{Mo} + ^{139}_{57}\text{La} + 2n + 7\beta + Q \qquad (2\text{-}49)$$

where ^{95}Mo and ^{139}La represent the light and heavy fission fragments of Table 2-8, and Q represents the energy of the reaction.

2-3.5 Recoil Energy

Neutron capture with the subsequent emission of a nuclear particle is always accompanied by recoil of the nucleus. A particular case of interest to radiation chemists is the production of a "hot" atom, which utilizes a nuclear reaction such as the (n, γ) re-action, to produce energetic recoil atoms. This is also discussed in Chap. 5.

In gamma emission the gamma ray has a momentum $p_\gamma = E_\gamma/c$ and an energy, $E_\gamma = p_\gamma^2/2m_o$. The recoil atom momentum p_{r_2} must equal p_γ, and the recoil atom will have an energy $E_r = p_\gamma^2/2m = E_\gamma^2/2Mc^2$, where M is the mass of the recoil atom. This same formula applies also for neutrino emission. Recoil energies are important in radiation damage studies in organic materials. For example, for a light element $(A = 20)$, the recoil energy can be of the order of 1000 ev.

EXAMPLE 2.6: Calculate the recoil energy of an atom of mass 10, following emission of a 2 Mev gamma ray.

SOLUTION: The energy equivalent to one mass unit is $E = mc^2 = 931 \times 10^6$ ev.

$$E_r = \frac{(2 \times 10^6)^2}{1862 \times 10^6 \times 10} = 214 \text{ ev}$$

or, alternatively,

$$E_r = \frac{E_\gamma^2}{2\,Mc^2}$$

$$= \frac{4 \times 10^{12} \text{ (ev)}^2}{2 \times 10 \dfrac{9}{\text{mole}} \times \dfrac{\text{mole}}{6.02 \times 10^{23} \text{ molec}} \times 9 \times 10^{20} \dfrac{\text{cm}^2}{\text{sec}^2}}$$

$$= \frac{4 \times 10^{12} \text{ (ev)}^2}{\dfrac{180 \times 10^{20} \text{ ergs}}{6 \times 10^{23} \text{ molecules}} \times \dfrac{\text{ev}}{1.6 \times 10^{-12} \text{ ergs}}}$$

$$= \frac{4 \times 10^{12} \text{ ev}}{186.2 \times 10^8 \text{ recoil}}$$

$$E_r = 214 \text{ ev/recoil}$$

PROBLEMS

2-1   What is the maximum range of a 4 Mev electron in steel?
In lead?

2-2   The number of ion pairs formed in air by a 10 Mev proton
is 1100 per mg/cm^2. How many ion pairs per mg/cm^2
would be formed by an α particle traveling with the same
velocity?

2-3   The energy loss for a 10 Mev proton in carbon is 4.2007×10^{-2} $Mev/mg/cm^2$. What would be the energy loss in air in
$Mev/mg/cm^2$ and Mev/cm^2? What would be the energy loss
of a deuteron having the same energy?

2-4   The range of a 2 Mev particle in air is 1 cm.
a. What is its range in water?
b. What is the range in water of a deuteron of equivalent
velocity?
c. What is the range in water of a deuteron of equivalent
energy?

2-5   Calculate and compare the energy loss of electrons by radiation and by collision with and without relativistic corrections
at 0.01, 0.1, 1.0, 10, and 100 Mev.

2-6   Calculate and compare the relative energy losses by collision and by scattering for 100 Mev electrons.

2-7   Using the photoelectric mass-energy absorption coefficient of
air for a 0.02 Mev photon, compute the coefficient of air and of
lead for a 0.1 Mev photon. Compare with the literature values.

2-8   What are the minimum- and maximum-energy gamma rays
that can result from a Compton collision of a 2 Mev incident
gamma with a free electron?

2-9   Show that it is impossible for a photon to transfer all its
energy to a free electron.

2-10 How many elastic collisions must a 5 Mev neutron undergo
in water before it is thermalized? Estimate how long the
neutron path will be.

2-11 The neutron absorption cross section for cadmium at 1 ev
is 20 barns. On the basis of the $1/\overline{V}$ law, what would you expect the cross section to be at 100 ev?

REFERENCES

1. H. A. Bethe and J. Ashkin, "Experimental Nuclear Physics," p. 166, John Wiley & Sons, Inc., New York, 1953.

2. H. A. Bethe, Properties of Atomic Nuclei. II. *Range-Energy Curves: Alpha Particles, Protons, and Mesons*, USAEC Report BNL-T7, Brookhaven National Laboratory, June 1949.

3. D. E. Lea, "Actions of Radiations on Living Cells," The Macmillan Company, New York, 1947.

4. R. T. Berger, *Radiation Res.*, **15:**1-29 (1961).

5. E. P. Blizard (ed.), Shielding, vol. III, Part B, "Reactor Handbook," Interscience Publishers, Inc., New York, 1962.

3

RADIATION SOURCES

Radiation sources can be divided into two broad categories: (1) sources comprising machines that accelerate charged particles to high energies by electrical means and (2) sources based on some form of nuclear reaction, such as radioactive isotopes and nuclear reactors. In each of these broad categories there exists a wide choice of designs, permitting great flexibility. As a result, sources are available for almost any chemical experiment of interest.

3-1 VOLTAGE MULTIPLIER AND ELECTRIC DISCHARGE DEVICES

Conceptually, the simplest form of accelerator is a direct-voltage machine consisting of a high voltage transformer and a discharge tube. Particles gain energy moving from the anode to the cathode or from cathode to anode, depending on their charge. A very simple device is the electric discharge tube, which can easily be operated from a 110 volt line with a 5000 volt transformer. Many experiments have been performed with this type of irradiator. The principal sources of difficulty in using the device are the variable ion energies, plus wall and photochemical effects.

3-1.1 Electric Discharges

Although the overwhelming number of radiation chemistry experiments use sources in the upper kilo-electron volt (kev) and lower mega-electron volt (Mev) range, an appreciable amount of work is done in the kv range with electric discharges. Figure 3-1 shows the three types of discharges, arc, glow, and silent, and the regions of their existence in terms of current density vs. the ratio of pressure to field in the discharge zone. The simplest (and probably the least expensive form of gas discharge equipment) is the Tesla coil. Depending on conditions (gas pressure, gap, etc.) this coil can be operated as a glow discharge or a spark discharge.

Silent discharges are usually observed for pressures close to atmospheric and low current densities. It is a discharge resulting from the conductivity of the gas owing to its residual ionization and is characterized by the absence of space-charge effects. As the

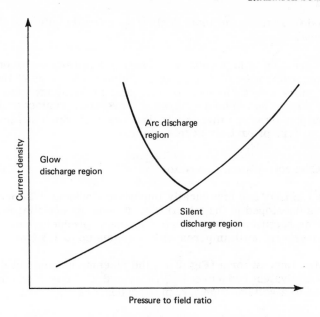

Fig. 3-1. Regions of existence of the basic types
of electric discharge.

potential is increased, a particular type of silent discharge called a *corona* appears. Coronas generally start near the electrodes in a nonhomogeneous field and are characterized by a glowing gas layer in which impact ionization of the gas takes place. Ozonizers, which represent a major industrial application of electric discharges, operate in the silent discharge region. When the current intensity is raised, the corona discharge becomes a spark discharge. The characteristic feature of a spark discharge is its discontinuous nature. After the discharge, the gas becomes conducting, and the discharge is quenched. 'The voltage then builds up, and another spark follows. When a capacitor is included in parallel with the discharge gap, as in an automobile ignition system, the discharge is called a *condensed spark discharge.*

Glow discharges are usually low pressure phenomena although under some conditions they can be made to occur at atmospheric pressures. The glow appears in the form of a fine sheath (cathode glow) separated from the anode by a dark layer (the Aston dark space) and passing into a weakly glowing layer (the cathode dark space). This distribution results from the complex voltage distribution and the various ion impact processes in the tube, which are discussed in a number of texts dealing specifically with gas discharge phenomena.

The creation of high voltages directly by batteries or motor-driven generators becomes impractical above a few tens of thousands of volts, hence methods for increasing the voltage from the primary source had to be developed. There are a variety of physical principles by which this can be done, each of which has produced a different type of particle accelerator.

3-1.2 Cockroft-Walton Generator

The familiar and historically important Cockroft-Walton machine was developed in the late 1920s. It consists of voltage-multiplying rectifier arrangements capable of producing particle beams of several milliamperes with energies up to 1.5 Mev.

In its simplest form (Fig. 3-2), the machine consists of three banks of equivalent condensers C_1, C_2, and C_3, one of which is connected to a voltage supply V, plus condensers C_{12} and C_{23}. In the

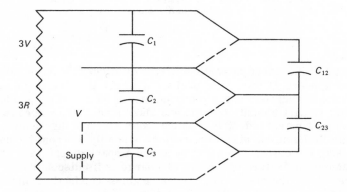

Fig. 3-2. Cockroft-Walton machine.

charge cycle, when C_{12} and C_{23} are connected to C_2 and C_3 (dotted lines), C_{23} is charged to a voltage V. The connections between the banks of condensers are then switched (solid lines), and C_{23} is made to share its charge with C_2. The voltage across C_{23} and C_2 is $1/2$ V if the capacitances are equal. In the next reversal, C_{23} is recharged, but C_2 then shares its charge with C_{12}. This pumping process is continued until the voltage $3V$ is developed across C_1. The voltage multiplication thus equals the number of primary, C_n, condensers.

The apparatus utilizes vacuum tube rectifiers instead of mechanical switches and embodies a number of other modifications. The Cockroft-Walton machine has found its major use as a positive-ion accelerator.

3-2 VAN DE GRAAFF ACCELERATOR

The basic principle of the Van de Graaff accelerator is that a charged conductor brought into contact with a hollow conductor will lose its charge to the hollow conductor, regardless of its own potential. Thus, were it not for insulation difficulties at the high voltage terminal and leakage from and to the charge transfer system, an infinite number of transfers could produce unlimited potentials.

As is seen in Fig. 3-3, the electric charge is carried to the high voltage terminal by an endless woven-cotton neoprene-impregnated belt. The charge is sprayed onto the belt within the field free region at ground potential by a controlled corona discharge from an array of steel needles or screens in close proximity to the belt. A regulated high voltage of 25 to 40 kv dc is applied between the pulley and the points to ionize the insulating gas in the gap. The charge remains on the belt surface.

The belt carries the charge (electrons) to the high voltage terminal, where it is transferred to the upper insulated shell by corona points located so as to permit the charged belt to rise in potential. Thus the charge flows into the terminal without assistance from a power supply. Since the voltage buildup is limited by the leakage in the system, the entire generator must be enclosed in a pressure vessel filled with dry compressed gas.

The high voltage terminal is a polished metal hemisphere supported by a number of equipotential metal planes separated by insulators. The charge bleeds through the column of planes by means of voltage dividing resistors that connect the planes consecutively and provide a controlled electric gradient.

The acceleration tube is a segmented tube made of glass toroids cemented to metal disks within the supporting column and electrically connected to it via the metal disks (planes). The acceleration tube, which must be maintained at pressures of 10^{-5} to 10^{-6} tors, is insulated so as to provide gradient control, focusing, and a uniform field within the tube. At the high voltage terminal, power is available for operating a filament to produce electrons or positive ions. The latter are obtained from a gas discharge (usually H_2).

The Van de Graaff generator can be operated in a pulsed mode. In this mode the capacitance of the high voltage terminal, rather

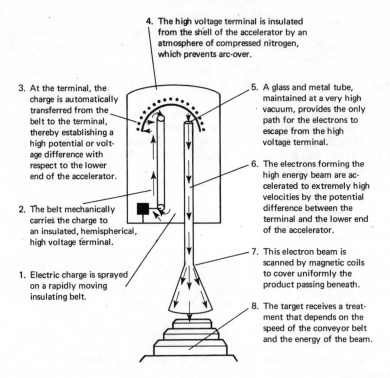

4. The high voltage terminal is insulated from the shell of the accelerator by an atmosphere of compressed nitrogen, which prevents arc-over.

3. At the terminal, the charge is automatically transferred from the belt to the terminal, thereby establishing a high potential or voltage difference with respect to the lower end of the accelerator.

2. The belt mechanically carries the charge to an insulated, hemispherical, high voltage terminal.

1. Electric charge is sprayed on a rapidly moving insulating belt.

5. A glass and metal tube, maintained at a very high vacuum, provides the only path for the electrons to escape from the high voltage terminal.

6. The electrons forming the high energy beam are accelerated to extremely high velocities by the potential difference between the terminal and the lower end of the accelerator.

7. This electron beam is scanned by magnetic coils to cover uniformly the product passing beneath.

8. The target receives a treatment that depends on the speed of the conveyor belt and the energy of the beam.

Fig. 3-3. Schematic diagram of a Van de Graaff accelerator.

than the total available power, governs the total energy available per pulse. Electron beam pulses of several hundred milliamperes peak at pulse lengths of several microseconds can be produced; however, special measures must be taken to minimize voltage drops during the pulse.

Although it is the most important, the Van de Graaff is not the only electrostatic accelerator. There has, of late, been a revival of interest, particularly in Europe, in the so-called "cylindrical" Felici generator, in which an insulating cylinder takes the place of the belt. This machine has a greater current carrying capacity than the Van de Graaff and is undergoing rapid development.

The Van de Graaff generator is basically a low current machine. Difficulties with space charge buildup at the point where the charges are sprayed on the belt, the unsuitability of the belt for carrying large currents, and limitations in belt speeds impose upper limits

on the output power. These inherent problems have led, in part, to
the development of a number of lower voltage, 3 Mev (and lower),
high current machines.

The electron beam of the Van de Graaff accelerator may be
converted to high energy X-rays (bremsstrahlung) by the use of a
heavy metal target. Neutrons may be produced by taking advantage
of many nuclear reactions, such as the (γ, n) on beryllium, or by
using a proton or deuteron beam for such reactions as (p, n) on
lithium.

3-3 RESONANT TRANSFORMERS

The resonant transformers currently being manufactured are
capable of producing 1-, 2-, and 4-Mev electrons at current ratings
up to 6 milliamp average beam current. The resonant transformer
was originally developed during the period 1937-1939 as an X-ray
source for the treatment of cancer, but in 1948 the machine was
modified to serve as an electron source. It is the high current
capability and the reliability of performance which make the machine attractive, particularly for industrial applications.

Figure 3-4 is a cutaway of a resonant transformer. A low
voltage, cone-shaped primary coil surrounds the lower end of the
high voltage secondary coil, which consists of a large number of
thin flat sections, each of which produce about 8.5 kv. The lower
end of the high voltage coil is grounded; the upper end is shielded.

The resonance principle has been explained by W. F. Westendorp[1] as follows:

"The high voltage coil has a large inductance which
is chosen to be in resonance with its terminal and distributed capacity at the operating frequency of 180 cycles
per second. To build this large resonance system up to
the amplitude of oscillation of a million or more volts
requires a relatively small input power which is needed
to operate the electron beam tube and supply the losses
of the transformer. Consequently the relatively small
cone-shaped primary windings will suffice to furnish this
power to the resonant system. The mechanical analogy
of the resonant transformer is the swinging pendulum or a
mechanical system in which a mass is oscillating at resonance with an elastic support. In such mechanical systems
a small force at the proper frequency can, with relatively
little power, maintain large amplitude oscillations containing much stored energy."

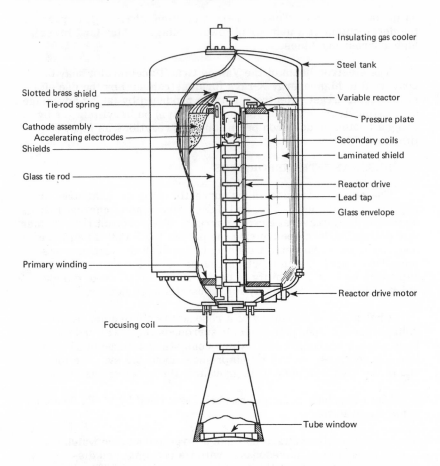

Insulating gas cooler

Steel tank

Slotted brass shield

Tie-rod spring

Cathode assembly

Accelerating electrodes

Shields

Glass tie rod

Primary winding

Variable reactor

Pressure plate

Secondary coils

Laminated shield

Reactor drive

Lead tap

Glass envelope

Reactor drive motor

Focusing coil

Tube window

Fig. 3-4. Schematic diagram of a resonant transformer.

The vacuum tube, which extends through the central space of the high voltage coil, consists of a cathode at the top followed by intermediate electrodes in the glass envelope and a grounded extension tube with a window through which the beam emerges. Power losses through the window are a problem with this machine. The high currents employed (6 ma) require a relatively thick window. In addition, the beam has energies substantially lower than the peak voltage. For a window consisting of 0.007 in. titanium, almost 20% of the beam energy is lost with a 1 Mev beam.

A very important auxiliary circuit in all machines is the sweep circuit, which distributes the beam over the conveyor system. In

machines with large window losses, these sweep systems also serve
the purpose of keeping the window temperature below failure temperature. Generally, a sweep yoke is used with a magnetic field
which sweeps the electron beam 180 times per second across the
conveyor belt. A simultaneous cross scan sweeps the beam in the
short window dimension at a frequency of 200,000 cycles to keep
the window from overheating.

For such machines as the resonance generators, the depth-dose
curves are complex functions of the window and machine parameters
since the beam is not monoenergetic.

3-4 INSULATING CORE TRANSFORMER

The insulating core transformer (ICT), which was invented by
Dr. Robert J. Van de Graaff, is one of the newest of the commercially available accelerators. It is primarily a low voltage industrial irradiation machine designed to provide high power outputs at
relatively low cost on a production line basis.

The machine consists of a series of secondary windings whose
ac output is rectified and connected in series to the preceding and
succeeding elements. The windings are excited by sections of core
that are insulated by contiguous rectifier and condenser assemblies.
The entire power supply is housed in a steel tank filled with insulating gas.

In the voltage generating system of the ICT, the magnetic core
is divided into segments that are insulated from each other so that
each core segment can be maintained at the total potential developed
at that stage. At the high voltage terminal, a large insulating gap
separates the terminal from the remainder of the core. The magnetic reluctance of the circuit is kept low by very short gaps provided between core segments and by a large surface area for the
long gap at the terminal. Thin plastic materials are used in the
small gaps.

Figure 3-5 is a schematic diagram of the transformer. The high
voltage terminal is at the bottom of the central column. The top of
the column and the outer shell of core material form the outer path
of the magnetic circuit and are at ground potential. Power is delivered to the primary coil by a motor generator or a signal generator at a frequency of about 10,000 cycles per second. Each core
segment is pancake-shaped and is surrounded by a ribbon winding
that is the secondary of the transformer circuit. A voltage of about
25 kv is induced in each secondary winding. The ac power developed in the secondary windings is converted to dc power by means
of a silicon rectifier and is a dc power supply. Voltage addition is
obtained along the column by the distributed series of capacitors

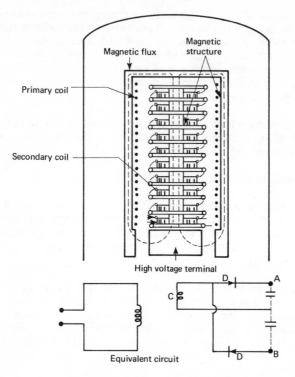

Fig. 3-5. Diagram of the insulating core transformer
without an electron acceleration system.

between the core segments. The latest versions of the ICT embody
three-phase systems and standard power frequencies.

3-5 DYNAMITRON

The Dynamitron, like the ICT and the resonance transformer,
is a relatively low voltage-high current machine. It is an accelerator that uses a cascaded rectifier system in which all rectifiers
are driven in parallel from a high frequency oscillator, as shown
in Fig. 3-6. Four large radio frequency (RF) electrodes situated
inside the cylindrical pressure vessel draw power from the oscillator. The RF potential is then capacitatively coupled to corona
rings, which are mechanically affixed to each rectifier tube through
a high pressure dielectric gas.

The same RF potential is impressed on each rectifier; and the
direct current then flows through the stack of rectifiers to establish

a large dc potential at the high voltage terminal. Charged particles
are produced by the ion source situated in the high voltage terminal
and are accelerated to ground through an evacuated beam tube.

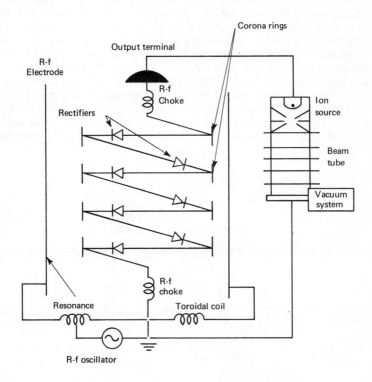

Fig. 3-6. Schematic diagram of a Dynamitron.

3-6 IMPULSE GENERATOR

In an impulse generator banks of capacitors are charged in
parallel from a relatively low voltage rectifier set and are discharged in series by spark-gap arrangements. The combination of
an impulse generator and a vacuum discharge tube was the basis of
a machine called the *Capacitron*, constructed by A. Brash, A. Waly,
and W. Huber. It was, along with the Van de Graaff, one of the
earliest machines to be used for radiation chemistry experiments.
It is no longer manufactured.

3-7 LINEAR ACCELERATORS

The insulation problems inherent in the direct-voltage devices described thus far must be avoided if high (>4 Mev) voltages are to be achieved at even reasonably high beam currents. There are two ways of doing this, both of which depend on a particle's transversing an electric or magnetic field many times and thus gaining its energy in small increments. One way is to have closed, or nearly closed, orbits as in the betatron, cyclotron, and synchrotron; the other is to accelerate along a linear path. The former method is suitable only for low current devices; the latter method is used in the high beam current-high voltage linear accelerators where a particle moves along in step with a traveling electromagnetic field or with the period of a radio frequency excitation. The basic components of the machine are shown in Fig. 3-7.

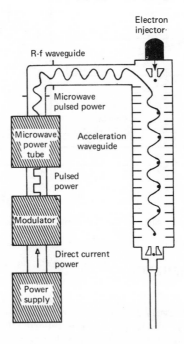

Fig. 3-7. Schematic diagram
of a linear accelerator.

The modern linear accelerator, with its large RF power requirement, is an outgrowth of wartime radar development in England and the United States. The English manufacturers based their machines on the efficient and compact magnetron RF sources; U.S. technology developed about the higher energy klystrons. Both types of power source are still used today.

Linear accelerators function by virtue of the axial component of an electric field that is established when RF power of the appropriate wavelength is propagated inside a hollow, smooth-walled metallic tube. The phase velocity of the traveling wave is matched to the velocity of the electrons by metallic disks or irises inserted into the tube to modify the phase velocity.

Electrons injected in pulses into the axis of the initial section will collect about some discrete phase of the wave and will move along in step with the wave, abstracting energy and being accelerated. Power tube and electron injector are synchronized by means of trigger pulses originating from a timing oscillator. For high energy to be attained in a practical length, the wave guides require accelerating fields of tens of kilovolts per centimeter. This, in turn, requires power inputs of the order of megawatts. The power sources must therefore be pulsed. Suitable pulsing equipment is based on the pulsed magnetron power sources developed for wartime radar.

Since 1949, when the first klystron-powered linear accelerator was built at Stanford, there has been a steady change from magnetron-powered to klystron-powered devices. The original machines had S-band (2855 mc) generators; however, since 1959 the 1300 mc L-band has also been used.

Linear accelerators have fewer limitations than any other type of accelerator. They can be built, for a price, to voltages in the billion electron volt region and with beam outputs as high as 40 kw at 100 Mev. Pulse lengths from the nanosecond to the millisecond range are now available, the longer pulse lengths having been made possible by the development of the L-band klystrons.

3-8 X-RAY PRODUCTION

Any of the machines previously discussed, as well as the simple Coolidge tube, can be used to produce electromagnetic radiation by allowing the electrons to strike a heavy-metal target. The sum of the bremsstrahlung produced when the electrons are decelerated in the fields of the nuclei and of the characteristic radiation emitted when electrons drop from the outer to the inner shell constitute the so-called "X-ray beam," which has the properties discussed in the following sections.

3-8.1 Angular Distribution

The angular distribution of the emitted radiation can be predicted theoretically. For thin targets at low energy, the distribution consists of two lobes at right angles to the original beam, similar to those for the photoelectric effect. At higher energies the lobes tilt forward to give a more nearly symmetrical distribution. This angular distribution is a strong function of target thickness and cannot be calculated for thick targets. For thick targets at 400 kev operating voltage, the intensity is distributed primarily at right angles to the incoming beam, but at energies above 1 Mev, it is primarily forward. With energies of 3 Mev, as much as 65% is emitted in the forward cone.

3-8.2 Spectral Distribution

The maximum photon energy is equal to the peak electron voltage; however, a very appreciable fraction of the photon energy is in the form of low energy radiation, much of which is absorbed in the target, which acts to some extent as a filter.

In addition to the target itself, an auxilliary absorber is customarily used to remove very low energy radiation in applications where very high surface doses must be avoided. The spectral density of the beam is customarily characterized in terms of the half-value layer (HVL), the thickness of absorber required to reduce the beam intensity by one half. At 400 kv, for instance, the HVL is about 4 mm of copper.

The HVL of the beam, as would be expected, is a function of filter thickness (Fig. 3-8). Shown also in Fig. 3-8 are the characteristic K and L peaks which, in practice, are either filtered off or constitute a negligible portion of the total intensity. Thus the curve of energy vs. intensity is generally treated as a continuous one.

3-8.3 Intensity

Total photon power output is the integrated area under any of the curves shown in Fig. 3-8. In practice, the total power output over a 4π angle is approximately linear with the atomic number of the target, and exponential with electron energy. The efficiency with which electron power is converted to usable photon power is thus a strong function of energy. At 200 kv it is about 0.2%; at 2 Mev it is, perhaps, 7%; at 3 Mev, 10%; and at 4 Mev 12%.[2] These low efficiencies demand that the targets have adequate cooling and thermal resistance. Figure 3-9 is a compilation of several measurements of forward-directed X-ray energy vs. bombarding electron energy for thick, heavy-atomic-weight targets.

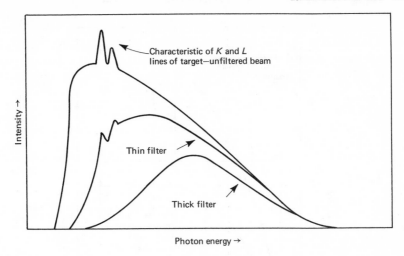

Fig. 3-8. Effect of filters on X-ray energy distribution.

3-9 NEUTRON PRODUCTION BY ACCELERATORS

Accelerators may be used to generate neutrons by (p,n), (d,n), and (γ,n) reactions. Some of the commonly used reactions are listed in Table 3-1. The neutron energy shown is a function of the nuclear reaction in the target, the energy of the incident particle, and the angle at which the neutron is emitted and thus may vary considerably, depending on the particular experiment.

The neutron yield is thus a complex function of the particular reaction as well as the bombarding energy, and the primary beam characteristics. Figure 3-10 is a compilation of neutron yields as a function of bombarding particle energy for most of the common nuclear reactions.

3-10 NUCLEAR REACTORS AS RADIATION SOURCES

A nuclear reactor is an extremely complex radiation source; the intensity, spectrum, and type of radiation are strong functions not only of the particular reactor but also of the position within a given reactor. The interest in reactors as sources is due to the large radiation volumes available, their stability, their future potential as large industrial radiation sources, and the extremely high dose rates obtainable (in contrast to isotope sources). Both particle and electromagnetic radiations are produced in a reactor.

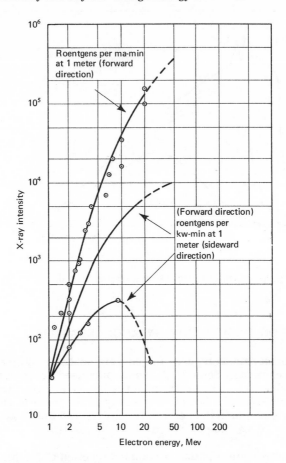

Fig. 3-9. Forward-directed X-ray production vs. bombarding electron energy for thick, heavy-atomic-weight targets, (Charlesby, op. cit.).

3-10.1 Neutrons

There are on the average 2.5 neutrons emitted per ^{235}U fission, and they have an average energy of about 2 Mev. In the reactor these "fast" neutrons are thermalized by collision with a moderator and then undergo absorption processes. Fast neutrons also undergo absorption but, as indicated in Chap. 2, the cross section for slow-neutron capture is considerably greater than that for fast.

The relation between average flux and reactor power in a thermal reactor is

Table 3-1. NUCLEAR REACTIONS USED TO PRODUCE NEUTRONS

Incident radiation	Reaction	Lowest neutron energy, Mev
Alpha particles	$^9Be(a, n)\ ^{12}C$	5.71
	$^{11}B(a, n)\ ^{14}N$	
	$^7Li(a, n)\ ^{10}B$	
Deutrons	$^2H(d, n)^3He$	2.45
	$^3H(d, n)^4He$	14.05
	$^9Be(d, n)\ ^{10}B$	
Protons	$T(p, n)\ ^3He$	1.19
	$^9Be(p, n)\ ^9B$	
	$^7Li(p, n)\ ^7Be$	1.88
Photons	$D(\gamma, n)\ H$	0.3
	$^9Be(\gamma, n)\ ^8Be$	0.16
	$^{238}U(\gamma, n)\ ^{237}U$	6.0
	$^2H(\gamma, n)\ ^1H$	0.1

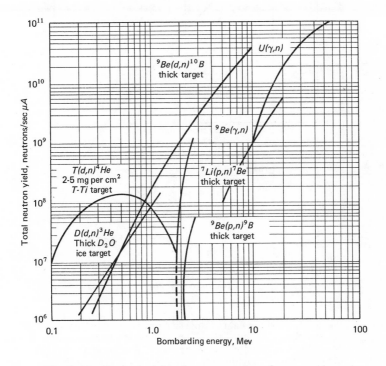

Fig. 3-10. Neutron yields from several nuclear reactions.

$$P = 5 \times 10^{-11} \ \phi_{av} \ G \tag{3-1}$$

where P = reactor power (in watts)

ϕ_{av} = average thermal-neutron flux (in neutrons/cm^2/sec)

G = reactor loading (in grams of ^{235}U)

The neutron spectrum 3 in. from the lattice of the Materials Testing Reactor (MTR), a light-water-moderated, enriched-uranium reactor is shown in Fig. 3-11. To the right of the figure, in the Mev range, are the fast neutrons, the pure fission spectrum being given by the dashed line. In general, the neutron energy spectrum is the most difficult of all reactor parameters to measure with precision. Measurement techniques as well as the neutron spectrum will be discussed in greater detail in Chap. 4.

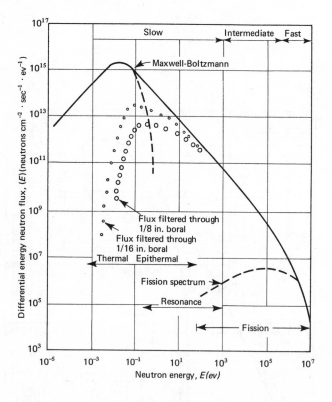

Fig. 3-11. Neutron energy spectrum of Materials Testing Reactor. (From C. D. Bopp and W. W. Parkinson, Jr., Nuclear Reactors as Sources of Radiation in A. Charlesby (ed.), "Radiation Sources," p. 8, Pergamon Press, Ltd., Oxford, 1964.)

3-10.2   Electrons

The radioactive fission products emit, among other things, large numbers of electrons. The average energy of the emitted electrons is 0.4 Mev, and their rate of production is described empirically by the equation $A = 3.8 \times 10^{-6}\, t^{-1.2}$, where A is electrons/sec/fission and t is days after fission.

Unless the fission products are separated or escape from the fuel, as in a chemonuclear reactor, the electrons will be largely absorbed and thus will not be available.

3-10.3   Gamma Radiation

In addition to the instantaneous gammas released in fission, there are appreciable amounts of electromagnetic radiation emitted by the fission products, and a lesser amount that results from neutron capture reactions and bremsstrahlung. Anywhere from 5.5 to 5.7% of the fission energy appears as gamma radiation.

3-11   LARGE ISOTOPE SOURCES

There are over 1300 isotopes that could, in principle, be used as radiation sources. These isotopes either can be manufactured in nuclear reactors by (γ, n), (n,p), and (n, α) reactions or can be made available as part of the hundreds of millions of curies of mixed and partially separated fission products that are the waste products of nuclear fuel reprocessing plants.

From among those isotopes that are solids at room temperature, are immediately or practicably available in reasonable quantities (in terms of the amount of activity), have reasonably long half lives, and are moderate in cost, the choice narrows down to those whose characteristics are given in Table 3-2. From the standpoint of readily available sources for use in radiation chemistry studies, this list can be reduced to two isotopes, ^{60}Co and ^{137}Cs. Cesium-137 source technology, however, is still being developed. Despite the fact that both Brookhaven National Laboratory and Harwell (England) have installed 500,000-curie ^{137}Cs sources, and that many teletherapy sources have been fabricated, this isotope is not in general use by radiation chemists.

Cobalt-60 is, by many orders of magnitude, the favorite isotopic radiation source. It is available in rods, tubes, strips, disks, and pellets, in specific activities ranging from 1 to over 500 curies/g, and in quantities of up to millions of curies. It also enjoys the unique and distinct advantage of being available from at least five primary sources: Brookhaven National Laboratory, Oak Ridge National Laboratory, Atomic Energy of Canada, Ltd., the

Table 3-2. CHARACTERISTICS OF RADIOISOTOPIC SOURCES

	^{60}Co	^{90}Sr	^{137}Cs	^{144}Ce	^{147}Pm	^{170}Tm	^{204}Tl
Watts/g (pure)[a]	17.4	0.95	0.42	25.6	0.33	15.6	0.67
Half life, years	5.3	28	30	0.78	2.7	0.35	4
Estimated isotopic purity, %	10	20	35	18	95	7.5[b]	20[c]
Compound form	Metal	SrTiO$_3$	Glass	CeO$_2$	Pm$_2$O$_3$[d]	Tm$_2$O$_3$	Tl$_2$O$_3$
Active isotope in compound, %	10	24	16	15	82	6.57	17.7
Watts/g (compound)	1.7	0.23	0.067	3.8	0.27	1.03	0.12
Density of compound, g/cm^3	8.9	4.6	3.2	6.4	6.6	7.7	9.0
Availability (annual kw$_t$, 1967)[e]	Avail.	Avail. (67)	Avail. (48)	Avail. (800)	Avail. (11)	Poten. avail.	Poten. avail.
Radiation (major)	γ,β	β	β,γ	β,γ	β	β	β
Shielding required	Heavy	Heavy	Heavy	Heavy	Minor	Minor	Minor
Biological hazard (MPC), μ c/cm^3	3×10^{-9}	3×10^{-10}	5×10^{-9}	2×10^{-9}	2×10^{-8}	10^{-8}	9×10^{-9}
Estimated cost, $/$g$ (pure)	570	18[e]	9[e]	23[e]	30[e]	156	67
Estimated cost, $/watt	33	19[e]	21[e]	1.00[e]	91[e]	10	100
Curies/g (pure)	1130	142	87	3180	914	6000	428
Curies/watt	65	150	207	124	2770	385	640

[a]Includes contributions from daughters at equilibrium (thermal watts).
[b]At this concentration ^{170}Tm is expected on ^{169}Tm irradiation without need for isotopic separation.
[c]At this concentration ^{204}Tl is probable only with isotopic separation or irradiation at very high flux.
[d]Metal may be preferred; mp=1080°C (F. Weigel, Angew. Chem., 75:451 (1963)) and expected power density=2.3 watts/cm^3.
[e](From proposed Hanford Isotope Plant, USAEC Report HW-77770); kw$_t$ = thermal kilowatts.

Table 3-2. CHARACTERISTICS OF RADIOISOTOPIC SOURCES (Continued)

	^{210}Po	^{228}Th	^{232}U	^{238}Pu	^{241}Am	^{242}Cm	^{244}Cm
Watts/g (pure)[f]	141	170	4.4	0.56	0.11	120	2.8
Half life, years	0.38	1.9	74	89	458	0.45	18
Estimated isotopic purity, %	95	95	85	80	90	90	90
Compound form	Metal	ThO$_2$	UO$_2$	PuO$_2$	Metal	Cm$_2$O$_3$	Cm$_2$O$_3$
Active isotope in compound, %	95	83	75	70	90	82	82
Watts/g (compound)	134	141	3.3	0.39	0.1	98	2.3
Density of compound, g/cm^3	9.3	9	10	10	11.7	11.75	11.75
Availability	Avail.	Poten. avail.	Poten. avail.	Limited avail.	Limited prod.	Poten. avail.	Poten. avail.
Radiation (major)	a	a,γ	a,γ	a	a	a,n	a,n
Shielding required	Minor	Heavy	Heavy	Minor	Minor	Minor[g]	Minor[g]
Biological hazard (MPC), μ c/cm^3	2 × 10^{-9}[b]	2 × 10^{-12}	9 × 10^{-12}	7 × 10^{-13}	2 × 10^{-12}	4 × 10^{-11}	3 × 10^{-12}
Estimated cost, $/g (pure)	2800[b]	6600	1540	500[i]	200[i]	2000[i]	1000[i]
Estimated cost, $/watt	20	40	350	894	1820	17	357
Curies/g (pure)	4500	4100[k]	114[k]	17	3.25	3310	84
Curies/watt	32	24	26	30	30	28	30
Spontaneous fission: half life, years			8 × 10^{13}	4.9 × 10^{10}	1.4 × 10^{13}	7.2 × 10^{6}	1.4 × 10^{7}

[f] Includes contributions from daughters at equilibrium (thermal watts).
[g] Except for shielding against neutrons.
[b] Upward revision of minimum costs shown in Holsted-Albaugh Hanford Diversification Report, p. 13, Jan. 15, 1964.
[i] (From AEC data; also Nucleonics, 21(3):63 (March 1963)).
[j] Anticipated costs with large-scale reactor fueling with plutonium (Pu at $10/g).
[k] Alpha disintegration curies including daughters at equilibrium.

United Kingdom Atomic Energy Authority, and the General Electric Co. More than 10 million curies of cobalt have been sold in the past 10 years, and the production capacity is essentially unlimited. Should the market warrant, the Savannah River Plant of the AEC, for instance, could produce up to 8 million curies per reactor-year as incidental production to their present operations.

Cobalt-60 sources, as well as other large isotope sources, can be grouped into three general categories with respect to their construction:

(1) Fixed-source, fixed-radiation cavity. In this type of instal- lation, the shipping container usually serves as the radiation facility.

(2) Movable-cavity, fixed-source design in which the source is held in place and the sample cavity is moved.

(3) Fixed-cavity, movable-source design in which the source emerges from a container or pit into the irradiation cavity only when required.

Most of the laboratory sources used by radiation chemists op- erating on limited budgets are of the fixed-source variety. Figure 3-12 is a schematic drawing of an early hollow-cylinder Brookhaven source. Fueled with from 50 to 3000 curies, sources of this general type deliver anywhere from a few thousand up to 10^6 rad/hr to samples whose size is usually limited to less than 1000 cm^3. One of the most popular of these sources is the Gamma-Cell.* In this motorized device the sample is placed in the radiation field by a movable, double-ended plug arrangement, making this a fixed- source, movable-volume irradiator.

Considerable ingenuity has been shown by economy minded radiation chemists, who have built a variety of small, earth-, oil-, water-, and concrete-shielded, fixed-source installations. All these installations are relatively inflexible, can accommodate only small samples, and provide very inefficient use of isotope power. To overcome the major limitations of the fixed-source installations requires going to the considerably more expensive movable-source installation. Here the source is stored in a container and is moved in and out of the radiation area, which may be relatively large and to which there is relatively free access. The most economic ver- sion of this source is one in which the shipping container is used as the isotope holder. The source is generally attached to a rod that moves axially through the storage cylinder into a concrete- or earth-shielded enclosure.

---

*Available from the Atomic Energy Establishment of Canada.

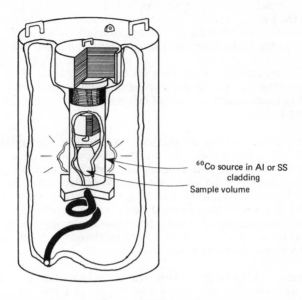

Fig. 3-12. Fixed volume, fixed source ^{60}Co irradiator.
[(From B. Manowitz, Nucleonics, 9, No. 2, 10 (1951))].

Large industrial installations are usually of the movable source variety. The sources are generally held in place, except during refueling, and the sample is passed by the source on overhead or belt-conveyer systems. A number of such source concepts and installations are described in the literature.[3,4] All are different, and each was engineered to do a specific processing job, such as pasteurization of food, sterilization of wool, sterilization of catgut sutures, and crosslinking of polyethelene coated wire. There are, however, certain physical principles, basic to isotope source design; the most important are those used in calculating the radiation flux. The flux must be known both for shielding design and for calculating process requirements.

3-11.1 Isotope Sources and Dose Field

Methods for evaluating the radiation field from isotopic sources of different geometric shapes have been developed. The main problem with all methods arises from the production of secondary photons. At any point in a medium, the flux of primary gamma rays (photons) can easily be calculated since the primaries penetrate a medium under narrow beam attenuation conditions. The scattered (secondary) photons influence the whole process of gamma ray penetration. The accumulation of scattered photons is related to the buildup factor, and in any shielding calculations the source geometry will determine the appropriate buildup factors. Tables of buildup factors for shielding calculations are available.[5]

In shielding design and other similar applications, it has become standard practice to use the narrow-beam total absorption coefficients and to compensate for broad beams by multiplying the flux by a buildup factor.

These buildup factors are difficult to calculate, being functions of the absorber material, photon energy, photon beam geometry, absorber geometry, and path length. Methods for calculating them include the moment, or polynominal method of Spencer, Fano, Goldstein and Wilkens, asymptotic methods, and Monte Carlo methods. The results of some of these calculations are plotted in Fig 3-13, which shows the buildup factor for point isotropic sources through various mediums as a function of shield thickness, source energy, and linear absorption coefficient.

The dose buildup factors, although not inappreciable, are not as important as a cursory examination of Fig. 3-13 might indicate. In general, for small variations in thickness, the buildup factors may be approximated by a linear equation of the form

$$B = 1 + a\mu x \qquad\qquad (3\text{-}2)$$

where the constant a is evaluated from the slopes of the individual curves of Fig. 3-13, μ is the linear attenuation coefficient, and x the shield thickness. This approximation is permissible because the attenuation through an absorber is exponential whereas the buildup factor is only a slowly increasing function of absorber thickness.

3-11.2   Isotope Sources — Self absorption

In large gamma sources, as well as in all sources that emit particle radiation, self absorption poses a serious problem. In addition to representing a loss of radiation power, the self absorbed flux generates an amount of heat which in some instances is adequate to calcine the sample. Indeed, in fission product processing the heat generated by self absorption is customarily used to evaporate liquid wastes. To calculate the amount of self absorption, one needs to know

(1) The specific activity of the source,

(2) The geometric distribution of the isotope in the source,

(3) The absorption coefficient path length of the radiation.

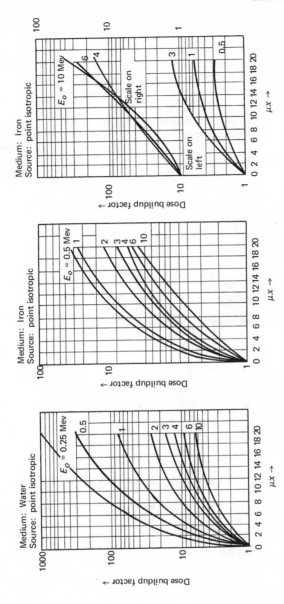

Fig. 3-13. Dose buildup factors for point isotropic sources as a function of shield thickness, x. (From B. T. Price, C. C. Horton, and K. T. Spinney, "Radiation Shielding," Pergamon Press, 1957).

3-12 ALPHA SOURCES

Among the isotopic sources of importance historically are the alpha emitters used in early studies of the effects of radiation on gases. Table 3-3 is a list of alpha-emitting isotopes and their pertinent characteristics.

Table 3-3. ALPHA RADIATORS*

Element	Energy, Mev	Half life	Range in air (15°C, 760 mm), cm	Initial velocity, 10^9 cm/sec	Number ($\times 10^5$) of ion pairs in air
^{238}U	4.180	4.55×10^9 years	2.73	1.39	1.25
^{235}U	4.350	8.52×10^8 years			
^{234}U	4.763	2.3×10^5 years	3.28	1.26	1.37
^{230}Th	4.68, 4.61	8×10^4 years	3.19	1.48	1.41
^{226}Ra	4.78 (94.2%), 4.59	1620 years	3.39	1.51	1.47
^{222}Rn	5.486	3.823 days	4.12	1.62	1.67
^{218}Po (RaA)	6.00	3.05 min	4.72	1.69	1.83
^{214}Bi (RaC) a(0.04%) β(99.96%)	5.505	19.72 min			
^{214}Po (RaC')	7.680	160 sec	6.97	1.92	2.37
^{208}Po		2.9 years			
^{232}Th	3.98	1.389×10^{10} years	2.90	1.44	
^{224}Ra (ThX)	5.86, 5.44	3.64 days	4.354	1.65	1.75
^{220}Rn (Tn)	6.282	54.5 sec	5.063	1.73	1.94
^{216}Po (ThA)	6.774	0.145 sec	5.683	1.80	2.09
^{212}Bi (ThC)	6.081	60.6 min	4.787	1.70	1.87
^{212}Po (ThC')	8.776	0.3 sec	8.617	2.05	2.71
^{236}Pu	5.862	2.7 years			
^{239}Pu	5.15	24,413 years			
^{240}Pu	5.246	6600 years			
^{239}Am	5.90	12 hr			
^{240}Cm	6.38	26.8 days			
^{241}Cm	6.20	35 days			

*From S. C. Lind, "Radiation Chemistry of Gases," p. 275, Reinhold Publishing Corporation, New York, 1961.

Of those listed, radon gas is, in principle, most suited for gas-phase experiments. Because RaA and RaC are deposited on the walls of experimental vessels, radon is usually confined in a thin-walled glass bulb, which is then suspended in the sample holder. In this form it has very few advantages over polonium, which can be obtained as a metal, plated on a stainless steel backing. Extensive discussions of the problems involved with sources of this type can be found in Lind.[6]

3-13 BETA EMITTERS

In addition to ^{90}Sr, whose properties are given in Table 3-2, gaseous tritium and, to a much lesser extent, krypton sources have been used by radiation chemists. Tritium, whose properties are given in Table 3-4, has many advantages for gas phase work. Like radon, it can be mixed directly with the gas being studied, and, because its radiation is soft (av. 5.69 kev) no auxiliary shielding is required.

Table 3-4. GASEOUS BETA SOURCES

Nuclide	Half life	Maximum β_n energy, Mev	Method of Production
^{3}H	12.46 years	0.018	^{6}Li (n, a)
^{85}Kr	10.6 years	0.67	Fission

3-14 ISOTOPIC NEUTRON SOURCES

Table 3-5 lists some of the radionuclides that can be used as photoneutron sources. The first two listed, the ^{124}Sb-Be, and ^{226}Ra-Be sources, are photoneutron sources and thus have large associated gamma fields. The last four sources are activated by alpha particles, the source emitter usually being thoroughly blended in with the target element, beryllium

Table 3-5. PROPERTIES OF ISOTOPIC NEUTRON SOURCES

Source	Half life	Actual yields, neutron/sec/curie	Average neutron energy
^{124}Sb-Be	60 days	1.6×10^6	24 kev
^{226}Ra-Be	1622 years	1.3×10^6	200 kev
^{239}Pu-Be	24,600 years	1.6×10^6	3 to 5 Mev
^{241}Am-Be	470 years	2.2×10^6	3 to 5 Mev
^{210}Po-Be	138 days	2.5×10^6	4 to 2 Mev
^{226}Ra-Be	1020 years	1.04×10^7	4 to 0 Mev

3-15 ON-SITE RADIATORS

A number of radiation sources are either presently available or potentially available only at nuclear reactor sites. These sources, though usually unsuitable for research purposes, represent potentially massive amounts of radiation power.

3-15.1 Gaseous Fission Products

An appreciable fraction of the fission products is in the form of the radioactive gases, xenon, krypton, and iodine. If these gases, which are primarily gamma emitters, could be made available in some external loop arrangement, as much as 0.7% of the fission energy could theoretically be recovered as radiation power.

3-15.2 Solid Fission Products

Figure 3-14 shows the gamma-radiation power from ^{235}U fission products with half lives greater than eight days. Because of the rapid decay of ^{140}La and other short-lived fission products, it is common practice to hold spent fuel elements at the reactor sites for a period of time so that they can be shipped more easily to the reprocessing plant.

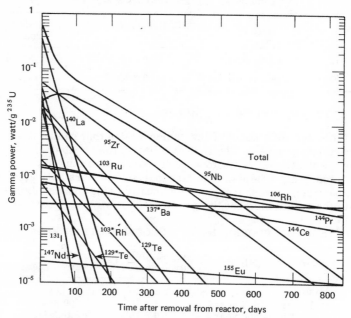

Fig. 3-14. Gamma-radiation power from fission products having half lives greater than eight days in ^{235}U fuel elements after 30 days of irradiation at a neutron flux of 2.10^{13} neutrons/cm^2/sec. (From S. C. Lind, "Radiation Chemistry of Gases," Reinhold Publishing Corporation, New York, 1961.)

A number of radiation facilities have been built at reactors to take advantage of the radiation from the "cooling" of spent fuel elements. One such English facility [7] uses the spent fuel elements (about 100,000 curies each) from the DIDO and PLUTO reactors. About 1 m^3 of material can be irradiated; the maximum dose rate is 5 megarad/hr.

3-15.3   Reactor Loops

Various concepts, all based on passing chemicals directly through the reactor core, have been repeatedly proposed. Reactors having such "loops" give promise of providing very inexpensive sources of radiation. One such design suggests that 80,000 lb of material could be exposed to a flux of 10 megarads for a total cost of $100. [8]

3-15.4   Secondary Reactor Loops

There have been repeated suggestions that an (n, γ) reaction be induced in a fluid inside a reactor and that the radioactive fluid then be pumped to an adjacent radiation facility where it could serve as a source of gamma rays. Radiation sources based on secondary circulating loops of liquid sodium, indium, and indium-gallium alloys have been suggested, and experimental facilities have been constructed.

3-15.5 Pulsed Radiation Sources

Machines and reactors capable of delivering significant radiation doses in times of the order of microseconds to nanoseconds are now in common use. The common reactor types are the TRIGA and the GODIVA and more recently the PULSTAR. The TRIGA reactor is a U-ZrH fueled reactor. When operated in the pulsed mode, it delivers up to thousands of megarads per pulse. The pulse width is in the order of a few milliseconds. The GODIVA at Los Alamos is an unmoderated, unreflected 50 kg metal assembly that gives power levels in thousands of megawatts per pulse. The pulse width is a few microseconds.

The Van de Graaff accelerator and the linear accelerator have both been adopted to the pulsed mode and can provide pulses in 10^{-9} - 10^{-6} second range. These and other pulsed machines are discussed in more detail in Chap. 6.

REFERENCES

1.   W. F. Westendorp, Resonant-transformer Electron-beam Generators, in A. Charlesby (ed.), "Radiation Sources," Pergamon Press, Ltd., Oxford, 1964.

2. D. A. Traegeser, High Voltage Engineering Co., personal communication.

3. O. A. Kuhl and D. S. Ballantine, Isotopic Sources of Radiation Power, in A. Charlesby (ed.), "Radiation Sources," Pergamon Press, Ltd., Oxford, 1964.

4. "Industrial Uses of Large Radiation Sources," vol. II, *Symposium Proceedings, Salzburg, 1963*, IAEA, Vienna, 1963 (STI/PUB/75).

5. E. P. Blizard (ed.), "Reactor Handbook," vol. III, part B, Shielding, 2d ed., Interscience Publishers, New York, 1962.

6. S. C. Lind, "Radiation Chemistry of Gases," Reinhold Publishing Corporation, New York, 1961.

7. S. Jefferson, Experience in Operating Large Gamma-radiation Installations, in "Industrial Uses of Large Radiation Sources," vol. II, *Symposium Proceedings, Salzburg, 1963*, IAEA, Vienna, 1963 (STI/PUB/75).

8. S. Mims, in "Large Radiation Sources in Industry," *Symposium Proceedings, Warsaw, 1959*, IAEA, Vienna, 1960 (STI/PUB/12).

4

RADIATION DOSIMETRY

A meaningful experiment in radiation chemistry requires a measurement of the amount of energy the sample absorbs and a determination of the chemical changes that occur. Surprisingly, the accurate measurement of an absorbed radiation dose, which is termed *dosimetry*, is often as difficult as the determination of the amount and type of chemical change produced. Difficulties may arise from (1) the nature and geometry of the source, (2) the nature and geometry of the sample, or (3) the physical conditions under which the irradiation is performed. Examples of difficulties arising from the nature of the source are problems involving mixed-pile or fission-product radiations. Examples of difficulties encountered under (2) and (3) are irradiation of heterogeneous samples, and irradiations performed at high temperatures or pressures.

There are several well-characterized methods of determining absorbed dose. These include ion chambers, calorimeters, power input measurements, and a chemical reaction that has been calibrated by some absolute method or by a precise knowledge of the beam energy and flux. Some of the dosimetry methods are absolute, or primary, insofar as they measure roentgens or rads directly. Thus ionization chambers, which measure roentgens, are primary, as are calorimeters, which measure rads. Secondary dosimeters must always be calibrated in terms of one of the primary dosimeters.

Any of the methods, if properly used, will accurately establish the radiation flux at the point where the measurement was made. The chemist may place his sample into the calibrated beam and state with confidence that it is being exposed to a certain flux expressed as energy/area/time.

4-1 MEASUREMENT OF ABSORBED DOSE WITH ION CHAMBERS

In principle, the method of determining absorbed dose with an ion chamber is to collect all the ions produced in a certain volume of gas, usually air. Knowing the amount of energy required to produce an ion pair in the gas, the chemist can calculate the amount of energy deposited in the volume of gas under consideration and thus determine the exposure dose. In practice, much care must be exercised if one is to determine accurately the absorbed dose with an ion chamber.

Several types of ionization chambers are used. These include the cavity and thimble chambers, the parallel-plate ionization chambers, the air-wall chamber (free-air chamber) and the extrapolation chamber. The most fundamental of the chambers is the air-wall chamber; it is the one usually used for calibration. The most practical is the cavity chamber, and it is the one most often employed by radiation chemists. The parallel-plate chamber is a variation of the air-wall chamber, and the extrapolation chamber is a cavity chamber designed for use with sources with a wide energy spectrum.

4-1.1 Cavity Chamber

The cavity chamber is a direct application of the Bragg-Gray relation. The principle involved is to measure the ionization in a gas cavity contained in a material, the cavity being sufficiently small that it is subjected to the same flow of ionizing particles as the material. The absorbed dose D (in ergs) in the material in which the cavity is contained is given by the relation

$$D = JWS_m \tag{4-1}$$

where J = number of ion pairs formed per gram of gas

W = energy required to form an ion pair in the gas, ev/ion pair

S_m = ratio of the mass stopping power of the material to that of the gas in the cavity for the ionizing particles in question

As stated previously, the cavity must be small, so small that the spectrum of secondary electrons traversing the cavity is identical in every respect with the spectrum of secondary electrons existing in the irradiated material before the introduction of the cavity. In short, charged particle equilibrium should exist. Such equilibrium requires that the amount of primary radiation interacting with the material in the cavity be negligibly small and that the walls of the chamber be of sufficient thickness to establish equilibrium between primary photons (or electrons) and their secondary electrons. This thickness is about as thick as the maximum range of the secondary electrons in the material from which the chamber is made.

The use of the cavity ionization chamber is generally restricted, for practical reasons, to X- or gamma radiation with quantum energies in excess of 20 kev and, with appropriate corrections, to neutrons. This restriction is due primarily to the difficulty in obtaining the condition of charged particle equilibrium, and in determining the values of S_m under nonequilibrium conditions with other radiation sources.[1] If charged particle equilibrium can be obtained or suitable corrections made, then in principle the cavity chamber may be used for almost any radiation source.

Charged particle equilibrium may not exist in these situations: (1) if a medium in which the cavity chamber is inserted is exposed to a beam that is appreciably attenuated in passing through the medium, (2) near a source where the intensity is changing rapidly with distance, and (3) near boundaries between materials of differing compositions.

Assuming conditions of electronic equilibrium, the absorbed dose at some point within an irradiated medium can be measured by a roentgen-calibrated chamber or an absolute ionization chamber if the chamber is properly positioned. The absorbed dose in air or air-equivalent material exposed to 1 roentgen of X- or gamma radiation is:

$$\frac{1 \text{ esu}}{0.001293 \text{ g air}} \left| \frac{2.082 \times 10^9 \text{ electrons}}{\text{esu}} \right| \frac{33.7 \text{ ev}}{\text{ion pair}} \left| \frac{1.602 \times 10^{-12} \text{ erg}}{\text{ev}} \right| \frac{1 \text{ rad}}{100 \frac{\text{erg}}{\text{g}}}$$

$$= 0.86 \text{ rad}$$

If a roentgen-calibrated chamber is placed in an absorbing medium and the chamber is sufficiently small so that there is no appreciable perturbation on the electronic equilibrium in the medium, the dose in the medium in rads is

$$D_{med} = 0.86 \left[\frac{(\mu_{en}/\rho)_{med}}{(\mu_{en}/\rho)_{air}} \right] X \tag{4-2}$$

where X is the dose in roentgens

4-1.2 Absolute Cavity Chamber

An absolute cavity chamber is constructed of air equivalent material containing an air filled cavity. Air equivalent material is material that has the same radiation absorption properties as air. It is material whose atomic number is about 6 (carbon) or whose average atomic number is about 6 (many plastics). When such a chamber is properly positioned in the medium it will give the absorbed dose in a thin layer of its own wall material:

$$D_{wall} = 0.86 (A)(S_m) \tag{4-3a}$$

where A = charge in esu carried by the ions of either sign produced per 0.001293 g of air in the cavity

The absorbed dose in the medium is given by

$$D_{med} = \left[\frac{(\mu_{en}/\rho)_{med}}{(\mu_{en}/\rho)_{wall}} \right] D_{wall} \qquad\qquad (4\text{-}3b)$$

Values of the mass-energy absorption coefficients for several common elements and for some selected materials when photons are the source are given in Table 4-1. A small correction factor may be needed in Eq. (4-3b) to account for the perturbation in the X-ray intensity due to the insertion of the chamber in the medium.

4-1.3   Average Energy to Produce an Ion Pair

The value of 33.7 ev for W is the weighted mean of several determinations for electrons in air. The value of W is different for different gases, as is to be expected; these values are summarized in Table 4-2. When alpha particles are the source of radiation, W is slightly different than for electrons; however, this is not true for the noble gases (except helium).

4-1.4   The Value of the Ratio S_m

The values of the ratio S_m vary, depending upon the material and the energy of the radiation. It is necessary therefore to know both of these quantities before appropriate values can be used. For cases where the conditions of electronic equilibrium are met, the values of S_m may be used directly from calculated values shown in Tables 4-3 and 4-3a. For materials composed of several elements for which S_m is not known, the value of S_m (relative to air) for each element comprising the material is calculated, multiplied by its proportion of weight, and summed over all the elements composing the materials of interest. It has been found that the summation rule for calculating S_m as given previously holds better if a distinction is made for values of S_m for hydrogen in saturated or unsaturated material. This distinction is made in the appropriate tables.

4-1.5   Measurement of Ion Currents

In an accurate ionization chamber the ion collection efficiency must be high. Ion collection is accomplished by applying an electric field across the walls of the chamber. The voltage so applied should be sufficient to produce a saturation current, i.e., the charge is collected at the electrodes at the same rate it is formed in the active volume. Failure to collect all the ions in an ionization chamber may be due to either initial or general recombination. Initial recombination appears to be independent of dose rate but may be a source of difficulty for slow particles, or when the chamber is operated at high pressures.

Table 4-1. VALUES OF THE MASS-ENERGY ABSORPTION COEFFICIENTS*

| Photon energy (Mev) | Mass-energy absorption coefficient (μ_{en}/ρ), cm^2/g ||||||||||||||||| $S_m = 0.86 \dfrac{(\mu_{en}/\rho)_{medium}}{(\mu_{en}/\rho)_{air}}$ |
	H	C	N	O	Na	Mg	Al	P	S	Ar	K	Ca	Poly-styrene $(C_8H_8)_n$	Perspex, plexi-glass, lucite $(C_5H_8O_2)$	Poly-ethylene $(CH_2)_n$	Bakelite $(C_{43}H_{38}O_7)$	Water	Air	Water/Air
0.010	0.0099	1.94	3.42	5.50	15.4	20.9	26.5	40.1	49.7	62.0	77.0	89.8	1.79	2.92	1.66	2.43	4.89	4.66	0.912
0.015	0.0110	0.517	0.916	1.49	4.43	6.09	7.65	11.9	15.2	19.4	24.6	28.9	0.478	0.788	0.444	0.651	1.32	1.29	0.889
0.020	0.0133	0.203	0.360	0.587	1.77	2.47	3.16	5.00	6.41	8.31	10.5	12.5	0.188	0.311	0.176	0.257	0.523	0.516	0.881
0.030	0.0186	0.0592	0.102	0.163	0.482	0.684	0.880	1.45	1.85	2.46	3.12	3.75	0.0561	0.0892	0.0534	0.0743	0.147	0.147	0.869
0.040	0.0230	0.0306	0.0465	0.0700	0.194	0.274	0.351	0.570	0.731	0.974	1.25	1.52	0.0300	0.0426	0.0295	0.0368	0.0647	0.0640	0.878
0.050	0.0270	0.0226	0.0299	0.0410	0.0996	0.140	0.176	0.282	0.361	0.484	0.626	0.764	0.0229	0.0288	0.0232	0.0259	0.0394	0.0384	0.892
0.060	0.0305	0.0203	0.0244	0.0304	0.0637	0.0845	0.104	0.166	0.214	0.284	0.367	0.443	0.0211	0.0243	0.0218	0.0226	0.0304	0.0292	0.905
0.080	0.0362	0.0201	0.0218	0.0239	0.0369	0.0456	0.0536	0.0780	0.0971	0.124	0.158	0.191	0.0213	0.0226	0.0224	0.0217	0.0253	0.0236	0.932
0.10	0.0406	0.0213	0.0222	0.0232	0.0288	0.0334	0.0372	0.0500	0.0599	0.0725	0.0909	0.111	0.0228	0.0235	0.0241	0.0227	0.0252	0.0231	0.948
0.15	0.0485	0.0246	0.0249	0.0252	0.0258	0.0275	0.0282	0.0315	0.0351	0.0368	0.0433	0.0488	0.0264	0.0267	0.0280	0.0261	0.0278	0.0251	0.962
0.20	0.0530	0.0267	0.0267	0.0271	0.0265	0.0277	0.0275	0.0292	0.0310	0.0302	0.0339	0.0367	0.0287	0.0289	0.0305	0.0283	0.0300	0.0268	0.973
0.30	0.0573	0.0288	0.0289	0.0289	0.0278	0.0290	0.0283	0.0290	0.0301	0.0278	0.0304	0.0319	0.0310	0.0311	0.0329	0.0305	0.0320	0.0288	0.966
0.40	0.0587	0.0295	0.0296	0.0296	0.0283	0.0295	0.0287	0.0290	0.0301	0.0274	0.0299	0.0308	0.0317	0.0319	0.0337	0.0312	0.0329	0.0296	0.966
0.50	0.0589	0.0297	0.0297	0.0297	0.0284	0.0293	0.0287	0.0288	0.0300	0.0271	0.0294	0.0304	0.0319	0.0320	0.0339	0.0314	0.0330	0.0297	0.966
0.60	0.0588	0.0296	0.0296	0.0296	0.0283	0.0292	0.0286	0.0287	0.0297	0.0270	0.0291	0.0301	0.0318	0.0319	0.0338	0.0313	0.0329	0.0296	0.966
0.80	0.0573	0.0288	0.0289	0.0289	0.0276	0.0285	0.0278	0.0280	0.0287	0.0261	0.0282	0.0290	0.0310	0.0311	0.0329	0.0305	0.0321	0.0289	0.965
1.0	0.0555	0.0279	0.0280	0.0280	0.0267	0.0275	0.0269	0.0270	0.0280	0.0252	0.0272	0.0279	0.0300	0.0301	0.0319	0.0295	0.0311	0.0280	0.965
1.5	0.0507	0.0255	0.0255	0.0255	0.0243	0.0250	0.0246	0.0245	0.0254	0.0228	0.0247	0.0253	0.0274	0.0275	0.0291	0.0270	0.0283	0.0255	0.964
2.0	0.0464	0.0234	0.0234	0.0234	0.0225	0.0232	0.0227	0.0228	0.0235	0.0212	0.0228	0.0234	0.0252	0.0252	0.0267	0.0247	0.0260	0.0234	0.966
3.0	0.0398	0.0204	0.0205	0.0206	0.0199	0.0206	0.0201	0.0204	0.0210	0.0193	0.0208	0.0213	0.0219	0.0220	0.0232	0.0216	0.0227	0.0205	0.962
4.0	0.0351	0.0184	0.0186	0.0187	0.0184	0.0191	0.0188	0.0192	0.0199	0.0182	0.0199	0.0204	0.0197	0.0198	0.0208	0.0194	0.0205	0.0186	0.958
5.0	0.0316	0.0170	0.0172	0.0174	0.0173	0.0181	0.0180	0.0184	0.0192	0.0176	0.0193	0.0200	0.0181	0.0183	0.0191	0.0179	0.0190	0.0173	0.954
6.0	0.0288	0.0160	0.0162	0.0166	0.0166	0.0175	0.0174	0.0179	0.0187	0.0175	0.0190	0.0198	0.0170	0.0172	0.0178	0.0168	0.0180	0.0163	0.960
8.0	0.0249	0.0145	0.0148	0.0154	0.0158	0.0167	0.0169	0.0175	0.0184	0.0172	0.0190	0.0197	0.0153	0.0156	0.0160	0.0153	0.0165	0.0150	0.956
10.0	0.0222	0.0137	0.0142	0.0147	0.0154	0.0163	0.0167	0.0174	0.0183	0.0173	0.0191	0.0201	0.0144	0.0147	0.0149	0.0144	0.0155	0.0144	0.935

*Adapted from Physical Aspects of Irradiation, National Bureau of Standards, Handbook 85, p. 3, U.S. Government Printing Office, Washington, 1964.

Table 4-2. W VALUES FOR ELECTRONS
FOR DIFFERENT GASES

Gas	Weighted mean ev/ion pair
H_2	36.6 ± 0.3
He	41.5 ± 0.4
N_2	34.6 ± 0.3
O_2	30.8 ± 0.3
Ne	36.2 ± 0.4
Ar	26.2 ± 0.2
Kr	24.3 ± 0.4
Xe	21.9 ± 0.3
Air	33.73 ± 0.15
CO_2	32.9 ± 0.3
CH_4	27.3 ± 0.3
C_2H_2	25.7 ± 0.4
C_2H_4	26.3 ± 0.3
C_2H_6	24.6 ± 0.4

General recombination is significant for those gases in which negative ion formation occurs, at very high dose rates, or in poor chamber design. In poor chamber design there may be regions in which the applied field is not sufficient to achieve saturation; thus recombination can occur. Figure 4-1 is a schematic diagram of a cavity ionization chamber that was developed for high intensity ^{60}Co sources.[2] More detailed accounts of ion chambers and their construction and operation may be found in Ref. 3.

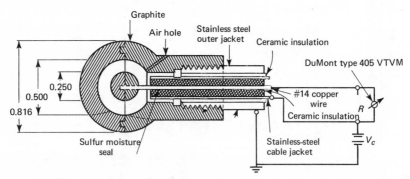

Fig. 4-1. Schematic diagram of cavity ionization chamber.
(Taimuty, 1959)

EXAMPLE 4-1: The ionization currents in a cavity chamber constructed of lucite irradiated with 1 Mev gamma rays were measured across a 1.013×10^6 ohm resistor with a calibrated vibrating reed electrometer. If the electrometer reading was 9.1 mv at saturation and the volume of the air filled cavity was 3.65 cm^3 at STP, calculate the dose rate.

Table 4-3. MEAN MASS STOPPING-POWER RATIOS, S_m, RELATIVE TO AIR AND CORRECTED FOR THE POLARIZATION EFFECT, FOR ELECTRONIC EQUILIBRIUM SPECTRA GENERATED BY MONOENERGETIC INITIAL ELECTRONS*

Initial energy, Mev	Hydrogen, (saturated molecule)	Hydrogen, (unsaturated molecule)	Carbon, (saturated molecule)	Carbon, (unsaturated molecule)	Carbon, (highly chlorinated)	Nitrogen, (amines, nitrates)	Nitrogen, (ring)	Oxygen, -O-	Oxygen, O=	Graphite	Al	P	Ca	Cu	Sn	Pb
						Element and state of molecular binding										
0.1	2.52	2.59	1.016	1.021	1.047	0.976	1.018	0.978	0.994	1.014	0.859	0.875	0.852	0.711	0.555	0.468
0.2	2.52	2.59	1.015	1.019	1.043	0.978	1.016	0.979	0.995	1.013	0.870	0.886	0.869	0.734	0.595	0.508
0.3	2.48	2.55	1.014	1.018	1.040	0.979	1.016	0.981	0.995	1.011	0.876	0.891	0.876	0.745	0.614	0.526
0.327	2.48	2.54	1.014	1.018	1.040	0.979	1.015	0.981	0.995	1.010	0.877	0.892	0.878	0.747	0.617	0.530
0.4	2.46	2.53	1.014	1.018	1.038	0.980	1.015	0.981	0.996	1.009	0.879	0.894	0.882	0.752	0.625	0.539
0.5	2.44	2.51	1.013	1.017	1.037	0.980	1.015	0.982	0.996	1.007	0.881	0.896	0.885	0.757	0.633	0.548
0.6	2.44	2.50	1.012	1.016	1.035	0.980	1.013	0.981	0.995	1.005	0.882	0.898	0.887	0.761	0.639	0.555
0.654	2.43	2.49	1.011	1.014	1.034	0.979	1.012	0.981	0.994	1.004	0.883	0.899	0.889	0.762	0.642	0.557
0.7	2.42	2.48	1.010	1.013	1.033	0.978	1.011	0.980	0.993	1.003	0.883	0.899	0.890	0.764	0.645	0.560
0.8	2.40	2.46	1.009	1.012	1.031	0.978	1.010	0.979	0.992	1.001	0.884	0.901	0.892	0.767	0.649	0.565
1.0	2.39	2.44	1.004	1.008	1.026	0.975	1.005	0.977	0.988	0.998	0.885	0.902	0.895	0.771	0.655	0.572
1.2	2.37	2.42	1.001	1.004	1.022	0.973	1.002	0.974	0.985	0.995	0.885	0.904	0.898	0.775	0.660	0.578
1.308	2.36	2.42	0.999	1.002	1.019	0.971	1.000	0.972	0.983	0.993	0.885	0.905	0.899	0.775	0.663	0.581
1.5	2.35	2.39	0.995	0.998	1.015	0.967	0.996	0.969	0.980			0.907	0.902		0.666	0.584

*Adapted from Physical Aspects of Irradiation, National Bureau of Standards, Handbook 85, p. 8, U.S. Government Printing Office, Washington, 1964.

Table 4-3a. MEAN MASS STOPPING-POWER RATIOS, S_m, RELATIVE TO AIR AND CORRECTED FOR THE POLARIZATION EFFECT, FOR ELECTRONIC EQUILIBRIUM SPECTRA GENERATED BY COMPTON RECOIL ELECTRONS

Gamma ray energy Mev	Element and state of molecular binding															
	Hydrogen (saturated molecule)	Hydrogen (unsaturated molecule)	Carbon, (saturated molecule)	Carbon, (unsaturated molecule)	Carbon (highly chlorinated)	Nitrogen, (amines, nitrates)	Nitrogen, (ring)	Oxygen, -O-	Oxygen, O=	Graphite	Al	P	Ca	Cu	Sn	Pb
0.15	2.73	2.85	1.020	1.027	1.058	0.970	1.022	0.972	0.992	1.017	0.835	0.823	0.776	0.657	0.458	0.380
0.25	2.62	2.72	1.017	1.022	1.050	0.974	1.019	0.976	0.994	1.015	0.853	0.850	0.816	0.696	0.538	0.443
0.4	2.55	2.63	1.016	1.020	1.045	0.977	1.017	0.978	0.995	1.013	0.866	0.867	0.842	0.723	0.575	0.487
0.6	2.50	2.57	1.014	1.018	1.040	0.979	1.016	0.980	0.995	1.011	0.874	0.879	0.857	0.740	0.605	0.518
1.0	2.44	2.50	1.008	1.012	1.032	0.977	1.009	0.978	0.991	1.005	0.881	0.888	0.873	0.758	0.634	0.548
1.5	2.39	2.45	1.001	1.005	1.023	0.972	1.003	0.973	0.985	0.999	0.883	0.894	0.883	0.768	0.650	0.567
2.0	2.36	2.42	0.994	0.997	1.014	0.966	0.995	0.967	0.978							
2.5	2.32	2.37	0.987	0.990	1.007	0.960	0.988	0.962	0.973							

SOLUTION:

$$D = JWS_m$$

$$D = \left(\frac{0.0091 \text{ volt}}{1.013 \times 10^6 \text{ ohms}} \middle| \frac{\text{electron (ion)}}{1.6 \times 10^{-19} \text{ coul}} \middle| \frac{33.7 \text{ ev}}{\text{ion pair}} \middle| \frac{}{3.65 \text{ cm}^3} \middle| \frac{\text{cm}^3}{0.001293 \text{ g}} \middle| \frac{0.0301}{0.0280} \right)$$

$$D = 4.3 \times 10^{14} \text{ ev}/g/\text{sec}$$

4-1.6   The Thimble Chamber

One of the most common of the small ionization chambers is the Victoreen condenser r-meter. This is a "thimble" chamber, which consists of a small air volume enclosed in a thin plastic cap. A suitable coating is applied to the inside of the wall of the chamber to make it conduct, and in the center there is a conducting wire insulated from the cap. The chamber is really a small condenser and before use is charged to some standard voltage. When the thimble is exposed to ionizing radiation, the charge is partially neutralized. The exposed chamber is inserted in a reading device that is also used to charge the chamber. The charge reader is a string electrometer, and the charge that remains on the chamber is measured by the electrometer, the deflection of the string being observed by means of a built-in microscope. The ocular scale of the microscope is calibrated in roentgens or milliroentgens.

4-1.7   The Free-air Chamber

The free-air chamber is essentially an ion collecting device. A collecting field of about 5 to 100 volts per centimeter is applied between the high voltage and collecting electrodes, which must be set sufficiently far apart to allow the secondary electrons (e_1, e_2, ...) in Fig. 4-2 to complete their tracks. This requirement restricts the practical use of free-ion chambers to relatively low energy radiation (50 to 200 kv). At higher energies either very large or pressurized chambers must be used. Figure 4-2 is a schematic diagram of a parallel-plate, free-air chamber.

For a determination of the number of roentgens, the ionizations from all the secondary electrons originating in 1 cm³ of air must be collected. This can be done only indirectly, since electrons are scattered both in and out of any given volume element. If, as shown in Fig. 4-2, the number scattered out equals the number scattered in, the system is said to be in electron equilibrium.

EXAMPLE 4-2: Calculate the dose in roentgens at position A (Fig. 4-2) given the following data:

$$A = \text{area of slit} = 3 \text{ cm}^2$$

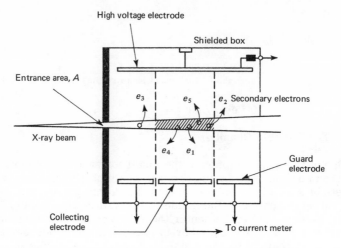

Fig. 4-2. Parallel-plate, free-air ionization chamber.

ΔV = voltage change across electrodes = 1 volt

ρ = density of air, 0.001293 g/cm^3

L = electrode length = 10 cm

C = capacity of measuring system = 100 $\mu\mu f$

SOLUTION: The total charge collected in the chamber is

$$Q = VC = (1)(10 \times 10^{-11})(3 \times 10^9) = 30 \times 10^{-2} \text{ esu}$$

According to the definition of the roentgen,

$$\text{Dose} = \frac{Q}{AL}\frac{0.001293}{\rho} = \frac{3 \times 10^{-1} \text{ esu}}{3 \text{ cm}^2} \left| \frac{}{10 \text{ cm}} \right| \frac{0.001293}{0.001293}$$

$$= 1 \times 10^{-2} \, r$$

4-1.8 Extrapolation Chamber

This chamber is of particular value when the source of radiation has a broad energy spectrum. The Bragg-Gray principle is applicable when electrons and neutrons, as well as other types of radiation sources, are used; however, as previously indicated, many problems arise with some sources or source configurations. These problems are primarily related to establishing the conditions discussed in Sec. 4-1.1. For example, if the source is a beta emitter, the electrons may have a very broad range of energies; this situation will make the condition of electronic equilibrium very difficult to achieve. The way to overcome such a situation is to construct a chamber so that the cavity can be made progressively smaller. Saturation currents are collected as the air cavity is made smaller and smaller; when the cavity becomes essentially zero, one obtains a limiting value of the ratio of the saturation current to the volume of the cavity. Thus the conditions for which the Bragg-Gray principle applies are satisfied.

The principal difficulty that arises with the extrapolation chamber is a choice of the values to be used for S_m. Some averaging method has to be used to obtain reasonably appropriate values. This problem is discussed by Failla.[4]

4-2 CALORIMETRY

Calorimetry is one of the primary methods for determining absorbed dose; it is a very direct approach but one that requires considerable experimental care. The technique if properly used, is capable of giving results which are just as accurate as ionization measurements. Calorimetric techniques do, however, have inherent disadvantages that have limited their general use. They have a low sensitivity (requiring dose rates usually in excess of 1000 rads per hour), are time consuming, and usually require complex and cumbersome equipment. Conversion of any of the absorbed energy into anything but heat (chemical change, for example) will produce an error. In most cases, however, adequate compensation for chemical changes or other disturbances can be made.

Calorimetric measurements of absorbed dose involve the measurement of the temperature rise in a small, thermally insulated mass of material. The system must be so designed that the insulating material does not appreciably perturb the radiation spectrum. Stirring devices, heaters, thermocouples, thermistors, etc., used in the measurement must be only a small fraction of the mass of material whose temperature rise is being monitored.

It is also necessary that electronic equilibrium be maintained in accurate calorimetry for the determination of absorbed dose. In addition, dose rates must be sufficiently high in relation to the rate of heat loss, and the absorbing volume should be sufficiently small to prevent intensity gradients.

Calorimetric measurements are usually made in terms of thermal power P or an energy Q. If a thermal power is produced (by absorption of radiation) in a material thermally insulated from the surroundings, its temperature will change as

$$\frac{dT_c}{dt} = \frac{[P - k(T_c - T_e)]}{C} \tag{4-4}$$

where T_c = temperature of the material in which the calorimeter measurement is being made

T_e = temperature of the surroundings

C = heat capacity of the material

k = coefficient of heat transfer through the insulating material

P = power, which is generally the sum of two parts, P_u, the power being measured, and P_o, which is any constant thermal powers generated in the system, such as those produced by stirrers, or the joule heat of resistance thermometers

t = time

4-2.1 Calorimetry: Types of Systems

Three principal types of calorimeters may be distinguished according to the method of control of T_e, the duration of measurement, the relative magnitudes of C and k, and whether calibration involves determination of C or k or both. These types are adiabatic, semi-adiabatic, and isothermal.

In adiabatic calorimeters T_c is maintained equal to T_e and the rate of temperature change is measured:

$$\frac{dT_c}{dt} = \frac{(P_u + P_o)}{C} \tag{4-5}$$

Calibration consists of determination of C. If the energy Q deposited in the calorimeter by a process of duration $t_f - t_i$ is to be determined, it is obtained from the expression

$$Q = C(T_f - T_i) - P_o(t_f - t_i) \tag{4-6}$$

where T_i and T_f are the initial and final temperatures of the calorimeter.

The semiadiabatic, method in calorimetry is used primarily for measurements of fairly short duration. The quantity T_e is maintained constant. The heat absorbed is given by

$$Q = C(T_f - T_i) + k \int_{t_i}^{t_f} (T_c - T_b) \, dt \tag{4-7}$$

where T_b is the balance or steady-state temperature which the calorimeter attains after infinite time:

$$T_b = T_e' + \frac{P_o}{k} \tag{4-8}$$

The value of k should be small so that the time-vs.-temperature curves before heating and after completion will be approximately linear. Calibration consists in determining C and k.

In isothermal calorimetry T_e is maintained constant, and the experiment is concluded when a constant steady-state value of T_c is attained. From (4-4)

$$T_c - T_e = \frac{P}{k} (1 - e^{-tk/C}) \tag{4-9}$$

at infinite time

$$P = k(T_c^{\infty} - T_e) \tag{4-10}$$

Thus $T_c^{\infty} - T_e$ is a measure of the heat flow from the sample at constant temperature. Calibration of the calorimeter consists only of a determination of k. The time constant of the calorimeter is C/k. The quantity C is kept small to decrease the time of measurement.

As indicated, it is possible that energy may be dissipated by mechanisms other than thermal, such as energy storage, as crystal lattice defects, chemical decomposition, etc. It appears probable that, for most elements and inorganic solids irradiated at ordinary temperatures, energy storage, while finite, is usually small;[6] however, graphite in reactors near room temperature may store more than 2000 joules per gram after prolonged irradiation.

In organic and many inorganic materials and aqueous solutions, chemical effects may be quite large. Milery and his co-workers[7] have discussed possible reactions in polystyrene. With water or aqueous solutions in a sealed vessel, it is usually assumed that after a certain length of time at constant irradiation an equilibrium pressure of H_2 and O_2 is established and no further net reaction occurs.

4-2.2 Measurement of Absorbed Dose by Calorimetry

Calorimetry has been used by radiation chemists primarily for calibration of chemical systems, such as the Fricke dosimeter, or for comparison with ionization chamber measurement. One of the first of these measurements was the calibration of the Fricke dosimeter by Hochanadel and Ghormley.[8]

The calorimeter used is shown in Fig. 4-3. It consisted of a cylindrical copper jacket that surrounded a thin-walled, silvered pyrex bulb containing 3 to 6 ml of water as the calorimetric body. The temperature was followed during irradiation by means of copper constantan thermocouples placed in the water and in the copper jacket. The jacket temperature was continually adjusted to that of the water by means of a heater placed in the cavity of the shield housing the ^{60}Co source (see Fig. 4-3). The ^{60}Co facility used gave dose rates of 25 to 225 r per second, which resulted in a temperature rise of 0.003 to 0.03 degrees per minute.

Temperatures were followed over 3- to 5-hr periods during which time steady state concentrations of water decomposition products (H_2, O_2, H_2O_2) were attained, and the small heat of reaction effects were eliminated.

In calculating the rate of energy absorption in the system, Hochanadel and Ghormley made the following assumptions:

(1) The temperature of the thermocouple junction immersed in the water was the same as the temperature of the water and of the bulb from which heat would be exchanged with the surrounding jacket.

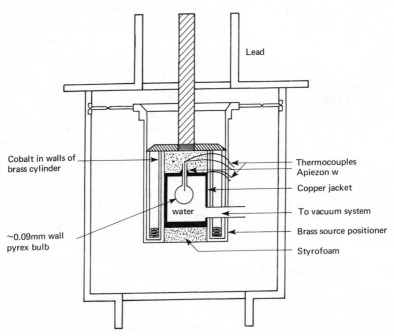

Fig. 4-3. Calorimeter for measurement of gamma-ray energy absorbed in water. (Hochanadel and Ghormley, 1953.)

(2) The total heat capacity (and energy absorption) could be calculated in accordance with the (known) heat capacities and weight fractions of the water and glass. The energy absorption in the thermocouple and in the thin silver coating on the outside of the pyrex glass was neglected.

After a determination of the energy absorption, the rate of ferrous sulfate oxidation in the identical geometry was determined and the G value (molecules converted per 100 ev absorbed) for ferrous ion oxidation calculated.

A typical set of experimental data is as follows:

Heating rate	$0.014°C/min$
Weight of water	$5.98\ g$
Weight of glass	$0.30\ g$
Total heat capacity	$6.03\ cal/deg$
Fe^{++} oxidation	69.0×10^{-6} moles/liter/min

The energy absorbed in the water in the calorimetry system is

$$\frac{0.014°C}{min}\ \left|\ \frac{6.03\ cal}{°C}\ \right|\ \frac{}{6.28\,g} = 0.0100\ cal/g\text{-}min$$

Assuming a density of 1.02, the energy absorbed in the ferrous solution is $(0.0100)(1.02) = 0.0102\ cal/g$-min. The G value is

$$G = \frac{69 \times 10^{-6}M}{liter\text{-}min}\ \left|\ \frac{g\text{-}min}{0.0102\ cal}\ \right|\ \frac{liter}{1000\ g}\ \left|\ \frac{6 \times 10^{23}\ mol\acute{e}c}{mole}\ \right|\ \frac{3.83 \times 10^{-18}\ cal}{100\ ev}$$

$$= 15.5\ \text{molecules of iron oxidized per 100 ev}$$

A series of determinations gave the value of 15.6 ± 0.3 for the molecules of Fe^{++} oxidized per 100 ev absorbed.

A number of subsequent calorimetric determinations of this system have been made with a similar calorimeter.[9,10] A different arrangement was that used by Brynjolfsson,[11] who used an ice calorimeter consisting of a 470 ml Dewar flask completely filled with ice and water and surrounded by ice and water in a cylindrical jacket. The volume change of the mixture in the flask was observed in a capillary tube outside the ^{60}Co irradiation facility. An advantage of the system was that any light energy produced by intermediate excited states would be retained in the calorimeter.

Keene and Law [12] measured power deposition in a magnesium calorimetric body operated semiadiabatically in a ^{60}Co irradiation facility; then they irradiated ferrous sulfate solutions in polyethylene containers of similar shape at the same position to determine the G value. The calorimetric body had internal voids to give the

same overall electron density as the solutions. Since Compton
scattering was the main mechanism of energy absorption, the dose
rate in the solutions was taken as the calorimeter power in watts
per gram multiplied by the ratio of the number of electrons per
gram in the solution and in magnesium.

Reid and Johns [13, 14] used twin semiadiabatic calorimeters with
small hollow cylindrical calorimetric bodies to determine W (air).
Gamma beams from a ^{60}Co or ^{137}Cs source or 22 Mev bremsstrahlung were used. The calorimetric body was small compared
with the cross sectional area and penetrating distance of the beam.
The measurement consists in comparing the energy absorbed per
unit mass of an ionization chamber wall with the number of ion
pairs produced in the chamber.

A micro-calorimeter for local dose determination in nonme-
tallic solids has been described [15] for high energy radiation. The
calorimeter is constructed of carbon or carbon particles in polystyrene to give a carbon to hydrogen ratio of 1 to 1. The calorimeter has been used with ^{60}Co radiation and electron beams with
energies up to 20 Mev. At 50 rads per minute or more, the calorimeter gives a precision of about 1%.

A calorimeter that has been proposed as a primary standard
for absorbed dose measurement [16] is one in which the calorimetric body is a graphite or aluminum sphere 1 cm in diameter
mounted on polystyrene pegs inside a spherical adiabatic jacket
1.4 cm in inside diameter and 2.2 cm in outside diameter. This is
shown in Fig. 4-3a. Temperatures are determined with chromel-
constantan thermocouples. A layer of conducting ink (250 ohms) is
used to cement the two hemispherical sections of the calorimetric
body and serves as the calibrating heater.

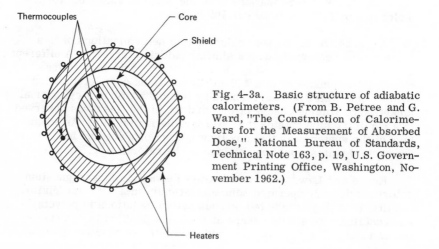

Fig. 4-3a. Basic structure of adiabatic
calorimeters. (From B. Petree and G.
Ward, "The Construction of Calorimeters for the Measurement of Absorbed
Dose," National Bureau of Standards,
Technical Note 163, p. 19, U.S. Government Printing Office, Washington, November 1962.)

4-3 MEASUREMENT OF ABSORBED DOSE BY POWER INPUT

In principle it would appear that absorbed dose can be accurately determined by delivering a measured amount of energy from a beam of ionizing particles to an appropriate system whose stopping power is known. This has been adequately demonstrated. The power input method can be used to measure radiation doses with an absolute accuracy of about 0.5%.

Figure 4-4 is a schematic diagram of a typical arrangement. The electron beam, whose voltage was determined by a calibrated generating voltmeter, exits from a Van de Graaff accelerator through a thin (3 mil) aluminum window. It then enters the absorption cell containing ferrous sulfate solution. The radius of the cell

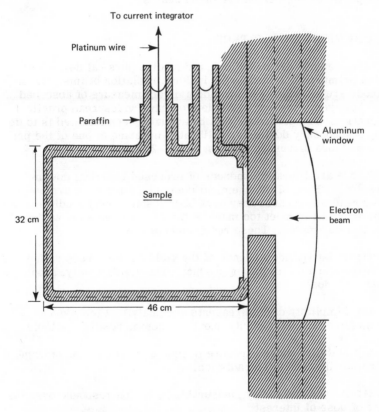

Fig. 4-4. Schematic diagram of apparatus used for determination of absolute value of Fricke dosimeter. [Adapted from J. Saldick and A. O. Allen, "The Yield of Oxidation of Ferrous Sulfate in Acid Solution by High-energy Cathode Rays," J. Chem. Phys., 22:439 (1954).]

is such as to ensure complete absorption of the electron beam. Beam currents of 6×10^{-11} to 7×10^{-7} amp were used in typical experiments. The current received by the solution was led out by a platinum wire through a shielded cable to a current integrating device that measures the total collected current.

There are several sources of error which must be corrected for: (1) the energy lost by the beam in passing through the various windows, (2) back scattered electrons which deliver some energy to the solution but which are not counted, (3) bremsstrahlung, (4) current leakage, and (5) electrons that are scattered from the defining orifice (see Fig. 4-4). When these corrections are taken into account, quite accurate measurements of absorbed dose may be made. The power input method has been used for electrons from Van de Graaff-accelerator[17,18] calibrated beta sources[19] and for protons and alpha particles [20,21] from cyclotron beams.

4-4 CHEMICAL DOSIMETERS

The methods described thus far involve physical devices designed primarily for measuring incident radiation beams. These methods are all sound and provide a direct measure of absorbed dose; however, none are convenient or have widespread practical application. The procedure that has usually been followed is to develop a secondary dosimeter calibrated in terms of one of the primary methods discussed in Secs. 4-1, 4-2, and 4-3.

There are literally hundreds of proposed chemical dosimeters.[22-28] Most of the chemical dosimeters reported are not in widespread use because they have been insufficiently studied or because they fail to meet too many of the requirements for an "ideal" chemical dosimeter. These requirements are

(1) Relative independence of the yield on the concentration of the reagent and the radiation product. The yield, ideally, should be linear with dose.

(2) Simplicity of both reagents and analytical techniques. Chemicals of adequate purity should be commercially available.

(3) Stability under exposure to light and heat and on storage before, during, and after radiation.

(4) A good and easily measurable radiation response over the range of dose of interest.

(5) Independence of dose rate over a very large range.

(6) No dependence on LET (linear energy transfer).

(7) Accuracy; an overall accuracy of about ±1%.

(8) Usability in a mixed radiation field.

There is no thoroughly tested chemical dosimeter that meets all these requirements; however, there are several that have been found to meet many of them.

The most commonly used and most thoroughly studied laboratory dosimeter is the Fricke ferrous sulfate dosimeter. This dosimeter and a number of the other systems in common use are detailed in the ensuing sections.

4-4.1 Ferrous Sulfate Dosimetry

An acid solution of ferrous sulfate, when irradiated, is oxidized to ferric sulfate. This fact was first reported by Hugo Fricke in 1927. Two years later Fricke proposed that ferrous sulfate in $0.8N$ sulfuric acid could be used as an X-ray dosimeter, this particular solution having been chosen to give an air chamber equivalent response.

The first step in the preparation of the solution is to purify the water and clean the glassware. Indeed, this is a necessary first step in any process involving the radiation chemistry of any aqueous system. The recommended procedures are described by Allen:[29]

> Pure water is obtained at Brookhaven by redistilling ordinary distilled water first from an acid dichromate solution, then from alkaline permanganate, and finally with no added reagent into a fused silica container. Each distillation is done through a column packed with glass helices; at the top of the column, a short section is heated externally to break the film of water on the inside of the column and prevent impurities from creeping over by capillarity. The distilled water feed is brought in through tubes that contain only metal and glass; the water must not come in contact with rubber or plastic. The stills are protected from dust or vapors in the outside air by tubes of activated charcoal.

Each of these precautions was found by experience to be necessary.

Other laboratories working in this field take similar precautions. Hart, in addition, during his distillations passes the steam through a tube heated to several hundred degrees centigrade to burn up the organic impurities.[30] Even after these treatments the water still contains impurities that affect such reactions as the formation of hydrogen peroxide in air saturated water. The purest water is probably obtained by gamma irradiation of triply distilled water containing air, which forms hydrogen peroxide and destroys organic matter; this is followed by destruction of the peroxide with ultraviolet light from a mercury resonance lamp.[31]

Even the most careful water purification is of no avail unless the irradiation vessels are cleaned with equal care. Apparently glassware that has been exposed to ordinary air picks up a film of grease or other organic matter. Much of this remains on the surface and can be removed by cleaning solution, but some seems to bury itself in submicroscopic fissures where it is not accessible to ordinary reagents. On irradiation by gamma or X-rays, this material comes out into the water and reacts with free radicals. Consequently it is necessary to preirradiate reaction vessels while they are full of purified water with $10^6 \gamma$ or more of radiation or enough to color the glass noticeably. Then the vessels are rinsed with purified water and kept full of water until they are used. It is a good idea to clean the vessels before preirradiation with a current of steam obtained by boiling purified water.*

The recipe for the dosimeter is to dissolve approximately 2 g $FeSO_4 \cdot 7H_2O$ or $Fe(NH_4)_2(SO_4)_2 \cdot 6H_2O$, 0.3 g NaCl, and sufficient concentrated (95 to 98%) H_2SO_4 to make the solution $0.8N$ in acid, in distilled water and to dilute to 5 liters. The solution is then $0.0014M$ in ferrous sulfate, $0.001M$ in NaCl, and $0.8N$ in sulfuric acid. Ferrous sulfate solutions slowly oxidize, but, if kept out of sunlight, they are reasonably stable up to two to three months.

Fricke originally determined the amount of oxidation by titration. This may also be done by following the disappearance of ferrous ion by o-phenanthroline complexing and subsequent spectrophotometric determination. It is now common practice to determine the ferric ion concentration by direct spectrophotometry at 305 mμ or 224 mμ (see Chap. 8).

Some of the problems associated with the use of ferrous-ferric dosimetry are listed here. Some of these can be obviated; others cannot.

(1) *Sensitivity to organic impurities.* The inordinate care with which the reagents and glassware need be cleaned is due to the sensitivity of the system to organic impurities. Dewhurst discovered that this sensitivity could be circumvented by the addition of small amounts of chloride ion. With the standard recipe given, only ordinary laboratory precautions need be taken.

---

*This practice is necessary for aqueous radiation chemistry, but it is not necessary for ferrous sulfate dosimetry. Ordinary care is all that is required, i.e., clean equipment and good distilled water. However, most laboratories use these careful procedures as a general precaution.

(2) *Temperature dependence of the extinction coefficient.* Absorbed dose is determined by spectrophotometric measurement of the ferric ion produced. Table 4-4 is a tabulation of the molar extinction coefficients, ε, at 3050 Å, reported by several investigators. Since ε has a large temperature coefficient at this wavelength (0.69% in the temperature interval 20 to 30° C), measurements must be made at 25° C or corrections made.

Table 4-4. REPORTED VALUES OF FERRIC-ION MOLAR EXTINCTION COEFFICIENT IN $0.8N$ H_2SO_4 at 25°C, 3050 Å

Institution	Name	Value
Argonne National Laboratory	Hart	2225
Cambridge University	Swallow	2167
Brookhaven National Laboratory	Allen	2195
Edinburgh University	Miller	2201
Oak Ridge National Laboratory	Hochanadel	2240
Sloan-Kettering Institute	Laughlin	2172
Paris	Lefort	2205
Average		2201
Standard deviation		0.4%

(3) *Absorbed dose range.* The G value for the oxidation is different for air saturated and deaerated solutions (see Chap. 8, Sec. 10). If one starts with an air saturated solution, all the oxygen is consumed by a dose of about 50,000 rads, and the G value changes from 15.5 to 8. Thus the "normal" upper range of utility for the Fricke system is about 50,000 rads. If the solution is initially saturated with oxygen instead of air, the range can be extended fivefold to about 2×10^5 rads, and, if oxygen is continually bubbled in or deaerated solutions used, doses up to 10^6 rads can be accurately determined.[32] Another method for extending the upper range for the Fricke dosimeter is by the addition of $0.1M$ copper sulfate. This reduces the G value for oxidation to 0.66, independent of the presence of oxygen; thus very high absorbed doses can be measured. At low absorbed doses (less than about 1000 rads), the use of the dosimeter is limited by the sensitivity of the analytical techniques.

(4) *Ambient conditions.* Response of the dosimeter, for practical purposes,* is not affected by temperatures from 0 to 65° C. It is also independent of ferrous-ion concentration between $5 \times 10^{-2} M$

---

*The temperature coefficient for the gamma-ray-induced oxidation has been found to be $0.04 + 0.03\%/°C$ between 0 and 70°C; however, with radiations of high LET the temperature coefficient is higher.

and $10^{-4} M$ and of sulfuric acid concentration between $1.5M$ and $0.1M$. Altering the heavy ion content, however, changes the mass absorption coefficient. The addition of high atomic-number elements, which do not change the G value, allows the mean atomic number of the dosimeter to be matched to that of almost any system under study.

(5) *Linear energy transfer.* Extensive compilations of G values as a function of LET for photon and particle irradiation are available. The data given in Table 4-5 and Fig. 4-5, as well as that given by Minder,[33] report an independence of yield for photons and electrons between 100 kev and 30 Mev. As shown in Fig. 4-5, which gives the G values for aerated and deaerated solutions, the yield begins to fall for LET values higher than 0.1 ev/Å and approaches an asymptotic value of 3 ± 0.9 for heavy fission products.

(6) *Dose rates.* There is little or no variation in response at dose rates up to 10^7 rads/sec. Between 10^7 and 10^{10} rads/sec, the yield falls from 15.5 to 8 (Table 4-6).

EXAMPLE 4-3: A 10 cm^3 air saturated Fricke dosimetry solution in a 1 cm diameter tube is irradiated for 10 min in the annulus of a cylindrical ^{60}Co gamma-ray source. The optical density, OD, measured at 3050 Å in a 1 cm light path at 30°C was 0.260 after irradiation and 0.003 before irradiation.

(1) What is the total dose in rads absorbed by the solution?

(2) If 10 cm^3 of methanol are irradiated for 10 min in the same vial, what is the absorbed dose in rads?

(3) If, instead of methanol, Pb(NO$_3$)$_2$ is irradiated in the same tube for 10 min, what is the absorbed dose?

SOLUTION: The molar extinction coefficient for ferric sulfate at 25°C (Table 4-4) is 2201. At 30°C it is $2201 [1 + 0.007(5)] = 2278$. The concentration in moles per liter is determined by Beer's law (see Chap. 6, Ex. 6-1). The density of the solution is 1.023; the G value is 15.5 molecules/100 ev. The total dose in rads is related to the change in optical density by

(1)

$$\frac{erg}{g} = \frac{(OD\ final - OD\ initial)\ mole}{l\varepsilon\ liter} \left| \frac{1\ liter}{1000\ cm^3} \right| \frac{cm^3}{\rho g} \left| \frac{6.023 \times 10^{23}\ molec}{mole} \right| \frac{100\ ev}{15.5\ molec} \left| \frac{1.6 \times 10^{-12}\ erg}{ev} \right.$$

$$rads = \frac{1}{100} \left| \frac{0.260 - 0.003}{(2278)(1)} \right| \frac{1}{1000} \left| \frac{1}{1.023} \right| \frac{6.023 \times 10^{23}}{} \left| \frac{100}{15.5} \right| 1.6 \times 10^{-12} = 6.87 \times 10^3$$

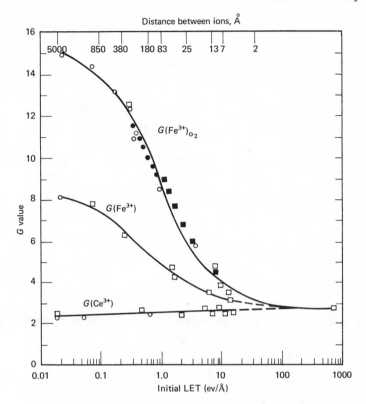

Fig. 4-5. Average yields for Fe^{2+} oxidation (in presence and absence of O_2), Ce^{4+} reduction, and H_2 formation as a function of initial LET of the impinging particle. Values for both multiply charged- and singly charged-particles are shown. The average distance between primary ions is shown at the top of the figure. [After Hochanadel, "Comparative Effects of Radiation," Burton, Kirby-Smith, Magee (eds.), John Wiley & Sons, p. 172 (1960).]

(2) Since the radiation is in the Compton region, the energy absorbed by each component will be assumed proportional to the number of electrons:

$$D_M = \frac{D_1(Z/A)_M}{(Z/A)_1} \qquad (4\text{-}13)$$

where subscript M applies to methanol and 1, the Fricke dosimeter.

Table 4-5. G VALUES FOR THE FERROUS SULFATE DOSIMETER

Radiation	$G(Fe^{3+})$	Method of energy measurement	Observers
160 Mev protons	16.5 ± 1	Proton flux from induced radioactivity	Ehrenberg and Saeland*
30 mvp X-rays (filtered, E = 7.6 Mev)†	16.3 ± 0.6	Ionization	Haybittle, Saunders, and Swallow*
2 mvp X-rays	16.0 ± 0.5	Ionization‡	Weiss, Bernstein, and Cupper*
60Co gamma rays (1.25 Mev)	15.5 ± 0.5	Ionization	Haybittle, Saunders, and Swallow*
	15.6 ± 0.3	Calorimetry	Hochanadel and Ghormley*
	15.7	Ionization‡	Hochanadel and Ghormley*
	15.8 ± 0.3	Calorimetry	Lazo, Dewhurst, and Burton*
2 Mev electrons	15.45 ± 0.11	Power input	Schuler and Allen*
32P beta particles (E_{av} = 0.70 Mev)	15.21 ± 0.04	4-π scintillation counting	Peisch and Steyn*
	15.39 ± 0.04	4-π proportional counting	Peisch and Steyn*
220 kvp X-rays (filtered 0.65 mm Al, E = 56 kev)†	15.0 ± 0.5	Ionization	Haybittle, Saunders, and Swallow*
60Co gamma rays	15.68 ± 0.7	Calorimetry	Ref. 11
60Co gamma rays	15.42 ± 0.04	Calorimetry	Ref. 12
100 kvp X-rays (filtered 0.65 mm Al, E = 33 kev)†	14.7 ± 0.5	Ionization	Haybittle, Saunders, and Swallow*

Table 4-5. G VALUES FOR THE FERROUS SULFATE DOSIMETER (Continued)

Radiation	$G(Fe^{3+})$	Method of energy measurement	Observers
50 kvp X-rays (unfiltered)	14.0 ± 0.8	(Not an absolute calibration)	Back and Miller*
8 kvp X-rays	13.4 ± 0.6	Ionization	Cottin and Lefort*
Tritium beta particles ($E_{av} = 5.5$ kev; internal source)	12.9 ± 0.2	Counting and gas-density determination	McDonnell and Hart*
12 Mev deuterons	9.81	Charge collection	Hart, Ramler, and Rocklin*
1.99 Mev protons	8.00	Charge collection	Hart, Ramler, and Rocklin*
3.47 Mev protons	6.90	Charge collection	Hart, Ramler, and Rocklin*
0.63 Mev protons	6.89	Charge collection	Hart, Ramler, and Rocklin*
$^6Li(n, \alpha)^3$ H recoil nuclei	5.69 ± 0.12	Neutron flux measurement	Schuler and Barr*
210 Po alpha particles (5.3 Mev; internal source)	5.10 ± 0.10	Absolute counting	Trumbore and Hart*
$^{10}B(n, \alpha)$ ^{7}Li recoil nuclei	4.22 ± 0.08	Neutron flux measurement	Hart, Ramler, and Rocklin*
^{235}U fission fragments	3.0 ± 0.9	Neutron flux measurement	Ehrenberg and Saeland*

*See Ref. 23, p. 111.
†Effective mean energy of radiation.
‡The G values based on ionization measurements have been adjusted, assuming W(air) = 34.0 ev/ion pair where the authors have used another value for this constant.

Table 4-6. EFFECT OF DOSE RATE ON $G(Fe^{3+})$
FOR FAST ELECTRON IRRADIATIONS*

(Fe^{++}), milli- moles	(Cl^-), milli- moles	E, Mev	Pulse length, μ sec	Dose rate, rad/sec	$G(Fe^{3+})$
1.0	1.0	1.0	Cont.	0.002×10^9	15.6 ± 0.5
1.0	1.0	2.0			
3.0		4.0	1.7	9.6×10^9	14.3
3.0	1.0	1.0–1.2	5.0	0.016×10^9	15.0 ± 1.6
3.0	1.0	1.0–1.2	5.0	0.18×10^9	13.4 ± 0.6
3.0	1.0	1.0–1.2	5.0	0.75×10^9	10.8 ± 0.9
3.0	1.0	1.0–1.2	5.0	2.4×10^9	10.1 ± 0.5
1.0	1.0	15	1.4	0.091×10^9	15.2 ± 0.4
1.0	1.0	15	1.4	0.69×10^9	14.5 ± 0.4
1.0	1.0	15	1.4	2.26×10^9	11.3 ± 0.5
1.0	1.0	15	1.4	2.92×10^9	12.2 ± 0.5
1.0	1.0	15	1.4	8.0×10^9	11.8 ± 0.5
1.0	1.0	15	1.4	8.0×10^9	13.0 ± 0.4
1.0	10.0	15	1.4	8.0×10^9	8.0 ± 0.5

*Adapted from "Physical Aspects of Irradiation," National Bureau of Standards, Handbook 85, p. 17, U.S. Government Printing Office, Washington, 1964.

For methanol: $-(Z/A)_M = (6 + 4 + 8)/32 = 18/32 = 0.562$

For the Fricke solution: $(Z/A)_1 = 0.553$

Hence $D_M = 6.87 \times 10^3 \ (0.562)/(0.533) = 7.22 \times 10^3$ rads.

(3) For $Pb(NO_3)_2$ there is considerable photoelectric absorption; so the electron fraction method (Eq. 4-13) cannot be used. The mass absorption coefficients for $Pb(NO_3)_2$ and for the Fricke dosimeter have been reported by Hochanadel and Davis[34] to be 0.0319 and 0.023 cm^2/g, respectively. The absorbed dose is

$$D_M = 6.87 \times 10^3 \ (0.0319/0.025) = 8.77 \times 10^3 \text{ rads}$$

A number of simplifying assumptions were made in solving Example 4-3:

(1) The substitution of methanol for ferrous sulfate solution was assumed not to change the secondary electron or primary beam spectra. Although this is reasonably correct for ^{60}Co as a general

rule, the mass-energy absorption coefficients would have to be calculated with due allowance for the degradation of the energy spectra occurring as the primary beam passes through matter. This effect has been determined theoretically and experimentally. Figure 4-6, for instance, shows the difference in mass absorption coefficients in $0.8N$ H_2SO_4 as a function of distance (in water) from a ^{60}Co gamma source. The increase in absorption coefficient is due to degradation of the primary and secondary spectra.

The electron fraction method, which applies only to the absorption of monoenergetic radiation in the Compton region of energies for both materials, is of questionable validity when applied to materials which differ greatly in atomic number; for example, $KNO_3/CsBr$ as compared to KNO_3/KNO_2 [in Eq. (4-13)]. The method assumes that all interactions (both primary and secondary) are in proportion to the number ratio of electrons. This is not strictly true.

(2) The intensity of the radiation beam throughout the sample container was assumed to be the same as that in the ferrous sulfate solution. For the type of source used, this is only approximately correct. (W. Bernstein and R. Schuler[35] have shown that about 2% of the

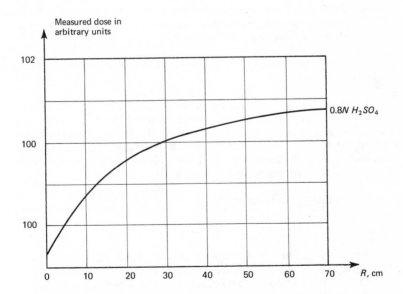

Fig. 4-6. Correction for the changed absorption coefficients due to spectrum degradation in $0.8N$ sulfuric acid as a function of the distance from ^{60}Co source. (Sehested, Brynjolfsson, and Holm, Riso Report No. 62 Danish Atomic Energy Commission, May, 1963.)

radiation in the annulus of a cylindrical ^{60}Co source is low energy radiation and therefore some photoelectric absorption occurs.)

4-4.2 Ceric Sulfate Dosimetry

The radiation induced reduction of ceric ion to cerous ion has found general acceptance as a dosimeter in the 10^5- to 10^8 rad range. It is particularly useful in intense radiation fields beyond the normal range of the ferrous-ferric system.

The use of ceric sulfate solutions as a dosimeter requires very special care in regard to cleanliness of the reaction vessel, etc., if reproducible results are to be obtained. All glassware must be thoroughly cleaned, and only triply distilled water prepared as discussed in Sec. 4-4.1 should be used in preparation of the solutions. The dosimeter is capable of a precision of ±1%. A small initial concentration of cerous ion ($>10^{-5}$ M) appears necessary for reproducible results.

The following procedure is recommended:

(1) Prepare a ceric sulfate solution that is 0.8N in sulfuric acid of such concentration (0.001M to 0.05M) that the radiation dose will reduce 20 to 80% of the available ceric ion. At higher ceric-ion concentration, the radiation response becomes nonlinear because $G(Ce^{3+})$ depends on both ceric and cerous ion concentrations at high cerous ion concentrations.

(2) Irradiate the solution in a container large enough to assure electronic equilibrium.

(3) Measure optical density at 3200 Å. The molar extinction coefficient at this wavelength is temperature dependent in the range 15 to 25°C and appears to vary with the pH. Several values have been reported in the literature; hence it is probably advisable to determine this independently. In 0.8N sulfuric acid, values of 5580 and 5565 have been reported.

(4) Compute the dose to the ceric solution.

(5) Convert the dose to the medium of interest.

The G value for the dosimeter is 2.5 ± 0.18, independent of temperature up to 35°C and of dose rates up to 2 × 10^6 rads/sec average and 2 × 10^8 rads/sec instantaneous. No dependence on LET is found for ^{60}Co gammas and electron energies up to 14 Mev. For more densely ionizing radiation, the dependence of the G value on LET is as shown in Table 4-7 and Fig. 4-5.

Table 4–7. G VALUES FOR THE CERIC SULFATE DOSIMETER[23]

Radiation	$G(Ce^{3+})$	Assumed $G(Fe^{3+})$ or method of energy measurement	Observers
8– to 14–Mev electrons	2.5 ± 0.18	Calorimetry	Taimuty and Towle Peterson
^{60}Co gamma rays (1.25 Mev)	2.5 ± 0.026	15.6	Taimuty and Towle Peterson
	2.33 ± 0.03	15.45	Barr and Schuler
	2.45 ± 0.08	15.5	Johnson and Weiss
	2.44 ± 0.03*	15.6	
200 kvp X-rays	3.15 ± 0.10	15.5	Johnson and Weiss
10 Mev deuterons	2.80 ± 0.04	Charge collection	Barr and Schuler
11 Mev helium ions	2.90 ± 0.06	Charge collection	Barr and Schuler
^{210}Po alpha particles (5.3 Mev; internal source)	3.20 ± 0.06	Absolute counting	Lefort and Tarrago
^{210}Po alpha particles (3.4 Mev; filtered through mica)	2.88 ± 0.02	4.7	Weiss and Miller
^{10}B(n, α) Li recoil nuclei	2.94 ± 0.12	4.22	Barr and Schuler

*This is the average of six independent literature values normalized to a standard set of conditions, in which 5609 liter/mole cm is taken as the molar extinction coefficient for ceric ion at 320 mμ.

4-4.3 Other Chemical Dosimeters

As previously indicated, a large number of chemical dosimeters have been proposed. Most of these dosimeters have been calibrated by comparison with the ferrous sulfate dosimeter and in a few cases with ionization chambers. One of the principal reasons for introducing a new dosimeter is that of sensitivity. For example, chemical dosimeters have been developed to detect absorbed doses as low as 0.5 rad.

Organic halogens, when exposed to radiation, liberate acids. Dosimeters based on this effect were reported in 1951 by Taplin, Douglas, and Sanchez[36] and by Henley and Miller.[37] Liquid hydrocarbons, such as chloroform, carbon tetrachloride, or tetrachloroethylene, may be incorporated into single phase, two phase, or emulsion systems. In the two phase and emulsion systems, the acid is extracted into the aqueous layer. The amount of acid produced over the usable range of the dosimeter, which is generally linear with dose, is determined by acidometric titrations or by color changes in pH-sensitive dyes, such as bromcresol purple.

Decomposition of the halogen compounds proceeds with a high G value of about 1000 and is very sensitive to oxygen. Since the G value is high, a small amount of radiation produces a great deal of chemical change, and very small doses of about 1 rad can be detected. By the addition of traces of organic inhibitor, alcohols and phenols in particular, the G value can be reduced to below 30, and doses as high as 10^6 rads can be measured.

In general, the chlorinated hydrocarbon systems are very sensitive to temperature, dose rate, and impurities. The presence of the high Z absorber, chlorine, makes them even more sensitive to LET effects. Most of the very considerable amount of work done on these dosimeters was sponsored by the U.S. Army in the hope that the halogenated hydrocarbons could be used as an inexpensive personnel dosimeter. There has been only limited application in the field.

Aqueous solutions of benzene and benzoic acid have been suggested as dosimeters. The principal products of benzene radiolysis are phenol and diphenyl, which are easily analyzed. Benzoic acid is oxidized to hydroxy benzoates, which are readily detected by fluorimetry.

Solutions of formic acid plus oxygen[38] have also been proposed for the high absorbed dose range (10^6 to 10^8 rads). The products of the reaction are hydrogen peroxide, carbon dioxide, and hydrogen.

Dosimetry in the gas phase has often presented a problem; a dosimeter that has been recommended and used with some success is acetylene.[39, 40]   At $30°$C $G(-C_2H_2)$ = 71.9. Nitrous oxide has also been used as a gas phase dosimeter. The proposed mechanism for nitrous oxide decomposition is

$$N_2O \xrightarrow{} N + NO \quad \text{or} \quad N_2 + O \qquad (4\text{-}11)$$

$$N + N_2O \longrightarrow N_2 + NO \qquad (4\text{-}12)$$

$$O + N_2O \longrightarrow 2\,NO \quad \text{or} \quad N_2 + O_2 \qquad (4\text{-}13)$$

$$2NO + O_2 \longrightarrow 2NO_2 \qquad (4\text{-}14)$$

A $G(-N_2O)$ of 12.8 for gamma and X-rays has been reported, however, at high absorbed doses ($> 10^4$ rads) back reaction occurs, thus limiting its use. This dosimeter has been used in mixed radiation fields and its use in this regard is discussed in the following section.

4-5 DOSIMETRY IN MIXED RADIATION FIELDS

In mixed radiation fields containing neutrons, several difficulties, in addition to induced radioactivity, are encountered. In aqueous dosimeters, for instance, the neutrons react with the water, producing protons, which are high LET sources. However, the fast capture cross section in water is small; hence aqueous dosimeters of some types can be used. The ceric sulfate dosimeter, for instance, has a fast neutron yield of 2.85 in contrast to the gamma yield of 2.40 and an effective yield of G = 2.70.

Absorbed dose in a mixed radiation field may in principle be determined with an ionization chamber. It is first necessary, however, to determine the percentage of the relative components and then make appropriate calculations. If the radiation field consists only of fast neutrons and hard X-rays or gamma rays, the situation is simplified enormously. This is discussed in the section on neutron dosimetry (Sec. 4-10).

Reactor radiation consists of a broad spectrum of neutron and photon energies, and it is in these situations that difficulty is experienced in accurately determining absorbed dose. Calorimetry is a method that has been used successfully; however, there are many limitations to its use, such as restricted space, remoteness from auxiliary equipment, and avoidance of materials with high neutron capture cross section. The method can, however, provide a good and reliable means of determining absorbed dose when properly used.[41-44] In general, however, dose limitations and other problems have led radiation chemists to seek other mixed radiation dosimeters. Some of these dosimeters are discussed in the following paragraphs.

A dosimeter based on the radiolytic decomposition of oxalic acid was originally proposed by Draganic.[45]   The procedure is as follows:

(1) Stock solutions of $0.05M$ oxalic acid are prepared.

(2) The dosimetry ampuls containing the solution are carefully evacuated.

(3) The solutions are irradiated; the decrease in oxalic acid concentration then being determined by measurement of the optical density at 248 mμ after addition of a complexing agent. The complexing agent is prepared from two solutions:

Solution A. 32.5 mg of benzidine are dissolved in 2 ml of 30% acetic acid and diluted with water to 250 ml.

Solution B. 125.0 mg of cupric acetate are dissolved in water and diluted to 250 ml.

Solutions A and B are mixed in equal parts, 4 parts of water are added, and then 1 ml of the resulting solution is added to 5 ml of sample.

The G value for the dosimeter is 4.9, and the accuracy is about 6% in the 1.6- to 160 Mrad dose range. The variation of yield with LET and dose rate has not been extensively studied; however, it is known that the G value for proton recoils and fission fragments is 0.9.

The formation of gaseous products by the decomposition of both organic and inorganic liquids has been extensively used for measuring large doses in mixed radiation fields. Cyclohexane, which produces gaseous hydrogen with a $G(H_2) = 5.25$ can be used in the 10^4- to 10^8 rad dose range with a precision of 3 to 6%. This dosimeter was first reported by Schuler and Allen[46] in 1955.

The use of nitrous oxide for reactor work in general and for fission fragment dosimetry in particular was proposed by Hartek and Dondes in 1956. This method, which is used at Brookhaven, Harwell, and other reactor sites, was reviewed recently.[47,48]   The dosimeter has the advantage of producing only gaseous products, consisting mainly of N_2, O_2, and NO_2. It appears to be completely independent of LET and consequently of dose rate. An added advantage is the temperature insensitivity of the reaction; the dosimeter can be used up to 150°C without thermal effects. The experimental procedure is as follows:

(1) The vessel, which is generally made of quartz for pressures below 5 atm and aluminum for higher pressures, is filled with N_2O.

(2) After irradiation the vessel is immersed in a liquid-nitrogen trap and connected to a vacuum rack. The noncondensible N_2 and O_2 are then measured. Next the vessel is raised to dry ice-acetone temperatures, and the N_2O pressure is measured. Finally, the sample is brought to room temperature, where the NO_2 is released.

(3) The total dose may be obtained from the NO_2, the $N_2 + O_2$ or the N_2O as follows:

$$E(NO_2) = 3.80 \times 10^{21} m \ (\%NO_2) \qquad (4\text{-}15)$$

$$E(N_2) = 1.59 \times 10^{21} m \ (\%N_2)^{1.064} \qquad (4\text{-}16)$$

$$E(N_2O) = 1.34 \times 10^{21} m \ (\%N_2O)^{1.04} \qquad (4\text{-}17)$$

where $E(NO_2)$, $E(N_2)$, and $E(N_2O)$ is the energy absorbed in electron volts, m is the weight of gas in grams, and (%) is the volume percent concentration.

The most serious drawbacks of the dosimeter are the relatively low accuracies (10%) and the corrections required because of neutron absorption reactions involving nitrogen.

EXAMPLE 4-4: Steinberg, Loffelholz, and Pruzansky [47] report the following experimental data for N_2O decomposition by fission recoils in a 22 cm^3 glass vessel:

Initial N_2O pressure	Temp	Irradiation time	Gas product analysis, %					G value		
			N_2	O_2	NO_2	N_2O	$(-N_2O)$	NO_2	$(-N_2O)$	N_2
2.55 atm	25°C	22.4 hr	0.32	0.04	0.16	99.48	0.4	3.90	9.74	7.80

Calculate the absorbed radiation dose and verify the G values reported.

SOLUTION: The weight of gas, according to the ideal gas law, is
$w = (MW) \ V/RT = 0.11$ g where

V = volume = 22 cm^3

MW = molecular weight = 44

R = gas constant = 82.06 atm-cm^3/°K-g mole

T = temperature = 298°K

P = pressure = 2.55 atm

By Eqs. (4-15) to (4-17),

$$E(\text{NO}_2) = 3.80 \times 10^{21}(0.11)(0.16) = 0.67 \times 10^{20} \text{ ev}$$

$$E(\text{N}_2) = 1.59 \times 10^{21}(0.11)(0.32)^{1.064} = 0.54 \times 10^{20} \text{ ev}$$

$$E(\text{N}_2\text{O}) = 1.34 \times 10^{21}(0.11)(0.4)^{1.04} = 0.58 \times 10^{20} \text{ ev}$$

The reason for the discrepancy is not clear. However, using average values, the absorbed dose is

$$E = \frac{0.6 \times 10^{20} \text{ ev}}{0.11 \text{ } g} \left| \frac{\text{rad } g}{6.24 \times 10^{13} \text{ ev}} \right. = 8.7 \times 10^{10} \text{ rads}$$

Number of molecules reacted:

$$\text{NO}_2 = \frac{22}{22,400} \left| \frac{2.55}{} \right| \frac{0.0016}{} \left| 6.02 \times 10^{23} \right. = 2.41 \times 10^{18}$$

$$\text{N}_2 = \frac{22}{22,400} \left| \frac{2.55}{1} \right| \frac{0.0032}{} \left| 6.02 \times 10^{23} \right. = 4.82 \times 10^{18}$$

$$\text{N}_2\text{O} = \frac{22}{22,400} \left| \frac{2.55}{} \right| \frac{0.004}{} \left| 6.02 \times 10^{23} \right. = 6.04 \times 10^{18}$$

$$G_{\text{NO}_2} = \frac{2.41 \times 10^{20}}{0.6 \times 10^{20}} = 4;$$

$$G_{\text{N}_2} = \frac{4.82}{0.6} = 8.02;$$

$$G_{-\text{N}_2\text{O}} = \frac{6.04}{0.6} = 10.5$$

4-6 PLASTIC FILM DOSIMETRY

The very low cost, negligible radiation attenuation, versatility, flexibility, and widespread commercial availability of polymeric materials such as cellophane, polyethylene, polyvinylchloride (PVC), and polyesters, make them attractive candidates as chemical dosimeters for applications where accuracy is not a primary consideration. As a result, dosimetry techniques based on plastic films were the first to gain industrial acceptance in drug and food sterilization, where extensive monitoring of individual samples is required. Other very important applications are in depth-dose determinations and in electron beam scanning.

Radiation induced changes in plastics include chemical changes, such as double bond formation, dehalogenation, crosslinking, polymerization, depolymerization, gas evolution, and the destruction by oxidation or reduction of dyes or other chemicals incorporated into the plastic matrix. These effects, as well as transient physical phenomena, such as electron trapping or crystallinity, can be recorded in terms of changes in light transmission, tensile strength, heat of fusion, color, free radical spectra, viscosity, solubility, density, hardness, elongation, plastic flow, or X-ray diffraction. All these methods have, at one time or another, been suggested and used for dosimetry. However, only three methods have gained widespread acceptance.

(1) Polyvinylchloride (PVC) turns green, yellow, amber, and then reddish-brown when irradiated. The color reaches a maximum in three to four days at room temperature, but at 80 to 85°C the maximum color is obtained in 5 to 10 min. The coloration, as measured by light absorption at 3960 Å, is proportional to absorbed dose in the 10^5 to 10^7 rad range. A rigid PVC of standard quality has been widely used in commercial sterilization quality control, the procedures being as described by Artandi and Stonehill.[49]

(2) Polymers containing dyes are discolored by radiation. Of the almost infinite combinations of polymers and dyes, commercial cellophane containing a blue dimethoxydiphenylbisazobis 8-amino-1-napthol-5, 7-disulphonic dye has been the most studied and used. Henley and Richman[50] give calibrations for 0.8-, 2-, and 3 Mev electrons and ^{60}Co gammas in the dose range 200,000 to 10×10^6 r. The dosage is determined by optical density measurements at 6500 Å.

(3) Although not as widely used as the other two methods cited, the trans-unsaturation induced in long chain paraffins, such as polyethylene, is also a convenient and widely used dosimeter. The unsaturation, which is measured in the infrared, is independent of intensity and temperature and is proportional to doses up to 100 Mrads.[51]

4-7 PHOTOGRAPHIC EMULSIONS

The latent images produced by charged particles passing through photographic emulsions constitute the earliest radiation detectors known. Upon development of the film, grains of silver appear along the track. These images, and those obtained from bubble chamber and cloud chamber photographs, constitute the principal techniques whereby atomic particles are discovered and characterized. Special emulsions having four times the silver bromide content and a much smaller grain size (0.1 to 0.6 μ) than that found for emulsions used in dosimetry applications are used for this work.

Nuclear track measurement is only one of the many dosimetry applications of photographic emulsions. They are widely used in autoradiography, where the geometric movement of a radioactive isotope must be followed. Personnel monitoring is another major application. By selection of suitable films, absorbed radiation doses between 0.1 and 1000 r can be monitored. The response of the films, which contain heavy metal ions, is a strong function of both photon and electron energies in the low energy region. The normal film packets worn for radiation monitoring purposes are therefore of rather sophisticated construction. They contain two or more films of different sensitivities for measuring different dose ranges, as well as stacked filters so that different particles can be distinguished.

High level, 10^4- to 10^8 r dosimetry with photographic film is a relatively new development. It has been made possible by a special photographic printout emulsion.[52]

Commercial X-ray film has also been used for high level dosimetry. Figure 4-7 shows the changes in net transmission density for Ansco Superay "A" and Kodak Type K X-ray film. Three stacks of films were used to increase the accuracy, which is said to be improved to ±5% by this technique. Although no dose rate dependence was observed for the Ansco film between 2×10^2 and 5×10^5 r/hr, an effect has been observed above 10^5 r/min. There is also a strong energy dependence below 0.6 Mev as well as a temperature dependence.

4-8 SOLID STATE DOSIMETERS

A large number of solid state dosimeters have been used. Photoluminescent and thermoluminescent materials; those materials that form permanent color centers (see Sec. 4-8.1); materials that undergo chemical decomposition, such as the nitrates; organic luminescent materials; and those materials that show a change in electrical conductivity (semiconductors) have all been used.

4-8.1 Glass Dosimetry

Although the radiation induced changes in glass are mostly physical rather than chemical, the application of these changes to dosimetry is typical of chemical dosimeters, and glass dosimeters are usually classified as such. The first type of glass dosimeter developed was the silver activated phosphate glass[53] now used by the armed forces as a personnel dosimeter. It is based on a radiophotoluminescence phenomenon, a postirradiation fluorescence stimulated by near ultraviolet radiation.

The function of the silver ions is to trap the electrons liberated in the glass by the radiation. In the process the silver ions are reduced to atoms, which serve as the center for both the photoluminescence and for the creation of color. These color centers can

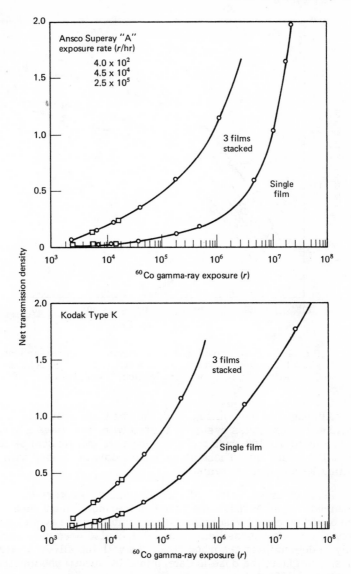

Fig. 4-7. Commercial X-ray film transmission densities for various exposure rates and doses from ^{60}Co source. (From H. F. Nitka, "Nucleonics," 17:10, 58, 1959.)

also be used for dosimetry purposes but in a much higher dose range, as is shown in Fig. 4-8. The dose is determined by optical density measurements with a spectrophotometer at 3500 Å.

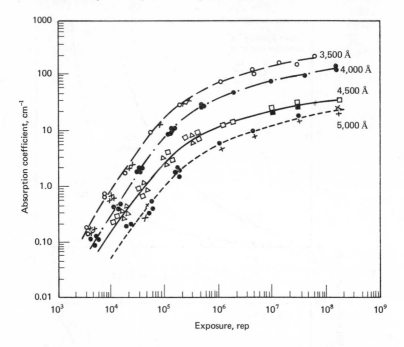

Fig. 4-8. Dose dependence of absorption of silver-activated glass for various wavelengths of light. (From J. H. Schulman, C. C. Klick, and H. Rabin, "Nucleonics," 13:30, February, 1955.)

Although, as seen in Fig. 4-8, the response above 10^6 rads is nonlinear, these glass systems, if used with care, have a precision of $\pm 2\%$ up to 5×10^6 rads and are dose rate independent up to at least 10^6 rads/sec. These glasses have only been used with penetrating X- and gamma radiation.

Many other variations of special glass dosimeters have been reported. Some of these are based on thermoluminescence; others are based on direct absorption in the visible or ultraviolet spectrum. Cobalt activated borosilicate glass[54] has also been used successfully in determining absorbed dose. As with the silver activated phosphate glass, the dose is determined by spectrophotometric absorption at 3500 Å.

4-8.2 Solid State Semiconductor Radiation Detectors

If a solid state diode is biased in the reverse direction, a large electric field is created in the "depleted" junction. The junction now acts exactly like a capacitance in that an ion pair created in the junction gives rise to an electric pulse that can be amplified and analyzed.

Since 1958 a wide variety of devices based on solid state semi-conductors has been made available. They have some unique advantages over ion chambers and scintillation devices. The pulse output is very fast, and only a few electron volts are required to raise an electron from a valence to a conduction band. This is about one tenth the energy required to form an ion pair and thus leads to improved counting statistics. Solid state devices also provide good linearity of pulse height vs. energy and high resolution.

Presently available devices also have some major disadvantages including: (1) small output signals, (2) variation of operating conditions with ambient conditions, (3) inability (because of their small linear dimensions) to stop long path length particles, and (4) susceptibility to radiation damage.

Two of the principal types of junction detectors used are shown in Fig. 4-9. In part (A) of Fig. 4-9 we see an example of an n^+ - p diffused junction, where the junction is made by diffusing a donor impurity such as phosphorus to a shallow depth into p-type silicon. Conversely, a diffused p^+ - n junction detector can be constructed by diffusing gallium or boron into n-type silicons.

Part (B) of Fig. 4-9 shows a surface-barrier junction detector. The p^+ surface layer is made by oxidation of chemically etched surfaces, the surface contact being made by the evaporation of a thin gold film. In operation the gold film on the p layer is biased negative to the n-type silicon crystal.

Figure 4-10, part (A), illustrates the use of an n-p-n junction as a radiation detector; part (B) is a block circuit diagram of a negatively biased semiconductor device.

Tremendous advances are being made in the field of semiconductor detectors, and it is not unreasonable to assume that in a few years they will replace ion chambers for many applications.

4-9 ABSORBED DOSE DETERMINED BY COUNTING TECHNIQUES

Absorbed dose may be determined by the use of counters, such as a Geiger-Mueller, proportional, or scintillation counter. In general counters usually only provide information concerning the number of particles per square centimeter; however, with certain equipment the energy and number of the particles can be obtained and can be related to the absorbed dose in the medium of interest.

4-9.1 Proportional Counters

Proportional counters are ion counting devices operating in such a manner that they produce a voltage drop that is proportional

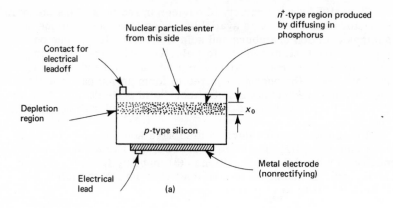

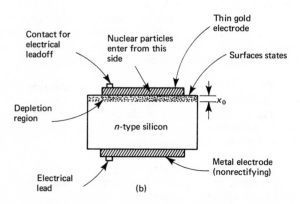

Fig. 4-9. Schematic representations (A) of diffused n^+-p junction detector and (B) of surface barrier junction detector. (After Price, 1964.)

to the number of ions created as well as to the number of events. A proportional counter can thus be used to establish both the number and the energy of charged particles. In theory this is true also for photons. In practice, however, energy discrimination is possible only at low photon energies where the differentiation is made on the basis of the energy of the ejected electron.

Energy discrimination in a proportional counter is achieved by arbitrarily rejecting pulses above or below certain levels. The number of counts can be controlled, to some extent, by increasing or decreasing the voltage difference between anode and cathode.

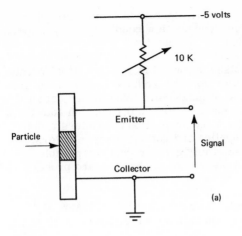

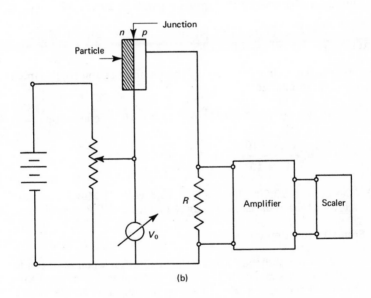

Fig. 4-10. Solid state radiation detector.

Proportional counters generally operate at atmospheric pressure and are often used as windowless flow counters with gas circulation between sample and ionization chamber.

Although the smaller pulses produced in a proportional counter, in contrast to a Geiger-Mueller counter, require greater amplification, the counters are capable of measuring much higher dose rates since resolving times can be made as low as 0.1 sec. In addition to requiring additional amplifiers, the proportional counters require stable high-voltage power supplies and voltage discriminators. Their cost therefore is considerably greater than comparable Geiger-Mueller counters. A discussion of the standard proportional counter is given in Ref. 55.

EXAMPLE 4-5: (1) What voltage is developed by a 3 Mev alpha particle in a proportional ionization counter having a 10 $\mu\mu$f capacity?

(2) If the counter gain is 10,000, what is the energy of an unknown alpha source that gives a pulse at 20 volts?

SOLUTION: (1) Assuming 35 ev per ion pair, the number of ion pairs is $3 \times 10^6/35 = 8.6 \times 10^4$.

The charge reaching the plate is the number of ion pairs times the electronic charge.

$$Q = (8.6 \times 10^4)(1.6 \times 10^{-19}) = 13.8 \times 10^{-15} \text{ coulombs}$$

$$V = \frac{Q}{C} = \frac{13.8 \times 10^{-15}}{10 \times 10^{-12}} = 1.38 \times 10^{-3} \text{ volts}$$

(2) The gain is 10,000; hence $V = 13.8$ volts/3 Mev. The unknown alpha thus has an energy of $(20)(3)/13.8 = 4.34$ Mev.

4-9.2 Scintillation Detectors

That certain substances emit visible radiation when exposed to ionizing radiation was known in the days of Roentgen, who used zinc sulfide luminescence as a qualitative dosimeter. The emission of light by substances exposed to radiation can be explained in some substances in terms of the return to the ground states by atoms that have been raised to excited states by energy absorption. The excited atoms return to their ground states with half lives characteristic of the process involved. If the decay constants are of the order of 10^{-8} to 10^{-9} sec, the scintillation process is called *fluorescence*. Longer-lived processes are often called *phosphoresences*.

Scintillation crystals used commercially today are largely organic hydrocarbon or sodium iodide crystals that yield about one photon per 100 ev of absorbed energy. Conversion of the light pulse into an electrical signal is accomplished by photomultipliers. Photomultiplier tubes consist of two elements: a normal photoelectric. surface that emits electrons when exposed to light and a series of metallic plates called dynodes, which are held at increasing voltages and which effect electron multiplication. Dynodes generally operate at 100 V and emit perhaps 3 or 4 electrons per incident electron. Typical tubes have 10 to 11 stages.

The number of electrons collected at the photomultiplier output is directly proportional to the energy lost in the crystal by the particle. Thus, if a 1 Mev beta particle produces a 1 V output, we would expect a 2 Mev particle to produce a 2 V output if no other factors be operative. The size of the voltage pulses from the phototube can thus be related to the energy of the incident particle, provided that accurate calibrations are possible and linear amplification of voltage signals is achieved.

Examples of the types of scintillators in use today are given in Table 4-8. Anthracene and trans-stilbene are examples of single-crystal organics. Liquid phosphors include materials such as p-terphenyl, 2-phenyl-5-(4-biphenyl)-oxazole, and other benzene-ring structures. Plastic phosphors are made by imbedding aromatic compounds in polymers like butadiene and polystyrene. The inorganic scintillators, lithium iodide or cesium iodide, generally contain small amounts of activators (europium or thallium).

4-10 NEUTRON DOSIMETRY

Neutron dosimetry is severely complicated by the fact that neutrons are nearly always accompanied by other types of radiation, gammas in particular. The simultaneous presence of both very low and very densely ionizing radiation raises immense problems of both dosimetry and data interpretation. Neutron interactions are also much more energy dependent than the interactions of electromagnetic or other forms of particulate radiation; thus spectrum measurements as well as dose measurements are necessary. Nuclear reactors, the chief source of neutrons for radiation chemistry, are remote-access installations. This often causes severe complications; the samples (and equipment) may become radioactive. In addition, then, to determining the observed dose due to the gamma- and neutron fluxes, one must also include the dose contributed by the induced radioactivity.

Since neutrons have no electrical charge, they are stopped largely by interactions with nuclei. Thus the electrical detection of neutrons must be based on secondary phenomena. Almost all

Table 4-8. PROPERTIES OF SCINTILLATORS*

Materials	Density, g/cm^3	Wavelength of maximum emission, Å	Relative beta-ray pulse height	Alpha-beta ratio, %	Decay time, sec
Anthracene crystal	1.25	4400	100	9	3×10^{-8}
Trans-stilbene crystal	1.15	4100	60	9	$4\text{-}8 \times 10^{-9}$ (β)
Liquid phosphors	0.86	3500-4500	40-60	9	$2\text{-}8 \times 10^{-9}$
Plastic phosphors	1.06	3500-4500	28-48		$3\text{-}5 \times 10^{-9}$
NaI(Tl)	3.67	4200	210	44	3×10^{-7}
LiI(Eu)	4.06	4700	70	95	1.2×10^{-6}
Cs(Tl)	4.51	4200-5700	55-95		1.1×10^{-6} (β) 0.43×10^{-6} (α)
ZnS(Ag) (powder)	4.10	4500	200	100	$4\text{-}10 \times 10^{-8}$ (fast component) $4\text{-}10 \times 10^{-5}$ (slow component)

*From W. J. Price, "Nuclear Radiation Detection," p. 162, McGraw-Hill Book Company, Inc., New York, 1964.

the neutron interaction mechanism detailed in Chap. 2 represents potential measurement techniques. If one is able to induce (n, α), (n, p), (n, γ), or $(n, fission)$ reactions, the problem reduces to one of knowing the reaction yield and of detecting the secondary radiation. Another alternative is neutron-induced transmutations resulting in radioactive products that can be identified by their characteristic decays. A third possibility is that of measuring charged recoil particles, such as protons.

4-10.1 Activation Detection and Spectrum Measurements

The detection of neutrons by the amount of radiation induced in a material of known cross section is an obvious extension of the principles discussed in Chap. 2. Neutron activation detectors have a number of advantages that make them well suited to the needs of radiation chemists.

(1) Wide range of fluxes. By choosing materials of high or low cross section radiation chemists can measure almost any neutron flux.

(2) Remote location readings. The dosimeters may be removed from the neutron beam and read at a later time at another location.

(3) Convenient physical dimensions. The detectors can be prepared in the form of thin foils, which can be attached to sample containers. These foils can be sufficiently small so that the neutron flux is not perturbed.

(4) Selectivity of energy response. This is the property which makes a determination of the neutron energy spectrum in a reactor possible.

Different elements have vastly different neutron capture cross sections at any given neutron energy. It is possible therefore to use multiple activations to determine neutron spectra. One particularly useful concept is that of threshold detectors, materials that do not become radioactive unless the neutron energy exceeds a certain minimum value. Table 4-9 is a listing of the more common threshold reactions. If several detectors, each having a different threshold, are used, it is possible, by substraction, to know the total flux between any two energy thresholds and thus to obtain histograms of the neutron spectrum.

Table 4-9. THRESHOLD REACTIONS

Reaction	Effective threshold Mev	σ_c, mb
^{237}Np(fission	0.2	
^{115}In(n, n)	0.45	0.223
^{238}U(fission)	1.45	540
^{31}P$(n, p)^{31}$ Si	2.5	75
^{58}Ni$(n, p)^{58}$ Co	2.9	420
^{32}S$(n, p)^{32}$ P	3.0	310
^{64}Zn$(n, p)^{64}$ Cu	4.0	320
^{54}Fe$(n, p)^{54}$ Mn	4.2	610
^{24}Mg$(n, p)^{24}$ Na	6.3	60
^{56}Fe$(n, p)^{56}$ Mn	7.5	110
^{27}Al$(n, a)^{24}$ Na	8.1	130
^{12}C$(n, 2n)^{11}$ C	20	
^{127}I$(n, 2n)^{126}$ I	10	

For the case of a very thin foil inserted in a nuclear reactor, the saturation activity, N_s, is given by

$$N_s = N \int_o^\infty \sigma_a(E)\, \phi(E)\, dE \qquad (4\text{-}18)$$

where N is the concentration of target atoms and where both the absorption coefficient, σ_a, and the flux ϕ, are energy dependent. Foils used in reactors are exposed to thermal $(0 < E < 0.4$ ev) neutrons, epithermal, or resonance $(0.4$ ev $< E < 10$ kev) neutrons, and fast $(10$ kev $< E < 10$ Mev) neutrons.

It may be assumed that the absorption coefficient σ_a for fast neutrons is negligible; so

$$N_s = N \left[\int_{thermal} \sigma_a(E)\,\phi(E)\;dE \right. $$

$$\left. + \int_{epithermal} \sigma_a(E)\,\phi(E)\;dE \right] \qquad (4\text{-}19)$$

Since in the thermal region the activation follows the $1/\overline{V}$ law, it is convenient to rewrite Eq. (4-19) in terms of a reference absorption coefficient σ_{oa}, neutron velocity, $\overline{V}_o$, and the thermal-neutron concentration, n_t. Thus Eq. (4-19) becomes

$$N_s = N \left[\int_{thermal} \frac{\sigma_{oa}\overline{V}_o}{\overline{V}} n_t(\overline{V})\;\overline{V}\,d\overline{V} \right. $$

$$\left. + \int_{epithermal} \sigma_a(\overline{V}) n(\overline{V})\;d\overline{V} \right] \qquad (4\text{-}20)$$

Denoting the two R.H.S. integrals by N_{st} and N_{se}, respectively,

$$N_s = N_{st} + N_{se} = N n_t \overline{V}_o\, \sigma_{oa} + N_{se} \qquad (4\text{-}21)$$

To distinguish between the activation due to the thermal neutrons, N_{st}, and epithermal neutrons, N_{se}, the foils are exposed bare and wrapped in cadmium sheets. Cadmium has an unusually large absorption coefficient for thermal neutrons (7200 barns); hence the activity induced in the cadmium-wrapped foils is proportional (primarily) to the epithermal flux. The cadmium ratio R_c is defined as the ratio of the saturation activity of the bare foil to that of the cadmium-covered foil:

$$R_c = \frac{N_s}{N_{se}} \qquad (4\text{-}22)$$

Substituting into Eq. (4-21),

$$\frac{N_{st}}{N_{se}} = R_c - 1 \qquad (4\text{-}23)$$

In actual practice the amount of activity induced in the cadmium-wrapped foil will be less than N_{se} by some factor because the cadmium also absorbs some epithermal neutrons. This correction factor, which depends on the ratio of foil-to-cadmium thickness, among other things, will be neglected in this simplified derivation.

A series of important relations may now be obtained by combining Eq. (4-23) with Eqs. (4-21) and (4-20).

$$R_c - 1 = \frac{n_t \overline{V}_o \sigma_{oa}}{\int_{0.4\,ev}^{\infty} \sigma_a(E)\,\phi(E)\,dE} \tag{4-24}$$

In the epithermal region the cross section of most absorbers varies as $1/E$, in contrast to the $1/E^{1/2}$ or $1/\overline{V}$ law prevailing at low energies. If we now say that the resonance flux, ϕ, is proportional to K/E, Eq. (4-24) becomes

$$(R_c - 1) = \frac{n_t \overline{V}_o \sigma_{oa}}{K \int_{0.4\,ev}^{\infty} \sigma_a(dE/E)} \tag{4-25}$$

K is a constant given by

$$K = \frac{n_t \overline{V}_o \sigma_{oa}}{(R_c - 1) \int_{0.4\,ev}^{\infty} \frac{\sigma_a(E)}{E}\,dE} \tag{4-26}$$

The integral in Eq. (4-25) is called the resonance integral and has been measured for a variety of activation detectors. Values of activation detectors, as well as some of the other important properties, are given in Table 4-10. The value of σ_{oa}, the reference thermal activation cross section, is normally taken at 0.025 ev, which corresponds to a neutron velocity of 2200 m/sec.

EXAMPLE 4-6: The cadmium ratio in a graphite uranium reactor is about 33 (Ref. 56). Calculate (1) the ratio of thermal activation to resonance activation for gold, assuming it is a $1/\overline{V}$ absorber in the thermal region and a $1/E$ absorber in the epithermal region and (2) the ratio of the thermal to epithermal neutron flux in any ln$e$ energy interval.

SOLUTION: (1) The ratio of σ_a thermal to $\int_{0.4}^{\infty} \sigma_a\,dE/E$ for a $1/\overline{V}$ ($1/E^{1/2}$) detector is

$$\frac{\sigma_a}{\int \sigma_a(dE/E)} = \frac{1/(0.025\,ev)^{1/2}}{\int_{0.4\,ev}^{\infty} E^{-3/2}\,dE} = \frac{1}{2}\frac{(0.4)^{1/2}}{(0.025)^{1/2}} = 2$$

Table 4-10. PROPERTIES OF ACTIVATION DETECTORS (THERMAL AND RESONANCE DETECTORS)*

Element	Detector material			Activation product		
	Thermal activation cross-section, barns†	Resonance energy, ev‡	Resonance activation integral, barns	Nuclide	Half life	Principal activity
Indium	145	1.45	2,640	^{116}In	54.1 min	β (1 Mev) γ (several energies)
Gold	96	4.9	1,555**	^{198}Au	27 days	β(0.963 and 0.41 Mev)
Iodine	5.5	20–200	140	^{128}I	24.99 min	β(2.0 Mev)
Dysprosium	2,600	54		^{165}Dy	139.2 min	β(1.25, 0.88, and 0.42 Mev) γ(0.09, 0.36, and 0.76 Mev)
Cobalt	34.0	135	49.3	^{60}Co††	5.28 years	β(0.31 Mev) γ(1.33 and 1.17 Mev)
Manganese	13.4	330	11.8	^{56}Mn	2.58 hr	β(2.81 Mev), γ (0.822 Mev)
Sodium	0.56	3,000	0.24	^{24}Na	15.0 hr	β(1.39 Mev) γ(1.37 and 2.75 Mev)
Vanadium	4.5	4,200; 13,000	2.2	^{52}V	3.76 min	β(2.1 Mev) γ (1.5 Mev)
Chlorine	0.56	26,000		^{28}Cl	37.5 min	β(5.0, 2.8, and 1.1 Mev) γ(2.2 and 1.6 Mev)

*Table taken from W. J. Price, "Nuclear Radiation Detection," p. 334, McGraw-Hill Book Company, Inc., New York, 1964.
†Taken at 0.025 ev. From J. Hughes and J. A. Harvey, "Neutron Cross Sections," McGraw-Hill Book Company, Inc., New York, 1955.
‡Location of principal peak. From J. Hughes and J. A. Harvey, "Neutron Cross Sections," McGraw-Hill Book Company, Inc., New York, 1955.
From R. L. Macklin and H. S. Pomerance, "Proceedings of the International Conference on the Peaceful Uses of Atomic Energy," Vol. 5, p. 96, United Nations, New York, 1956.
From J. M. Hollander, I. Perlman, and G. T. Seaborg, Table of Isotopes, Revs. Mod. Phys. 25:613 (1953).
**From C. N. Kelber, "Resonance Integrals for Gold and Indium Foils," Nucleonics, 20(8):162 (1952). This reference also includes values corrected for the effect of foil thickness.
††The 10.7-min ^{60}Co decays into the 5.28-year ^{60}Co.

Thus for gold the $1/\overline{V}$ contribution is $0.5(96) = 48$, whereas the resonance integral is 1555 barns (Table 4-10).

(2) The ratio of thermal-to-resonance flux in any $dE/E = \ln e$ interval is Eq. (4-25)

$$(R_c - 1) = 2 \; \frac{n_t \overline{V}_o}{K} = (33 - 1)$$

or

$$\frac{n_t \overline{V}_o}{K} = 16/\ln e \text{ interval}$$

Once the reactor neutron flux and spectrum have been measured, it is possible to calculate absorbed doses, provided that gamma fluxes as well as neutron fluxes have been established. The calculations must allow for all possible modes of energy transfer, as is demonstrated in Example 4-7.

EXAMPLE 4-7: Fenger[57] reports a series of experiments wherein the gamma flux in a thermal column of Danish reactor Dr2 was calibrated with an oxalic acid dosimeter. To find the gamma flux, it is necessary to determine the fraction of the total dose due to neutrons. In particular, corrections must be made for energy absorption due to: (1) gamma recoil, (2) thermal neutron capture gammas, (3) elastic scatter of fast neutrons, and (4) scattering of (intermediate energy) neutrons.

The oxalic acid was irradiated at 25° C in quartz ampules 5 cm long and 8 mm in diameter in a thermal beam hole containing only gamma rays and neutrons. The neutron flux, as measured by foil activation methods, was: thermal $E_n < 0.4$ ev, 4.55×10^{12} neutrons/cm^2/sec; fast neutrons, 8×10^9 neutrons/cm^2/sec, average energy of 2 Mev; epithermal flux, 5×10^{10} neutrons/cm^2/sec, average energy of 2 Mev; epithermal flux, 5×10^{10} neutrons/cm^2/sec. Thirty percent of the oxalic acid was decomposed in 2.8 hours. Calculate the total gamma radiation dose and the fraction of the dose due to neutrons. It is assumed that negligible activation of the glass ampules occurred.

SOLUTION: (1) Gamma recoil. The thermal neutron cross sections for the (n, γ) reactions of the elements in the mixture are

$$\sigma_H = 0.0332 \times 10^{-24} \text{ cm}^2$$

$$\sigma_o = \; < 2 \times 10^{-28} \text{ cm}^2$$

$$\sigma_c = < 4.5 \times 10^{-27} \text{ cm}^2$$

It is apparent that σ_o and σ_c are negligibly small compared to σ_H.

The gamma ray energy released by the (n, γ) reaction is 2.23 Mev. The recoil energy is

$$E_r = E_\gamma^2/1862M = 1330 \text{ ev}$$

where E_γ is the gamma energy and M the mass of the recoiling atom.

The total number of recoils is

$$\frac{4.55 \times 10^{12} \text{ neutron}}{\text{cm}^2\text{-sec}} \left| \frac{3600 \text{ sec}}{\text{hr}} \right| \frac{2}{18} \left| 6.02 \times 10^{23} \right| 0.332 \times 10^{-24} \text{ cm}^2$$

$$= 3.64 \times 10^{14} \frac{\text{absorptions}}{\text{ml-hr}}$$

The energy in rads per hour is

$$3.64 \times 10^{14} \frac{\text{absorptions}}{\text{ml-hr}} \left| 1330 \text{ ev} \right| \frac{1.6 \times 10^{-14} \text{ rad-}g}{\text{ev}} \left| \frac{\text{ml}}{g} \right.$$

$$= 7.75 \times 10^3 \frac{\text{rads}}{\text{hr}}$$

(2) Capture gammas. The $H(n, \gamma)D$ gamma reaction releases a 2.23 Mev gamma, for which the absorption coefficient is 0.027 cm^2/g = 0.027 cm^{-1} in the medium.

The average track length in the 5 cm long, 8 mm diameter tubes is estimated to be 0.30 cm.

The gamma-ray energy deposited inside the dosimeter is

$$\frac{3.64 \times 10^{14} \text{ absorps}}{\text{ml-hr}} \left| \frac{2.23 \text{ Mev}}{\gamma} \right| \frac{0.027}{\text{cm}} \left| 0.3 \text{ cm} \right| \frac{1.6 \times 10^{-8} \text{ rad-}g}{\text{Mev}} \left| \frac{\text{ml}}{g} \right.$$

$$= 1.05 \times 10^5 \frac{\text{rads}}{\text{hr}}$$

(3) Fast neutrons $(E_n > 1 \text{ Mev})$, $E_{av} = 2$ Mev. The mean loss on collision is

$$\ln \frac{E_o}{E} = 1 + \frac{(A - 1)^2}{2A} \ln \frac{(A - 1)}{(A + 1)}$$

where E_o = 2 Mev, A = 2 and E = 1 Mev.

The cross section for scattering, $\sigma_{scatter}$, is 0.037 cm^{-1}. Assuming there is only one scattering interaction per neutron,

Absorbed energy

$$= \frac{8 \times 10^9 \text{ n}}{\text{cm}^2\text{-sec}} \left| \frac{3600 \text{ sec}}{\text{hr}} \right| \frac{1 \text{ Mev}}{\text{n}} \left| \frac{0.137}{\text{cm}} \right| \frac{1.6 \times 10^{-8} \text{ rad}}{\text{Mev}} \left| \frac{\text{g cm}^3}{\text{g}} \right.$$

$$= 6.3 \times 10^3 \; \frac{\text{rads}}{\text{hr}}$$

This total energy transfer due to fast-neutron scatter is obviously too small to justify a more detailed calculation for the number of scattering interactions.

(4) Resonance energy neutrons (0.4 ev $< E_n <$ 10 kev). In the intermediate energy region, there is a considerable variation in both the energy spectrum and the cross section. It is therefore necessary to calculate an average value for the scattering cross section:

$$\sigma_{av} = \int_{0.4 \text{ ev}}^{\text{Mev}} \sigma_s(E_n) dE_n$$

Fenger obtained a value of 7×10^{-18} ev-cm^2 for this integral by using the measured spectrum and integrating the cross section curve for hydrogen.

The intermediate energy neutrons, like the fast ones, lose 0.5 of their energy in each collision; hence the total dose due to intermediate energy neutrons is

$$\frac{0.5}{} \left| \frac{5 \times 10^{10} \text{ n}}{\text{cm}^2\text{-sec}} \right| \frac{3600 \text{ sec}}{\text{hr}} \left| \frac{7 \times 10^{-18} \text{ ev-cm}^2}{} \right| \frac{6.7 \times 10^{22} \text{ H atoms}}{\text{g}} \left| \frac{1.6 \times 10^{-14} \text{ rads-g}}{\text{ev}} \right.$$

$$= 0.68 \times 10^6 \; \frac{\text{rads}}{\text{hr}}$$

A summary of the preceding calculations is:

Interaction	Dose, rads/hr
Gamma recoils	7.75×10^3
Capture gammas	1.05×10^5
Fast neutrons	6.30×10^3
Epithermal neutrons	0.68×10^6

The LET for the 0.5 Mev recoil protons produced in the neutron scatter and the recoil processes is about 7 ev/Å. The G value for heavy particles of this type is about 0.9, in contrast to the 4.9 acid molecules decomposed per 100 ev by the gamma radiation (Sec. 4-5). The total amount of acid decomposition due to the high LET transfer processes is

$$\frac{(6.3 \times 10^3 + 6.8 \times 10^5 + 7.75 \times 10^3)\ \text{rads}}{\text{hr}} \left| \frac{0.9\ \text{molec}}{100\ \text{ev}} \right| \frac{\text{ev}}{1.6 \times 10^{-14}\ \text{rad-g}} \left| \frac{\text{mole}}{6.02 \times 10^{23}\ \text{molec}} \right.$$

$$= 6.47 \times 10^{-7}\ \text{moles/g}$$

The total amount of the 0.05 molar acid destroyed is $(0.05)(0.3)/1000 = 1.5 \times 10^{-5}$ moles/g.

The amount of acid destroyed by capture gammas is

$$\frac{1.05 \times 10^5\ \text{rads}}{\text{hr}} \left| \frac{4.9\ \text{molec}}{100\ \text{ev}} \right| \frac{\text{ev}}{1.6 \times 10^{-14}\ \text{rad g}} \left| \frac{\text{mole}}{6.02 \times 10^{23}\ \text{moles}} \right.$$

$$= 5.34 \times 10^{-7}\ \text{moles/g}$$

The total dose due to the reactor gamma flux is

$$\frac{(150 - 1.5 - 5.34) \times 10^{-7}\ \text{moles}}{\text{g}} \left| \frac{1}{2.8\ \text{hr}} \right| \frac{6.02 \times 10^{23}\ \text{moles}}{} \left| \frac{100\ \text{ev}}{4.9\ \text{molec}} \right| \frac{1.6 \times 10^{-14}\ \text{rad-g}}{\text{ev}}$$

$$= 276 \times 10^4\ \frac{\text{rads}}{\text{hr}}$$

PROBLEMS

4-1 What voltage is developed across a 1 $\mu\mu f$ capacitor under conditions such that there is a 10^{-10} coulomb charge separation?

4-2 A 2 Mev particle enters an air-filled proportional counter with a gain of 1000 and a capacity of 10 $\mu\mu f$. How large a voltage pulse is developed?

4-3 A calibrated proportional counter gives a 30 V pulse for a 3 Mev alpha particle. An unknown source of alphas is found to give two pulses in two groups, one group of 40 V pulses and one group of 38 V pulses. What are the alpha energies observed?

4-4   A 1 Mev gamma ray has an average path length of 7 cm in a KI scintillation crystal of 3.13 specific gravity. If the quantum yield for photon emission is 1 per 50 ev absorbed and if 80% of the photons reach the photomultiplier, which has a phosphor-electron conversion efficiency of 7% and 10 4-stage dynodes, what voltage pulse is produced in a 10 $\mu\mu f$ capacitor? What would be the equivalent voltage pulse for a 1.25 Mev gamma ray?

4-5   Calculate the anticipated pressure buildup due to the absorption of 10^7 rads in the cyclohexane, water, and nitrous oxide dosimeters.

4-6   The total heat transfer coefficient for an adiabatic calorimeter is estimated to be 0.01 Btu/(hr)(sq ft)(°F). The absorbing volume is a sphere of carbon 2 cm in diameter, and the temperature regulation maintains a 1°C differential between the dosimeter and the adiabatic wall. Make a plot of expected temperature vs. time if the dosimeter is used in radiation fields of 10^4, 10^5, 10^6, and 10^7 r/hr. Would this calorimeter be adequately sensitive to calibrate a 1 curie ^{90}Sr source?

4-7   The optical density of a ferrous-ferric solution measured in a 1 cm cell at 25° C increases by 0.34 because of radiation. To what dose was the dosimeter exposed if it has been subjected to bombardment by (1) 0.01 Mev betas, (2) 1 Mev X-rays, (3) fission recoils, and (4) 40 Mev betas? Calculate the dose in rads and electron volts per milliliter.

4-8   A solidly packed sample of $Pb(NO_3)_2$ is irradiated in the same 3 cm diameter, 0.3 cm wall-thickness test tube used in (ferrous-ferric) source calibrations that gave a value of 10^3 rads per hour. The source is an infinite slab; the tube is 5 cm from the source. What dosage is absorbed by the lead nitrate if the source is (1) ^{60}Co, (2) 0.7 Mev beta particles, (3) ^{210}Po alpha particles, and (4) 100 kvp X-rays?

4-9   Gross and Murphy, "Selected Topics in Radiation Chemistry," p. 549, IAEA, Vienna, 1961, have proposed the solid-state neutron-gamma dosimeter shown in Fig. P4-9. In this device the Compton electrons which are ejected in the forward direction, constitute a current, the intensity of which is proportional to the gamma flux. The insulated metal block is sufficiently thick to stop almost all, if not all, the gamma rays entering. Under these conditions the metal will acquire a negative charge. Calculate the current produced by this device from a 1 r/sec ^{60}Co beam.

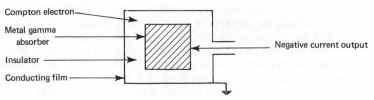

Fig. P4-9. Compton Electron Collector

4-10 Estimate the current obtained in a Faraday cup from a 3 Mev electron beam delivering 5000 rads/min to an aqueous solution.

4-11 Calculate the counts per second per unit flux obtained in a BF_3 neutron counter if the device has a total volume of 60 cm^3 and is filled with BF_3 gas at 100 mm torr. The average neutron path length is 5 in. The boron cross section is 750 barns for the 2200 m/sec neutrons being measured.

4-12 The cross section of ^{10}B for neutrons is 750 barns at 0.025 ev. What is its cross section at 10 kev, assuming the $1/\bar{V}$ law holds?

4-13 One can obtain 0.1 curies of ^{32}P by irradiation of an ^{32}S threshold detector for 1 hr. Calculate the fast neutron flux which exists.

4-14 The cadmium ratio for cobalt foils placed in a reactor is 81. If the thermal neutron flux is 10^{10} particles/cm^2/sec, what is the neutron flux in the energy internal 2.7 to 2700 ev?

4-15 Wright, [*Trans. Faraday Soc.*, *12*: 65 (1952)] reports that, for the Harwell pile, gold foils showed a count of 1000/min-mg, corresponding to a thermal neutron dose of 5.42×10^{12} m/cm^2-sec. The cadmium ratio was 2.70. The fast neutron dose was 2×10^9 neutrons/cm^2-sec. Calculate the anticipated oxidation of ferrous ion due to neutrons in this reactor in molecules per cubic centimeter-hour.

REFERENCES

1. "Physical Aspects of Irradiation," National Bureau of Standards, Handbook 85, U.S. Government Printing Office, Washington, 1964.

2. S. I. Taimuty, "Obtaining a System of Dosimetry," USAEC File number NP-7613, Stanford Research Institute, March 1959.

3. W. J. Price, "Nuclear Radiation Detection," McGraw-Hill Book Company, Inc., New York, 1964.

4. G. Failla, Dosimetry of Ionizing Radiations, *Proc. Intern. Conf. Peaceful Uses At. Energy, Geneva*, vol. 14, pp. 239-245, 1956.

5. J. Coops, R. S. Jessup, and K. van Ness, "Experimental Thermochemistry," F. D. Rossini (ed.), Interscience Publishers, New York, 1956.

6. E. R. Johnson and J. Forten. Radiation-induced Decomposition of Inorganic Nitrates, *Discuss. Faraday Soc.*, 31:238 (1961).

7. P. Milery, N. Barr, J. Geisselsoder, and J. S. Laughlin, in B. Rajewsky (ed.), "International Congress of Radiology," vol. 2, p. 1348, George Thieme Verlag, Stuttgart, Germany, 1961.

8. C. J. Hochanadel and J. Ghormley, Calorimetric Calibration of Gamma-ray Actinometers, *J. Chem. Phys.*, 21:880 (1953).

9. R. M. Lazo, H. A. Dewhurst, and M. Burton, The Ferrous Sulfate Radiation Dosimeter: A Calorimetric Calibration with Gamma Rays, *J. Chem. Phys.*, 22:1370 (1954).

10. L. T. Zimmer, "Dosimetry of Kilocurie ^{60}Co Sources," USAEC Report AECU-3446, Argonne Cancer Research Hospital, October 1956.

11. A. Brynjolfsson, in "Papers Presented at the First Nordic Meeting on Food Preservation by Ionizing Radiations Held at Risö, April 25-26, 1960," pp. 17-20, Danish Report R150-16, July 1960.

12. J. P. Keene and J. Law, Determination of the G Value of Ferrous Sulfate for ^{60}Co Radiation Using Calorimetric Dosimetry, *Phys. Med. Biol.*, 8(1):83 (1963).

13. W. B. Reid and H. E. Johns, Measurement of Absorbed Dose with Calorimeter and Determination of W, *Rad. Res.*, 14:1-16 (1961).

14. W. B. Reid and H. E. Johns, *Rad. Res.*, 7:217 (1957).

15. J. Geisselsoder, K. Keopke, and J. S. Laughlin, *Rad. Res.*, 20(2):423 (1963).

16. B. Petree and G. Ward, "The Construction of Calorimeters for the Measurement of Absorbed Dose," National Bureau of Standards, Technical Note 163, U.S. Government Printing Office, Washington, November 1962.

17. J. Saldick and A. O. Allen, Yield of Oxidation of Ferrous Sulfate in Acid Solution by High-energy Cathode Rays, *J. Chem. Phys.*, 22:438 (1954).

18. R. H. Schuler and A. O. Allen, Yield of the Ferrous Sulfate Radiation Dosimeter: An Improved Cathode-ray Determination, *J. Chem. Phys.*, 24:56 (1956).

19. D. M. Donaldson and N. Miller, Quantitative Studies of Radiation-induced Reactions. III. Oxidation of Ferrous Sulfate by Beta Particles, *J. Chim. Phys.*, 52:578 (1955).

20. R. H. Schuler and A. O. Allen, Radiation Chemistry Studies with Cyclotron Beams of Variable Energy — Yields in Aerated Ferrous Sulfate Solution, *J. Amer. Chem. Soc.*, 79:1565 (1957).

21. E. J. Hart, W. J. Ramler, and S. R. Rocklin, Chemical Yields of Ionizing Particles in Aqueous Solutions: Effect of Energy of Protons and Deuterons, *Rad. Res.*, 4:378 (1956).

22. B. T. Price, C. C. Horton, K. T. Spinney, "Radiation Shielding," Pergamon Press, 1957.

23. J. W. T. Spinks and R. J. Woods, "An Introduction to Radiation Chemistry," John Wiley and Sons, New York, 1964.

24. J. F. Kircher, "Effects of Radiation on Materials and Components," Kirchman and Bowman (eds.), Reinhold, 1964.

25. F. H. Attix, *Nucleonics*, 17:10 (1959).

26. C. Artandi, *Nucleonics*, 17:61 (1959) and V. Chandler, Nucleonics, 17:63 (1959).

27. P. Shall, *Nucleonics*, 17:68 (1959).

28. D. E. Harmer, *Nucleonics*, 17:72 (1959).

29. A. O. Allen, "Radiation Chemistry of Water and Aqueous Solutions," p. 19, D. Van Nostrand Company, Inc., Princeton, N.J., 1961.

30. E. J. Hart, Mechanism of the Gamma-ray Induced Oxidation of Formic Acid in Aqueous Solution, *J. Amer. Chem. Soc.*, 73:68 (1951).

31. A. O. Allen and R. A. Holroyd, Peroxide Yield in the Gamma Irradiation of Air-saturated Water, *J. Amer. Chem. Soc.*, 77:5852 (1955).

32. F. J. Haasbrock, "Extending the Range of the "Fricke" Dosimeter up to 10^6 Rads," USAEC Report BNL-763, Brookhaven National Laboratory, April 1962.

33. W. Minder, Selected Topics in Radiation Dosimetry, "Symposium Proceedings," pp. 315-323, IAEA, Vienna, 1961, STI/PUB/25.

34. C. J. Hochanadel and T. W. Davis, Radiolysis of Solid Nitrates, *J. Chem. Phys.*, 27:333 (1957).

35. W. Bernstein and R. H. Schuler, Low-energy Scattered Radiation Inside a Cylindrical Cobalt-60 Source, *Nucleonics*, 13(11):110 (1955).

36. G. V. Taplin, C. H. Douglas, and B. Sanchez, *Nucleonics*, 9(2):73 (1951).

37. E. J. Henley and A. Miller, Gamma-ray Dosimetry with Polyvinyl Chloride Films, *Nucleonics*, 9(6):62 (1951).

38. E. J. Hart and P. D. Walsh, Dosimetry of Gamma Ray and Neutron Fluxes in CP-5, *Proc. Second U. N. Int. Conf. Peaceful Uses At. Energy, Geneva*, vol. 29, p. 38, 1958.

39. L. M. Dorfman and F. J. Shipko, Beta-particle Radiolysis of Acetylene, *J. Amer. Chem. Soc.*, 77:4723 (1955).

40. F. H. Field, Benzene Production in the Radiation Chemistry of Acetylene, *J. Phys. Chem.*, 68(5):1039 (1964).

41. W. B. Lewis, *Trans. Amer. Nucl. Soc.*, 6:73 (1963).

42. C. D. Bopp, W. W. Parkinson, O. Sisman, R. L. Towns, and W. K. Kirkland, pp. 95-102, in "Solid State Division Annual Progress Report for Period Ending August 31, 1961," USAEC Report ORNL-3213, Oak Ridge National Laboratory, December 1961.

43. A. R. Anderson and J. K. Linacre, Calorimetric Dosimetry of Reactor Radiation, in "Selected Topics in Radiation Dosimetry, Symposium Proceedings, Vienna, 1960," pp. 609-621, IAEA, Vienna, 1961, STI/PUB/25.

44. "Measurement of Absorbed Dose of Neutrons and Mixtures of Neutrons and Gamma Rays," National Bureau of Standards Handbook 75.

45. Ivan Draganic, Oxalic Acid: The Only Aqueous Dosimeter for In-pile Use, *Nucleonics*, 21(2):33 (1963).

46. R. H. Schuler and A. O. Allen, Radiation-chemical Studies with Cyclotron Beams, *J. Amer. Chem. Soc.*, 77:507 (1955).

47. M. Steinberg, M. M. Loffelholz, and J. Pruzansky, in "Industrial Uses of Large Radiation Sources, Conference Proceedings, Salzberg, Austria. 1963," vol. II. p. 89, IAEA, Vienna, 1963, STI/PUB/75.

48. F. S. Dainton, Chemical Dosimetry, Radiation Research, in G. Silini (ed.), "Proceedings of the Third International Congress of Radiation Research," North-Holland Publishing Co., Amsterdam, 1967.

49. C. Artandi and A. A. Stonehill, Poly (vinyl chloride) — New High-level Dosimeter, *Nucleonics*, 16(5):118 (1958).

50. E. J. Henley and D. Richman, Cellophane-dye Dosimeter for the 10^5 to 10^7 Röntgen Range, *Anal. Chem.*, 28:1580 (1956).

51. A. Charlesby and W. H. T. Davison, Temperature Effects in the Irradiation of Polymers, *Chem. Ind. (London) (Rev.)*, p. 232 (1957).

52. H. F. Nitka, Photographic Methods, *Nucleonics*, 17(10):59 (1959).

53. J. H. Shulman, C. C. Klick, and H. Rabin, Measuring High Doses by Absorption Changes in Glass, *Nucleonics*, 13(2):30 (1955).

54. N. J. Kreidl and G. E. Blair, Recent Developments in Glass Dosimetry, *Nucleonics*, 14(3):82 (1956).

55. E. B. Wagner and G. S. Hurst, Advances in the Standard Proportional Counter Method of Fast-neutron Dosimetry, *Rev. Sci. Instrum.*, 29:153 (1958).

56. D. J. Hughes, Pile Neutron Research, p. 63, Addison-Wesley Publishing Company, Inc., Reading, Mass., 1953.

57. J. Fenger, "Measurement of Gamma Flux in a Thermal Column with an Oxalic-acid Dosimeter," Danish Report RISÖ-67, September 1963.

5

CHEMICAL CONSEQUENCES
OF THE ABSORPTION OF
HIGH-ENERGY RADIATION

A charged particle passing through matter interacts with the planetary electrons of a substrate molecule to varying degrees — from simple excitation to multiple ionization. Thus, in any system exposed to high energy radiation, we may expect to observe molecules that have one or more electrons in an excited state, ions, excited ions, and free radicals.

5-1 TIME SCALE FOR THE PRIMARY PROCESS

Figure 2-7 shows the events that occur when a charged particle passes through a liquid. The primary particles produce secondary electrons of varying energies, and these in turn may produce other electrons. For a system exposed to ^{60}Co radiation, most of the electrons ejected in the primary act will have energies ranging only up to a few thousand electron volts. These electrons can excite and ionize molecules in small volume elements called *spurs*. The exact shape of the spurs depends upon how closely they are formed; it will be assumed for the present that they are spheres having diameters of about 20 Å.

The time scale for primary events depends upon the velocity of the ionizing particle, since the velocity determines the time required for the particle to traverse a molecule. For a 1 Mev electron and an average size molecule, this time is about 10^{-18} sec. The time scale for the subsequent events has been established with reasonable certainty only for water. As shown in Table 5-1, a 1 Mev electron will come to rest in about 10^{-9} seconds. In the spurs and delta-ray branches, there will be ions, excited molecules, excited ions, radicals, excited radicals, and electrons with an average energy of about 6 ev. These electrons, which are called *subexcitation* electrons, are reduced to thermal energies by exciting molecular vibrations and by dipolar interactions. In the condensed state, the subexcitation electron is either captured by a positive ion or polarizes the molecules in the medium and is then trapped in a potential well. In water this trapped electron is called the *hydrated* electron, and in other systems (methanol and ethanol, for example) it is the *solvated* electron.

Table 5-1. TIME SCALE FOR RADIATION EVENTS IN WATER

Time, sec	Event
10^{-18}	1 Mev electron traverses a molecule
10^{-18}	Excitation or ionization
10^{-16}	10 ev electron traverses a molecule
10^{-14}	Period of molecular vibration
	Dissociation of excited molecules
	Time for an ion-molecule reaction
10^{-13}	Collision time in liquids
	Internal conversion between electronically excited states
	Secondary (subexcitation) electrons reduced to thermal energy
10^{-12}	Radical moves one jump if diffusion coefficient is $\sim 5 \times 10^{-5}$ cm^2/sec
10^{-11}	Dielectric relaxation time for dipoles
10^{-10}	Collision time in gas
10^{-10} to 10^{-8}	Radical-radical (diffusion controlled) reactions nearly complete in spurs and a-track
10^{-9} to 10^{-8}	Fluorescence
	Radiative lifetime of singlet excited state
10^{-7} to 10^{-5}	Lifetime of hydrated electron
10^{-7} to 10^{-5}	Reaction time for radical with solute (depends on activation energy)
10^{-4} to 10^{-3}	Time for radical to diffuse, ~ 5000 Å (distance between primary Mev electron events)
10^{-3}	Radiative lifetime of triplet state

5-2 DESCRIPTION OF REACTIVE INTERMEDIATES

Table 5-1 lists a number of reactive intermediates, not all of which may be familiar. They will be explained in subsequent sections.

5-2.1 Radicals

Radicals are atoms or molecules containing an unpaired electron that is free to form a chemical bond. The unpaired electron may or may not be stabilized by any appreciable amount of resonance energy. Examples of unstabilized free radicals are CH_3, H, C_2H_5, and CH_2. Examples of relatively unreactive radicals stabilized by appreciable amounts of resonance energy are NO, NO_2, and ClO_2. Examples of radicals that may be considered as being intermediate in stability between the two types shown above are triphenyl methyl (Ph_3C) and diphenyl-picryl-hydrazyl (DPPH).

5-2.2 Ions

Normally the ions dealt with in radiation chemistry are atoms or molecules that have an excess of positive or negative charge. These charges are not stabilized by an associated negative or positive ion.

5-2.3 Excited Ions

An excited ion is an ion in which one or more of the electrons is not in the ground state.

5-2.4 Excited Radicals

An excited radical is a radical that has one or more electrons not in the ground state.

5-2.5 Radical Ions

A radical ion is a radical that has an excess of positive or negative charge, i.e., a radical that has excess positive or negative charge in addition to unpaired electrons.

5-3 EXCITED STATES

An excited molecule is one that is not in the ground state electronically, vibrationally, or rotationally; thus it has excess energy. The ground state is the state of lowest energy. Figure 5-1 shows the electronic ground state of a diatomic molecule as well as the vibrational and rotational energy levels. Excited electronic states have associated with them excited vibrational and rotational states unless the excited state is repulsive, i.e., has no minimum in the potential energy curve (upper curve in Fig. 5-3).

5-3.1 Dissipation of Excitation Energy

The absorption or emission of radiation takes place during a time interval that is very small compared with that of a molecular vibration; hence vertical lines may be drawn upward from the points in the path where the nuclei are most likely to be found to the curve of the excited state (Fig. 5-2, vertical arrow). If the excited state is repulsive, as in Fig. 5-3, the molecules will dissociate in the period of one vibration, $\sim 10^{-13}$ sec; for nonrepulsive excited states dissociation may take 10^{-4} sec and even longer.

If the excited state has a potential energy curve similar to that shown in Fig. 5-2, it can return to the ground state by emission of a photon. This process is called *fluorescence*. If the molecule has lost some vibrational energy by collision with other molecules before

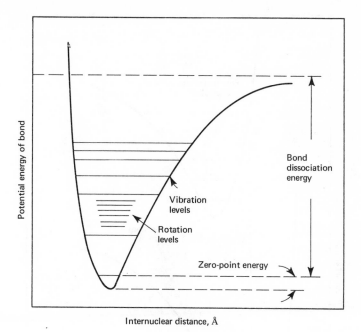

Fig. 5-1. Electronic ground state of
a diatomic molecule.

returning to the ground state the fluorescent radiation will have a
longer wavelength (less energy) than that of the absorbed photon. If
the excited molecule loses all its excess vibrational energy, it would
be at the lowest vibrational state (E in Fig. 5-2). The excited molecule may remain in this state for a relatively long time ($t_{1/2} \sim 10^{-8}$
sec) since electronic energy is not lost as readily as vibrational
energy. The observed fluorescence from an excited molecule is
usually characteristic of the lowest electronically excited state of a
given multiplicity even though higher excited states were initially
formed.

Normally the electrons in a shared electron bond are paired;
i.e., the spins of the electrons are opposite in sign. Excitation to
an excited singlet state occurs when one of the electrons by the absorption of energy is translated to a higher energy orbit without a
change in electron spin; i.e., the spins are still paired. Excitation
to a triplet state involves the translation of one of the electrons to a
higher energy orbit but with an inversion of spin so that the spins of
the two electrons are parallel. A triplet level is usually the lowest

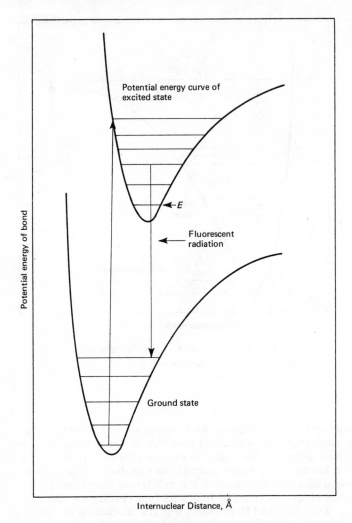

Fig. 5-2. Potential energy diagrams of
ground state and excited state.

electronically excited state of the molecule. Triplet states have importance in radiation chemistry since they may act as biradicals. For every excited singlet state, there is a corresponding triplet state. It must not be assumed, however, that all triplet states are associated with excited molecules. The ground state of oxygen is a triplet state, which accounts for many of its reactions.

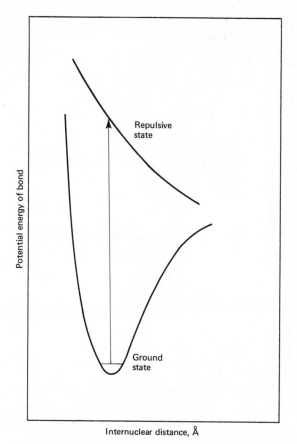

Fig. 5-3. Potential energy diagram of transition between ground state and repulsive state.

5-3.1a <u>Intersystem Crossing</u>. When the potential energy curve of an excited state is crossed by a second excited state of different multiplicity (Fig. 5-4), it is possible for the molecule to cross to the other excited state at the point of intersection, provided the vibrational level is below that to which the molecule had been originally excited. The particular diagram shown in Fig. 5-4 shows an excited singlet state and its excited triplet state. According to the laws of quantum mechanics, triplet $\rightarrow$ singlet state transitions are highly forbidden, since transitions are allowed only when there is no change in spin; i.e., $\Delta s = 0$.

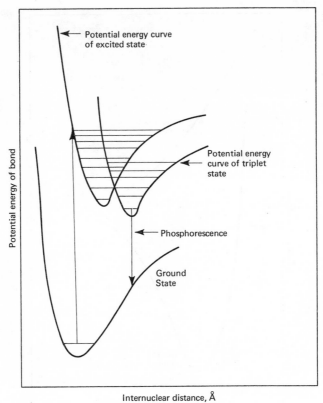

Fig. 5-4. Potential energy diagram showing excited
singlet and triplet states.

Triplet excited states have lifetimes longer than singlet states.
Excited triplet state lifetimes vary; most are 10^{-4} to 10^{-3} sec
although lifetimes as long as seconds are not uncommon. The radiation emitted when an excited triplet state drops to the ground state
has a longer wavelength than the corresponding fluorescence and
is called *phosphorescence*. The lifetime of triplet excited states is
strongly influenced by the physical state of the medium; this is not
true of singlet states.

There are many ways in which the excited molecule can lose its
excitation energy: internal conversion, energy transfer, predissociation, unimolecular reaction, and bimolecular (chemical) reaction.

5-3.1b Internal Conversion. Internal conversion is a process in which the electronic energy of the excited state is transferred to a high lying vibrational level of the ground state. This process occurs when the potential energy curve of the excited state crosses the potential energy curve of the ground state at a vibrational level that is lower than that to which the molecule was originally excited. The molecule will have excess vibrational energy, but this is rapidly lost to the surrounding molecules. This results in a nonradiative conversion to a state of the same multiplicity (Fig. 5-5).

5-3.1c Energy Transfer Reactions. The transfer of electronic excitation energy to another molecule may occur in a variety of ways; however, in all cases the excitation energy of the donor molecule must be greater than the excitation energy of the receptor molecule. A simple form of energy transfer occurs when an excited molecule collides with another molecule and transfers its excitation energy. The resultant excitation of the receptor molecule can be sufficient to cause dissociation, as in a mercury-photosensitized decomposition. These reactions occur when mercury vapor excited by ultraviolet light (2537 Å) is in contact with, for example, hydrogen or acetone. The excited mercury atoms transfer their energy, and decomposition occurs. Transfer of energy may also occur by the fluorescing of a donor molecule and by the absorption of the fluorescent radiation by an acceptor molecule. In solids excitation energy may migrate very rapidly through the crystal by a process called *exciton migration*. If the crystal contains an impurity molecule that has an excited state lower in energy than the host molecules, it can capture the excitation energy and fluoresce, the fluorescent radiation being typical of the impurity molecule.

Intramolecular energy transfer also occurs. For example, in acetone the initial absorption of energy may occur at the carbonyl group, but it is the carbon-carbon bond which breaks. Electronic excitation energy in a molecule is most often distributed rather rapidly; therefore it is necessary to consider the molecule as a whole to be excited rather than to think of the excitation being confined to a particular bond. Processes such as

$$C_2H_6 \rightarrow C_2H_4 + H_2$$

$$CH_4 \rightarrow CH_2 + H_2$$

are known to occur and are of great importance in radiation chemistry.

5-3.1d Predissociation. Predissociation occurs when the excited state of a molecule crosses another state which is dissociative (Fig. 5-6). It is possible for the molecule to pass into the dissociative state, but it is also possible for the molecule to return to

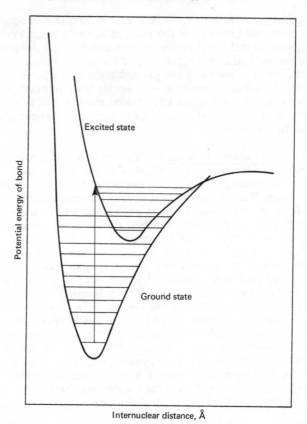

Fig. 5-5. Schematic of internal
conversion process.

the ground state by fluorescence. The process in which the excited
molecule passes into the dissociative state is called predissociation.

There are several other mechanisms whereby an excited molecule may lose or transfer its energy, but these are primarily some
combination of those referred to previously or those discussed below.

5-3.1e <u>Unimolecular Reaction</u>. An excited molecule may lose its
excitation energy and attain a stable state by molecular rearrangement processes, such as an isomerization reaction (*trans → cis*).
It is also possible that the excitation energy is sufficient to cause
bond cleavage. If the potential energy curve of the excited state is
repulsive, then dissociation would occur in a period less than one
vibration (10^{-13} sec).

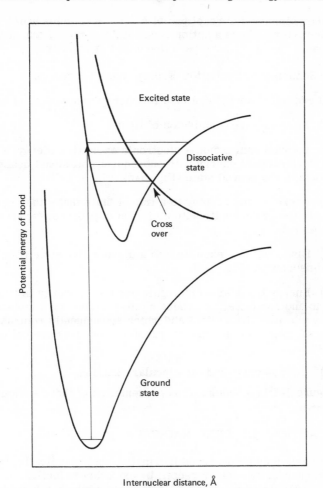

Fig. 5-6. Schematic of one type
of predissociation process.

5-3.1f <u>Bimolecular Reaction</u>. An excited molecule may also enter
into a bimolecular reaction with a molecule that is either in the
ground state or in an excited state. For example, it has recently
been suggested that part of the "molecular yield" of hydrogen (see
Chap. 8, Sec. 3) arises from the reaction of two excited water
molecules:

$$2H_2O^* \rightarrow H_2 + 2OH$$

Other bimolecular reactions of excited molecules which have been characterized are addition reactions and energy transfer reactions. The latter have been discussed previously.

5-3.2 Summary of Excitation Energy Loss Processes

An excited molecule can lose its energy in a variety of ways:

(1) Fluorescence — emission of light.

(2) Internal conversion — electronic excitation energy is converted to vibrational energy with subsequent collisional deactivation and return to the ground state (Fig. 5-5).

(3) Intersystem crossing to a triplet state that either reacts or returns to the ground state with emission of phosphorescent radiation (Fig. 5-4).

(4) Dissociation — excitation to a dissociative state (Fig. 5-3) or predissociation (Fig. 5-6).

(5) Energy transfer — electronic excitation energy is transferred to another molecule producing dissociation or a molecule which is vibrationally excited and which subsequently returns to the ground state. These energy transfer processes are called *quenching* .

(6) Unimolecular and bimolecular reaction.

Figure 5-7 is a schematic representation of these various processes.

5-4 REACTIONS OF FREE RADICALS

Radicals may be produced thermally, photochemically, by microwave discharge, by nuclear recoil, by oxidation reduction, or by charged particle interactions. Many of the methods for producing radicals are well established, and detailed descriptions of the techniques are available.[1,2]   The reactivity of a radical depends on its structure and mode of formation. The discussion in this chapter will be limited to those radicals which are reactive: N, H, OH, CH_3, CH_2, C_2H_5, propyl, isobutyl, etc.

When possible radical reactions are being considered, the energetics of the reaction should be examined. For instance, if a free radical X is to react with molecule AB

$$X + AB \rightarrow AX + B$$

the energetics must be correct; i.e., the overall reaction must be exothermic for the reaction to have a reasonable probability of occurring. The reaction

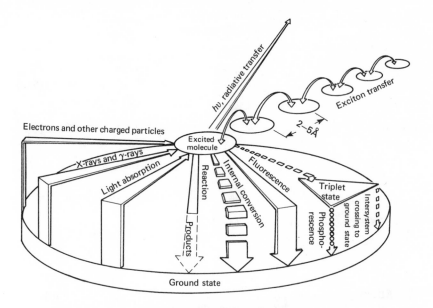

Fig. 5-7. Summary of excited states. (From M. Windsor, Technique of Organic Chemistry, Weissberger and Fox, Editors, Interscience Publ., N.Y., 1965.)

$$I + H_2 \underset{k_r}{\overset{k_f}{\rightleftharpoons}} HI + H$$

is quite improbable because the energy of the hydrogen-hydrogen bond is considerably greater than the hydrogen-iodine bond. Unless the iodine atom can supply the necessary activation energy, this reaction has a very low probability.

A crude but reasonably good approximation often used to determine the probability of a particular reaction is to examine the ratio of the forward rate constant k_f to the reverse rate constant k_r for the reaction. Assuming that the rate constant can be expressed by an equation of the form

$$\text{Rate constant} = A \exp - \Delta E/RT \qquad (5\text{-}1)$$

Where A is a constant (pre-exponential factor) and ΔE is the activation energy,

$$\frac{k_f}{k_r} = \frac{A_f \, \exp(-\Delta E_f /RT)}{A_r \, \exp(-\Delta E_r /RT)}$$

assuming $A_f = A_r$,

$$\frac{k_f}{k_r} = \exp \left[\frac{(\Delta E_r - \Delta E_f)}{RT} \right] \qquad (5\text{-}2)$$

EXAMPLE 5-1: Calculate the relative rate of the reaction at 300°K of

$$H + Br_2 \xrightarrow{k_1} HBr + Br \qquad \Delta E_1 = 0.9 \text{ kcal}$$

$$Br + HBr \xrightarrow{k_2} Br_2 + H \qquad \Delta E_2 = 41.4 \text{ kcal}$$

SOLUTION: According to Eq. (5-2),

$$\frac{k_1}{k_2} = \exp \frac{(41.4 - 0.9)}{600} \cong e^{70}$$

Although the energetics of a reaction usually play the dominant role, steric and other factors must be considered.

5-4.1 Reactions of Free Radicals: Abstraction

A common radical reaction is abstraction. For example,

$$CH_3 + C_2H_6 \rightarrow CH_4 + C_2H_5 \qquad (5\text{-}3)$$

$$n\text{-}C_3F_7 + H_2 \rightarrow n\text{-}C_3F_7H + H \qquad (5\text{-}4)$$

$$H + C_2H_6 \rightarrow H_2 + C_2H_5 \qquad (5\text{-}5)$$

$$C_2H_5 + C_6H_{14} \rightarrow C_2H_6 + C_6H_{13} \qquad (5\text{-}6)$$

These reactions are often called transfer reactions and have the general designation

$$R + XH \rightarrow RH + X \qquad (5\text{-}7)$$

whenever a hydrogen atom is transferred.

In Table 5-2 are listed the activation energies of several radical abstraction reactions as obtained from thermal data. We see that a reaction between iodine atoms and molecular hydrogen is very much less probable than the reaction between hydrogen atoms and iodine for example.

Table 5-2. ACTIVATION ENERGIES FOR
RADICAL REACTIONS*

Reaction	ΔE, kcal/mole
$CH_3 + C_2H_6 \rightarrow CH_4 + C_2H_5$	10.4
$CH_3 + CH_4 \rightarrow CH_4 + CH_3$	14.3
$H + C_2H_6 \rightarrow C_2H_5 + H_2$	6.4
$Cl + H_2 \rightarrow HCl + H$	6.0
$Br + H_2 \rightarrow HBr + H$	17.6
$I + H_2 \rightarrow HI + H$	33.4
$H + Cl_2 \rightarrow HCl + Cl$	2.4
$H + Br_2 \rightarrow HBr + Br$	0.9
$H + I_2 \rightarrow HI + I$	0
$OH + C_2H_6 \rightarrow H_2O + C_2H_5$	5.5

*Data are taken from S. W. Benson, "The Foundations of Chemical Kinetics,"
McGraw-Hill Book Company, Inc., New York, 1960.

5-4.2 Reactions of Free Radicals: Combination

The activation energies for radical combination are very small
and are usually taken to be zero, combination being considered as
occurring on first collisions (Table 5-3). Combination of atoms,
however, usually requires the presence of a third body to remove
the excess energy since, unless this is done, the atoms dissociate
again. For polyatomic radicals (except methyl at low pressure), a
third body is not necessary since the excess energy can be absorbed
in the various molecular vibrational degrees of freedom. At high
pressures (> 100 torr) the third body requirement for methyl may
also be ignored.

Table 5-3. ENERGIES OF ACTIVATION FOR
RADICAL COMBINATION

Reaction	ΔE, kcal/mole
$N + N + N_2 \rightarrow 2N_2$	0
$I + I + M \rightarrow I_2 + M$	0
$Br + Br + M \rightarrow Br_2 + M$	0
$CH_3 + CH_3 \rightarrow C_2H_6$	1.7
$C_2H_5 + C_2H_5 \rightarrow C_4H_{10}$	0
$CH_3 + C_2H_5 \rightarrow C_3H_8$	0
$CF_3 + CF_3 \rightarrow C_2F_6$	0
$C_2H_5 + C_2H_5 \rightarrow C_2H_4 + C_2H_6$	0.8

Typical radical combination reactions are

$$H + H + M \text{ (third body)} \rightarrow H_2 + M \qquad (5\text{-}8)$$

$$N + N + M \rightarrow N_2 + M \qquad (5\text{-}9)$$

$$n\text{-}C_3H_7 + n\text{-}C_4H_9 \rightarrow C_7H_{16} \qquad (5\text{-}10)$$

$$CH_3 + CH_3 \rightarrow C_2H_6 \qquad (5\text{-}11)$$

$$CF_2Cl + CF_2ClCF_2 \rightarrow C_3F_6Cl_2 \qquad (5\text{-}12)$$

$$C_2H_5 + C_2H_5 \rightarrow C_4H_{10} \qquad (5\text{-}13)$$

5-4.3 Reaction of Free Radicals: Disproportionation

Disproportionation is a reaction whereby two radicals combine to give two stable molecules, one more unsaturated than the other. Disproportionation reactions are competitive with combination, but appear to have slightly higher activation energies. For example the ratio k_d/k_c for the reactions shown below is 0.14

$$2C_2H_5 \rightarrow C_4H_{10} \qquad k_c \qquad (5\text{-}14)$$

$$2C_2H_5 \rightarrow C_2H_6 + C_2H_4 \qquad k_d \qquad (5\text{-}15)$$

The ratio of the rate constant for disproportionation to combination for most radical systems studied is less than 1; i.e., $k_d/k_c < 1$. Values for the ratio of k_d/k_c for representative systems are given in Table 5-4.

5-4.4 Reactions of Free Radicals: Addition Reactions

The addition of radicals to unsaturated molecules to form a new radical is a characteristic radical reaction:

$$CH_3 + C_2H_4 \rightarrow C_3H_7 \qquad (5\text{-}16)$$

$$H + C_2H_4 \rightarrow C_2H_5 \qquad (5\text{-}17)$$

Reaction (5-17) has been found to be an important one in the radiolysis of hydrocarbons for hydrogen atoms at thermal energies. When this type of reaction occurs with great efficiency, the neutral molecule is called a *radical scavenger* and the reaction, a *scavenger reaction*. Another radical scavenger reaction that is also an addition reaction is

$$CH_3 + NO \rightarrow CH_3NO \quad \text{or} \quad CH_2NOH \qquad (5\text{-}18)$$

Table 5-4. RATIO OF DISPROPORTIONATION TO
COMBINATION FOR ALKYL RADICALS

	k_d/k_c
$2(C_2H_5)$	0.14
$2(n-C_3H_7)$	0.16
$2(i-C_3H_7)$	0.64
$2(n-C_4H_9)$	0.7
$2(i-C_4H_9)$	0.17
$2(t-C_4H_9)$	~3.0
$2(cyclo-C_5H_9)$	0.2
$2(cyclo-C_6H_{11})$	0.5
$CH_3 + C_2H_5$	0.06
$CH_3 + n-C_3H_7$	0.05
$CH_3 + t-C_4H_9$	0.70
$C_2H_5 + s-C_3H_7$	0.43

Radical induced polymerization reactions are also good examples of additions of a radical to a stable molecule.

The activation energies for the addition of alkyl radicals to unsaturated molecules is about 6 to 8 kcal per mole. This is quite low; thus it would be expected that radical addition reactions occur in many radiation chemistry systems, especially if the olefin concentration is appreciable.

5-4.5   Reactions of Free Radicals: Decomposition

Alkyl radicals decompose if sufficient activation energy is available. Radicals smaller than pentyl decompose to yield a hydrogen atom or a methyl or an ethyl radical.

$$C_2H_5 \rightarrow C_2H_4 + H \tag{5-19}$$

$$CH_3CH_2CH_2 \rightarrow CH_3 + CH_2CH_2 \tag{5-20}$$

$$CH_3CH_2CH_2CH_2 \rightarrow C_2H_5 + C_2H_4 \tag{5-21}$$

$$C_7H_{15} \rightarrow C_6H_{12} + CH_3 \tag{5-22}$$

The activation energies appear to be about 40 to 50 kcal per mole for decomposition to hydrogen atoms [Reaction (5-19)] and about 20 to 30 kcal per mole for decomposition into a radical [Reactions (5-20) to (5-22)].[3] For radicals such as CH_3COO and C_2H_5COO, the activation energy for decomposition is only about 5 kcal per mole. For radicals that are stabilized by resonance, such as the benzyl radical, the activation energy is quite high.

5-4.6   Detection of Radicals

One of the most widely used indirect techniques in determining the presence of radicals or other reactive intermediates is the effect of intensity and/or intermittency of the energy input. The intensity, which is the rate of energy deposition in unit time, can be varied in several ways, such as, for example, interposing absorbers between the source and sample. Intermittency is achieved by some rapid method of turning the source on and off or by moving the sample in and out of the field.

Normally the energy is added to the system continuously; i.e., for a period of time the sample is continuously exposed to a radiation source. Reactive intermediates then build up to a steady-state concentration, the concentration being essentially constant during the course of an exposure. If the steady-state concentration of radicals is changed, the rate of the reaction may change. If the reaction rate is directly proportional to radiation intensity, it will be proportional to the average rate of absorption of energy no matter how the energy is distributed in time. If the rate is not proportional to the first power of the intensity, then intermittency of energy input will affect the rate.

The intermittency of the radiation must be adjusted to the half life of the reactive intermediate. In photochemical experiments this is done by placing a rotating disk (with sectors cut out) in front of the energy source. The speed of rotation of the disk determines the rate at which energy enters the cell.

Changing the radiation intensity (without intermittency) also provides valuable insights into reaction mechanisms. The steady-state concentration of radicals or other reactive intermediates varies with intensity, and this directly affects the rate of reaction as is demonstrated by the following simple kinetic scheme:

$$R_2 \overset{k_1}{\to} R + R \tag{5-23}$$

$$R + A \overset{k_2}{\to} B + C \tag{5-24}$$

$$R + R \overset{k_3}{\to} R_2 \tag{5-25}$$

where R_2, A, B, and C are stable molecules and R is the reactive intermediate. If the radical concentration is high, then the probability of radical combination [Reaction (5-25)] is high. If the radical concentration is low, then Reaction (5-24) may predominate.

Indirect and direct detection of radicals has been accomplished by a variety of techniques. In the gas phase radical scavengers such as NO, propylene, and I_2 are frequently used. A relatively new technique uses a combination of electric-dipole and magnetic-dipole epr spectroscopy.[4]   In solids, gases, and liquids, direct observation of radicals by spectroscopic means has been used. In liquids radical scavengers and epr techniques have both been used successfully. In solids epr has been found to be useful.

5-5 REACTION OF IONS

Ions undergo a variety of reactions, several of which may be readily anticipated. They can capture an electron and become neutralized, react with a negative ion, decompose to yield reactive products (or stable molecules) plus an ion, and undergo charge exchange or ion-molecule reactions. All these processes occur and must be considered as a source of products.

5-5.1   Neutralization Processes

Ions, as a result of the energy expended in the ionization process, have a very large amount of potential energy; therefore, in the neutralization process, dissociations are common.

The ionization potential of water is 12.61 ev; hence the reaction $H_2O^+ + e^- \rightarrow H_2O$ produces H_2O molecules in a highly excited state. The neutralization of H_2O^+ has therefore been postulated as a source of H and OH radicals since the neutralization energy is more than the bond dissociation energy of the water molecule. It is also not surprising that the radicals so produced often have additional excess kinetic energy (hot radicals).

Most of our knowledge of the reactions of ions comes from mass spectrometry; however, several reactions have been inferred from the kinetics. Although reactions of positive ions with negative ions have not been characterized to any appreciable extent, it is known that the neutralization process is very rapid.

5-5.2   Electron Capture

Molecules can attach electrons to form negative ions with varying degrees of endothermicity. Electron capture is a resonance process, and, when it occurs with electrons that have energies above thermal energies, dissociation always occurs. However, dissociative electron capture also occurs with electrons that have thermal energies.

Some dissociative electron-attachment reactions are:

$$Cl_2 + e^- \rightarrow Cl^- + Cl \qquad (5\text{-}26)$$

$$HCl + e^- \rightarrow Cl^- + H \qquad (5\text{-}27)$$

$$SO_2 + e^- \rightarrow SO^- + O \tag{5-28}$$

$$C_2H_5I + e^- \rightarrow C_2H_5 + I^- \tag{5-29}$$

$$H_2O + e^- \rightarrow H + OH^- \tag{5-30}$$

$$O_2 + e^- \rightarrow O + O^- \tag{5-31}$$

The negative ions formed may undergo a variety of reactions, the principal one being neutralization by a positive ion. Other negative ion reactions may lead to the formation of new products.

$$O^- + H_2O \rightarrow 2OH^- \tag{5-32}$$

$$H^- + H_2O \rightarrow H_2 + OH^- \tag{5-33}$$

$$O^-_{aq} + H_2 \rightarrow OH^-_{aq} + H \tag{5-34}$$

$$H^- + H_2O \rightarrow OH^- + H_2 \tag{5-35}$$

$$SO^- + SO_2 \rightarrow SO_2^- + SO \tag{5-36}$$

The rates of reactions and cross sections of the few gas phase negative ion reactions that have been studied are similar to those of positive ions. Many negative ion reactions in solution have been studied, particularly in aqueous solution.

5-5.3   Decomposition Reactions

Ions, when formed, can decompose to yield radicals plus one or more ions.

$$CH_3OH^+ \rightarrow CH_3O^+ + H \tag{5-37}$$

$$CH_4^+ \rightarrow CH_3 + H^+ \tag{5-38}$$

$$C_4H_8^+ \rightarrow C_3H_5^+ + CH_3 \tag{5-39}$$

$$C_8H_{16}^+ \rightarrow C_7H_{13}^+ + CH_3 \tag{5-40}$$

$$CH_3CH_2CH_2NH_2^+ \rightarrow C_2H_5 + CH_2NH_2^+ \tag{5-41}$$

It is generally believed that the observed mass spectrum of a particular molecule arises from the unimolecular decay of the parent molecule ion and to a more limited extent from the decomposition of some product ions. To some extent there is a relation between the strengths of a bond broken and the relative abundance of the ions that make up the mass spectral pattern. This generalization cannot be carried too far since it is known not to apply in several cases; however, as shown in a later chapter, the relative probabilities for decomposition of the different ions may be roughly estimated by the strength of the various one-electron bonds.

5-5.4   Charge Exchange

Charge exchange is a very important reaction in radiation chemistry in both gas and liquid systems. Some examples of charge exchange are

$$He^+ + Ne \rightarrow Ne^+ + He \tag{5-42}$$

$$H_2^+ + H_2O \rightarrow H_2O^+ + H_2 \tag{5-43}$$

$$Ar^+ + C_2H_4 \rightarrow Ar + C_2H_4^+ \tag{5-44}$$

Charge exchange is a resonance process and is favored by small differences in ionization potentials between the two species. When charge exchange occurs, the energy difference between the ionization potentials is liberated in the process. This energy may be retained by the product ion and may be sufficient to cause dissociation.

$$Ar^+ + CH_4 \rightarrow Ar + CH_3^+ + H \tag{5-45}$$

5-6 ION-MOLECULE REACTIONS

Ion-molecule reactions are one of the most important reactions in radiation chemistry systems, and are the subject of a great deal of theoretical and experimental effort, not only in the context of radiation chemistry but as an important class of chemical reactions. Ion-molecule reactions may be broadly characterized as reactions between ions and molecules. They are thought to occur by the formation of a collision complex with subsequent rearrangement of the atoms to give the observed products. Ion-molecule reactions may be classified into three general categories: (1) single particle transfer reactions, (2) condensation reactions, and (3) association reactions.

5-6.1   Single Particle Transfer

$$H_2O^+ + H_2O \rightarrow H_3O^+ + OH \tag{5-46}$$

$$CH_4^+ + CH_4 \rightarrow CH_5^+ + CH_3 \tag{5-47}$$

$$CH_3OH^+ + CH_3OH \rightarrow CH_3OH_2^+ + CH_3O \tag{5-48}$$

$$H_2^+ + H_2 \rightarrow H_3^+ + H \tag{5-49}$$

$$Ar^+ + H_2 \rightarrow ArH^+ + H \tag{5-50}$$

Equations (5-46) to (5-50) represent hydrogen atom transfer reactions. These are among the most intensely studied of the ion-molecule reactions. The rate constants are generally very high (this is true for almost all ion-molecule reactions) and are among the most important reactions that occur, especially in gas phase radiolysis. Another type of single particle transfer reaction is proton transfer. In the higher alkanes, proton transfer is dissociative. For example, $C_3 H_9^+$ is not observed in the $C_3 H_8$ systems, but $C_2 H_5^+$ and $C_3 H_7^+$ are. These presumably arise from $C_3 H_9^+$. There are many proton transfer reactions,[5] including

$$CH_5^+ + NH_3 \rightarrow NH_4^+ + CH_4 \tag{5-51}$$

$$C_2 H_5^+ + NH_3 \rightarrow NH_4^+ + C_2 H_4 \tag{5-52}$$

$$C_2 H_5^+ + H_2 O \rightarrow H_3 O^+ + C_2 H_4 \tag{5-53}$$

$$CH_5^+ + CH_4 \rightarrow CH_5^+ + CH_4 \tag{5-54}$$

$$H_3^+ + cyclo\text{-}C_3 H_6 \rightarrow H_2 + sec\text{-}C_3 H_7^+ \tag{5-55}$$

$$CH_5^+ + cyclo\text{-}C_4 H_8 \rightarrow CH_4 + sec\text{-}C_4 H_9^+ \tag{5-56}$$

Organic molecules with a permanent dipole moment, such as alcohols and amines, appear to show a marked preference for proton-transfer reactions.

5-6.1.1 Hydride Ion Transfer

Hydride ion transfer, the transfer of an H^- to a positive molecule ion, is a very important reaction between alkyl ions and neutral alkane molecules. In several cases it is the only reaction of the alkyl ion other than neutralization. Hydride ion transfer between alkyl ions and olefins also occurs but to a much more limited extent. The reaction appears to be the only one occurring between the cycloalkanes and alkyl ions (except cyclopropane). Examples of hydride ion transfer are

$$C_4 H_8 D^+ + (CH_3)_2 CDCH_2 CH_3 \rightarrow C_4 H_8 D_2 + C_5 H_{11}^+ \tag{5-57}$$

$$C_2 H_5^+ + C_3 H_8 \rightarrow C_2 H_6 + C_3 H_7^+ \tag{5-58}$$

$$C_2 D_3 H_2^+ + C_6 H_{12} \rightarrow C_2 D_3 H_3 + C_6 H_{11}^+ \tag{5-59}$$

$$C_3 H_5^+ + C_3 H_8 \rightarrow C_3 H_6 + C_3 H_7^+ \tag{5-60}$$

Hydride ion transfer often is a very efficient reaction. Reaction (5-58), for example, is practically the only reaction of the ethyl ions produced in methane radiolysis. It occurs when only

0.01% C_3H_8 is added to the reaction mixture. Hydride ion reactions are most important for the higher alkanes. Table 5-5 summarizes some relative rates of hydride ion transfer for a few molecule ions.

Table 5-5. RELATIVE RATES OF HYDRIDE
TRANSFER REACTIONS AT $300°K$[*]

	$C_4D_9^+$	$C_3D_7^+$	$C_2D_5^+$
Cyclopropane		< 0.02	< 0.05
i-Butane		0.58	0.87
n-Butane		0.78	
Cyclobutane	1.00	1.00	1.00
Neopentane		0.049	1.05
i-Pentane	1.26	1.04	1.09
n-Pentane	1.42		1.07
Cyclopentane	1.56	1.44	1.14
n-Hexane	2.37	2.13	
Methyl cyclopentane	2.36	1.91	1.29
Cyclohexane	3.51	2.41	1.36
n-Heptane	4.04	3.88	1.65
Methyl cyclohexane	3.50	2.69	
Cyclopentane		0.71	0.34
Cyclohexane		0.81	0.49

[*]Data from P. Ausloos, S. G. Lias, and A. A. Scala, "Advances in Chemistry Series," 58:264 (1966).

The transfer of H_2^- in ion-molecule reactions may also be considered in this category. This reaction is characterized as

$$C_m H_{2m}^+ \; + \; RH_2 \rightarrow \; C_m H_{2m+2} \; + \; R^+ \tag{5-61}$$

where $C_m H_{2m}^+$ is a lower olefinic ion and RH_2 is a saturated hydrocarbon. This is not to be interpreted too generally since saturated hydrocarbons can also transfer a hydride ion to an olefinic ion; i.e., Reaction (5-62) may also occur.

$$C_m H_{2m}^+ \; + \; RH_2 \rightarrow C_m H_{2m+1} \; + \; RH^+ \tag{5-62}$$

Some H_2^- transfer reactions that have been observed are:

$$C_2 H_4^+ \; + \; C_3 H_8 \rightarrow \; C_2 H_6 \; + \; C_3 H_6^+ \tag{5-63}$$

$$C_3 H_6^+ \; + \; cyclo\text{-}C_5 H_{10} \rightarrow \; C_3 H_8 \; + \; C_5 H_8^+ \tag{5-64}$$

$$C_2 H_4^+ \; + \; C_4 H_8 \rightarrow \; C_2 H_6 \; + \; C_4 H_6^+ \tag{5-65}$$

$$C_2 H_4^+ \; + \; cyclo\text{-}C_6 H_{12} \rightarrow \; C_6 H_{10}^+ \; + \; C_2 H_6 \tag{5-66}$$

$$C_4H_8^+ + cyclo\text{-}C_6H_{12} \rightarrow C_6H_{10}^+ + C_4H_{10} \tag{5-67}$$

Another particle transfer reaction that has been characterized is the transfer of H_2. Both the transfer of H_2 and H_2^- appear to occur as a single entity transfer from adjacent carbon atoms. Some H_2 transfer reactions are

$$cyclo\text{-}C_6H_{12}^+ + C_4H_8 \rightarrow C_6H_{10}^+ + C_4H_{10} \tag{5-68}$$

$$cyclo\text{-}C_6H_{12}^+ + C_3D_6 \rightarrow C_6H_{10}^+ + C_2D_6H_2 \tag{5-69}$$

$$cyclo\text{-}C_6H_{12}^+ + cyclo\text{-}C_3D_6 \rightarrow C_6H_{10}^+ + C_3D_6H_2 \tag{5-70}$$

$$cyclo\text{-}C_5H_8^+ + C_3D_6 \rightarrow C_3D_6H_2 + cyclo\text{-}C_5H_6^+ \tag{5-71}$$

The relative rates of H_2 and H_2^- transfer reactions follow the same trends, but there is a wide variation in rates, depending on the entities involved.

5-6.2 Condensation

Condensation reactions are characterized by a considerable rearrangement of the collision complex, whereas particle transfers of ion molecules are not. Examples of condensation reactions are

$$CH_3^+ + CH_4 \rightarrow C_2H_5^+ + H_2 \tag{5-72}$$

$$CH_2^+ + CH_4 \rightarrow C_2H_4^+ + H_2 \tag{5-73}$$

$$C_2H_4^+ + CH_4 \rightarrow C_3H_6^+ + H_2 \tag{5-74}$$

$$C_2H_2^+ + C_2H_2 \rightarrow C_4H_2^+ + H_2 \tag{5-75}$$

$$C_4H_6^+ + C_4H_6 \rightarrow C_7H_9^+ + CH_3 \tag{5-76}$$

$$I^+ + C_2H_5I \rightarrow HI_2^+ + C_2H_4 \tag{5-77}$$

5-6.3 Association

In association reactions the collision complex is the final product:

$$C_3H_7I^+ + C_3H_7I \rightarrow (C_3H_7I)_2^+ \tag{5-78}$$

$$C_2H_5Br^+ + C_2H_5Br \rightarrow (C_4H_{10}Br_2)^+ \tag{5-79}$$

$$C_2H_4^+ + C_2H_4 \rightarrow C_4H_8^+ \tag{5-80}$$

The lifetimes of these complexes as observed in the mass spectrometer are at least 10^{-6} sec.

Ion-molecule reactions have rate constants that are generally very high (up to 2×10^{-9} cm^3 per molecule-sec). Such high rate constants imply that the reaction phenomenological cross sections are equal to or greater than the geometrical cross sections. Table 7-3 summarizes a number of ion-molecule reactions.

5-7 HOT ATOMS AND RADICALS

A "hot" atom or radical is one that is not in thermal equilibrium with its neighbors and thus possesses excess kinetic and/or electronic energy. Hot atoms are usually produced by nuclear recoil reactions such as

$$^6\text{Li } (n, \gamma) \, ^3\text{H} \qquad\qquad\qquad (5\text{-}81)$$

$$^3\text{He } (n, p) \, ^3\text{H} \qquad\qquad\qquad (5\text{-}82)$$

The recoil tritium atom produced by Reaction (5-81) has an energy equivalent of 2.73 Mev, whereas that produced in Reaction (5-82) has an energy equivalent of 0.19 Mev.

Hot atoms and radicals are produced by other processes too; for instance, hot methylene radicals may be produced during some photochemical reactions. The same is true for hydrogen atoms. The term *hot* is of course relative, the excess energy ranging from just a few hundredths of an electron volt to several million electron volts. In the photolysis of hydrogen iodide with 2537 Å light, hot hydrogen atoms with some 41 kcal of excess translational energy are produced. When hot radicals are produced, the excess energy that is not distributed in the internal degrees of freedom is converted to kinetic energy.

5-8 RADIATION CHEMISTRY AND PHOTOCHEMISTRY

In any system exposed to ionizing radiation, the reactions of excited molecules and ions must be considered when attempting to develop a mechanism. The amount of the energy deposited in a system that results in direct electronic excitations which subsequently leads to product molecules or reactive intermediates, as compared with the energy expended in forming ions that subsequently leads to products, has not been established with any certainty for aqueous, nonaqueous, or gaseous systems. The role of excited states as precursors for observed reactive intermediates or products is a problem that is of major concern to radiation chemists.

Many radiation chemists use parallel photochemical experiments in an attempt to elucidate observed reactions. In photochemical experiments the method of attack generally used is to obtain some knowledge of the absorption spectrum of the molecule under study to determine what part of the molecule absorbs a particular wavelength of light. Light of this selected wavelength is then used, and the subsequent reaction is followed by chemical analysis, supported often by detailed studies of fluorescent or phosphorescent emission spectra. Light absorbed in one part of the molecule is often found to be transferred to other parts of the molecule where bond cleavage may occur. For instance, energy absorbed by the carbonyl group in acetone is transferred to the carbon bond, resulting in carbon-carbon bond cleavage.

$$CH_3COCH_3 \xrightarrow{h\nu} CH_3 + COCH_3 \qquad (5-83)$$

Photochemists studying this type of reaction have been able to show some of the various mechanisms whereby electronic excitation energy can be transferred intramolecularly, and in this manner they have contributed a great deal to our understanding of energy transfer. In this respect photochemistry and radiation chemistry are very similar. Radiation chemistry departs from photochemistry in several important respects: (1) Electronic excitation is given to a molecule by direct perturbation of the electrons; hence it is very possible to have excited molecules undergoing "forbidden transitions" to excited states not normally populated in photochemical experiments. (2) Excitations in radiation chemistry studies may be multiple; i.e., several electrons are simultaneously excited. (3) In radiation chemistry we have reactions of ions produced with varying energies.

In recent years, however, the development of vacuum ultraviolet photochemistry has permitted photochemists to employ monochromatic light of energies capable of ionizing most molecules of interest. Such studies permit studies of the reactions of ionic species in the gas phase.

The photochemists use the term *quantum yield* to describe the energy efficiency of a photochemical reaction. The quantum yield is the amount of chemical reaction observed in the form of a particular product molecule, or the disappearance of the parent molecule, per quantum of light absorbed. The similarity between the quantum yield and G value is readily seen. Photochemists, like radiation chemists, must have a method of determining the amount of energy absorbed during a radiation exposure. In photochemistry the dosimetry systems used are called actinometers. The best known actinometer is uranyl oxalate solution that decomposes via

$$(UO_2^{++}) + (COOH)_2 \xrightarrow{h\nu} UO_2^{++} + CO_2 + CO + H_2O \qquad (5-84)$$

The number of molecules reacting per quantum, the quantum yield, which is 0.5 at standard conditions, varies with wavelength, temperature, the relative concentrations of the uranyl and oxalate ions, pH, and the addition of other ions. It is independent of intensity and whether or not the light is continuous or intermittent.

The energy of a quantum is

$$E = h\nu = h\frac{c}{\lambda} \qquad (5\text{-}85)$$

The fractional degree of absorption of light in an infinitesimal layer of absorber of thickness dl is proportional to the concentration of the absorbing substance.

$$\frac{dI}{I} = -kCdl \qquad (5\text{-}86)$$

where I = intensity of the light

k = constant of proportionality

C = concentration

Integration over a finite thickness gives the famous Lambert-Beer law

$$\ln\frac{I}{I_o} = -kCl \qquad (5\text{-}87)$$

When C, the concentration, is expressed in moles per liter, k is the molar extinction coefficient, and I_o and I are the incident and emergent intensities.

A molecule that has absorbed a quantum of light to become electronically excited, if isolated, will reemit the quantum by fluorescence and return to the ground state.

$$A + h\nu \rightarrow A^* \quad (\text{rate} \propto I_a) \qquad (5\text{-}88)$$

$$A^* \xrightarrow{k_e} A + h\nu \qquad (5\text{-}89)$$

The rate of fluorescence is

$$\frac{-d(A^*)}{dt} = k_e(A^*) \qquad (5\text{-}90)$$

In the presence of other gas molecules, the excited molecule may transfer its excitation energy in a collision and become "quenched." In the presence of other gas molecules, therefore, there is competition between fluorescence and quenching.

$$A* + M \xrightarrow{k_q} A + M*$$ (5-91)

The total rate of loss of excited atoms is given by

$$\frac{-d(A*)}{dt} = k_e(A*) + k_q(A*)(M)$$ (5-92)

The fluorescence yield is given by

$$\frac{I_e}{I_a} = \frac{k_e(A*)}{k_q(A*)(M) + k_e(A*)}$$ (5-93)

where I_e is the quanta of light emitted and I_a is the quanta of light absorbed.

Measurement of the fluorescence yield aids in giving insight to energy transfer efficiency.

5-9 KINETICS: NOTATION AND CONVENTIONS

Rate constants are customarily expressed by the Arrhenius equation

$$k = Ae^{-\Delta E/RT}$$ (5-94)

where A is the preexponential factor and ΔE is the activation energy.

The rate constant k is usually determined indirectly, but, when it is determined directly, as, for example, by measuring either the disappearance of a particular reactant or the appearance of a product by a direct method, it is called an *absolute* rate constant. Most of the rate constants that have been determined for the reaction of the hydrated electron with various substances, for example, are absolute rate constants.

The units for a first order rate constant are

$$k = \frac{1}{time}$$ (5-95)

and for a second order rate constant

$$k = concentration^{-1}\ time^{-1}$$ (5-96)

and for a third order constant

$$k = concentration^{-2}\ time^{-1}$$ (5-97)

Concentration may be expressed in molecules per cubic centimeter or moles per liter, in which case Eq. (5-96) becomes

$$k = cm^3 \ molecules^{-1} \ sec^{-1} \tag{5-98}$$

or

$$k = liters \ moles^{-1} \ sec^{-1} \tag{5-99}$$

A convention often used when expressing the concentration in moles per liter for second order reactions is

$$k = M^{-1} \ sec^{-1} \tag{5-100}$$

where M is the molarity.

All three methods of expressing the second order rate constant are used in this text.

The half life (or half time) of a reaction is the time required for the concentration to fall to one half its initial value. The mean life of a reaction is the time for the concentration of reactants to fall to $1/e$ of its initial value, where e is the base of the natural logarithms.

For a chemical reaction such as

$$2A \rightarrow B \tag{5-101}$$

the rate of the reaction may be written as

$$\frac{-d(A)}{dt} = k(A)^2 \tag{5-102}$$

However, when rate constants are being compared, the expression commonly used is such as to indicate that two molecules of A are disappearing; therefore

$$rate = 2k(A)(A) \tag{5-103}$$

In tables of rate constants, therefore, it is very common to see this notation used; however, normally the rate constant is written as shown in Eq. (5-102). In general, square brackets are used to denote concentrations.

5-9.1 Competition Kinetics

Competition kinetics are very common in aqueous systems where the principal radicals are often in competition for the same solute or where one of the radicals, H, for example, is reacting with two different solutes.

If a radical R is reacting with two different solutes A and B, the probability of reaction with A is $k_A A$, and with B, $k_B B$. If reactions with the solutes A and B are the only reactions of radical R, then the probability of reaction with A is just

$$\frac{k_A[A]}{k_A[A] + k_B[B]} \tag{5-104}$$

or, more generally, for several solutes Eq. (5-104) is written as

$$\frac{k_A[A]}{\Sigma k_i[i]} \tag{5-105}$$

where $k_i[i]$ is the probability for reactions with the ith solute.

If the total concentration of the reactive intermediate R is known, then, in the situation where the competition is between reaction with A or B, the fraction reacting with A over some time interval is given by

$$f = \int_{t=t'}^{t=t''} \frac{k_A[A][R]}{[R_o]}\, dt \tag{5-106}$$

If the only reaction of radical R is with itself or with the solute B to form stable products,

$$R + R \rightarrow RR \qquad 2k_1[R][R] \tag{5-107}$$

$$R + B \rightarrow RB \qquad k_2[R][B] \tag{5-108}$$

$$\frac{-d[R]}{dt} = 2k_1[R]^2 + k_2[R][B] \tag{5-109}$$

The concentration of R at any time, t, is found by integrating Eq. (5-109) assuming $[B]$ constant

$$[R] = \frac{k_2[B]}{[C \exp k_2[B]\, t] - 2k_1} \tag{5-110}$$

The integration constant, C, is evaluated by appropriate boundary conditions consistent with the experiment. Usually a time is chosen which gives the total (or maximum) concentration of the radical R_o. If this is when $t = 0$, then

$$C = \frac{k_2[B] + 2k[R_o]}{[R_o]} \tag{5-111}$$

where $[R_o]$ is the concentration of R at $t = 0$.

Substitution into Eq. (5-110) gives

$$[R] = \frac{k_2[B][R_o]}{[k_2[B] + 2k_1[R_o]][\exp k_2[B]t] - 2k_1[R_o]} \qquad (5\text{-}112)$$

The fraction of radicals $[R]$ reacting with $[B]$ in the time interval $t = 0$ to $t = t''$ is

$$f = \int_{t=o}^{t=t''} \frac{k_2[B][R]}{[R_o]} \, dt \qquad (5\text{-}113)$$

Substitution for $[R]$ from Eq. (5-112) gives

$$f = \int_{t=o}^{t=t''} \frac{[k_2[B]]^2 [R_o]}{R_o[k_2[B] + 2k_1[R_o]][\exp k_2[B]t] - 2k_1[R_o]} \, dt$$

$$(5\text{-}114)$$

PROBLEMS

1. Using the relation

$$\ln K^{\circ} = -\frac{\Delta G}{RT} = \frac{\Delta H}{RT} + \frac{\Delta S^{\circ}}{R} \text{ and } \ln k_r = \ln A - \frac{\Delta E}{RT} ,$$

   show that for a reaction

   $$A + B \rightarrow C + D$$

   the difference in activation energies is proportional to the heat of the reaction assuming $\Delta C_p = 0$.

2. For the radiation-induced decomposition of KNO_3, the following reaction scheme has been shown to provide a kinetic expression consistent with the observed rate

   $$NO_3^- \rightarrow NO_2^- + O$$

   $$O + NO_3^- \rightarrow O_2 + NO_2^-$$

   $$O + NO_2^- \rightarrow NO_3$$

   With this scheme derive the integrated rate expression for the nitrite yield:

   $$Ax^2 + x = bt$$

where x is the concentration of NO_2^-, bt is a quantity proportional to absorbed dose at any time t, and A is a constant.

3.   Calculate the number of molecular collisions in H_2 gas at 1 atm pressure and 300°K. The molecular diameter is 2.72 Å.

4.   Show that the collision theory predicts a temperature dependence of the frequency factor A.

5.   What might you predict about the relative G values for the reactions

$$H_2 + Cl_2 \rightarrow 2HCl$$

$$H_2 + Br_2 \rightarrow 2HBr$$

$$H_2 + I_2 \rightarrow 2HI$$

REFERENCES

1.   E. W. R. Steacie, "Atomic and Free Radical Reactions," A.C.S. monograph no. 125, Reinhold Publishing Co., New York, 1954.

2.   A. F. Trotman-Dickenson, "Free Radicals," Methuen, London, 1959.

3.   J. A. Kerr and A. F. Trotman-Dickenson, G. Porter (ed.), "Progress in Reaction Kinetics," Pergamon Press, Inc., New York, 1961.

4.   C. C. McDonald and R. J. Goll, *J. Phys. Chem.*, 69:293 (1965).

5.   P. Ausloos, *Ann. Rev. Phys. Chem.*, 1965.

6

MODERN TECHNIQUES IN RADIATION CHEMISTRY

Science progresses in steps; some large, some small. The steps of progress are usually marked by new theoretical advances, but every so often they are marked by new experimental tools or techniques. Since 1950, chemists have seen the introduction of new techniques such as flash photolysis, electron spin and nuclear magnetic resonance spectroscopy, gas chromatography, pulsed radiolysis and high resolution mass spectrometry. These experimental tools have been applied to great advantage by radiation chemists and four of the most important — flash photolysis, pulsed radiolysis, electron spin resonance and mass spectrometry — are described in this chapter.

6-1 FLASH PHOTOLYSIS

In flash photolysis a bank of capacitors is discharged through an inert gas such as argon or krypton, producing a brilliant flash of light with an energy up to 10^5 joules, for a duration of about 10^{-4} seconds. As a result of the absorption of this intense burst of light, extensive photolysis occurs in the reaction system with the consequent production of excited molecules, radicals, and other transient species. A secondary source of light traverses the system and a spectrophotometric or spectrographic record is made of the absorbing specie. (See Fig. 6-1.)

This technique is uniquely valuable for detecting reactive intermediates and in studying the lifetimes and modes of decay of excited molecules, because in the usual photochemical experiment one does not produce a sufficiently high concentration of these reactive intermediates to observe them directly. This is readily seen from the energy requirements for a flash photolysis experiment.

EXAMPLE 6-1:

(1) Calculate the radical concentration required in a flash photolysis experiment to produce an optical density of 0.1 if the molar extinction coefficient is 5000.

(2) If the cell dimensions are r = 1 cm, length = 100 cm, how many quanta must be absorbed?

177

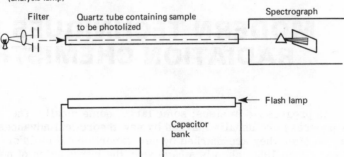

Fig. 6-1. Schematic of flash photolysis experiment.

(3) If the mean life of the radical or specie to be observed is 10^{-3} sec calculate the number of quanta per second needed.

(4) If the average wavelength of the light from the flash is 3000×10^{-8} cm and only 1% of this is available for reaction calculate the total flash energy required.

SOLUTION: From Beer's law

$$ln\ \frac{I_o}{I} = D = \varepsilon[C]l$$

where I_o = intensity of incident light

I = intensity of emergent light

D = optical density

$[C]$ = concentration in moles per liter

ε = molar extinction coefficient

l = path length

(1) $0.1 = 5000 \times [C] \times 100$ cm

$[C] = 2.0 \times 10^{-7}$ moles per liter

(2) Volume of the cell is $(100\ \pi r^2) \mathrm{cm}^3$ or $\pi/10$ liters

$(\pi/10) \times 2 \times 10^{-7} = 6.28 \times 10^{-8}$ moles

$$= 3.77 \times 10^{16} \text{ molecules (radicals)}$$

Photochemists employ the term *einstein* ($Nh\nu$) to designate 1 mol of quanta ($h\nu$). Therefore, since $N = 6.023 \times 10^{23}$, $6.28 \times 10^{-8} \times 6.023 \times 10^{23} = 3.77 \times 10^{16}$ quanta are required.

(3) If the mean life τ of the radical or specie is 10^{-3} sec, the stationary state concentration is $I_a \tau$ where I_a is the light intensity. To produce 3.77×10^{16} radicals or specie a light intensity of 3.77×10^{19} quanta per second is required.

(4) If the average wavelength from the flash is 3000×10^{-8} cm the flash energy required is obtained by multiplying the light energy per quanta by the moles to be reacted.

$$\frac{\text{energy}}{\text{einstein}} = 6.023 \times 10^{23} \frac{\text{molecules}}{\text{mol}} \times \frac{6.62 \times 10^{-27} \text{ ergs-sec}}{10^7 \dfrac{\text{ergs-molecule}}{\text{joule}}}$$

$$\times \ 3 \times 10^{10} \ \frac{\text{cm}}{\text{sec}} \times \frac{1}{3000 \times 10^{-8} \text{ cm}}$$

$$= 390{,}000 \text{ joules/einstein}$$

energy $= 390{,}000 \times 6.28 \times 10^{-8} = 0.024$ joules

Since only 1% of the flash energy is utilized, the total flash energy required is:

total flash energy $= \dfrac{.024}{.01} = 2.4$ joules

There are many inefficiencies involved in delivering the energy from the condenser bank to the absorbing system. Flash energies of the order of 20 to 100 joules are usually required in most flash photolysis experiments. This is due to the many variable factors such as lifetimes, and extinction coefficients of the absorbing species.

The maximum energy which can be obtained from a flash lamp is equal to that stored in the capacitor bank. This is equal to $1/2\ CV^2$ where C is the capacitance in farads and V the voltage. For example if the capacitance is 10 μf and the voltage 20 kv, the energy in joules is

$$E = \frac{1}{2} (10 \times 10^{-6}) \times (2 \times 10^4)^2 = 2000 \text{ joules}$$

6-1.1 Flash Photolysis — Flash Duration

Flash duration is often considered as the time during which the intensity exceeds half its peak value. The more widely accepted definition, however, is the time taken to fall $1/e$ of its peak value where e is the base of natural logarithms.

Flashes of very short duration can be obtained providing energy is not an important criterion. Indeed, flash lamps are available with duration times of 10^{-9} sec; however, the energy is only microjoules per flash. The duration is related to the capacity and tube length, and to some extent the voltage. Table 6-1 summarizes the pertinent characteristics of some available equipment.

Table 6-1. FLASH PHOTOLYSIS LAMPS

Duration, sec	Output joules	Reference
8×10^{-10}	6×10^{-6}	Q. A. Kerns, F. Kersten, G. C. Cox, Rev. Sec. Instr., 30:31 (1959). [See also J. T. D'Alessio, P. Ludwig, M. Burton, Rev. Sec. Instr., 35(8), 1015 (1964).]
2×10^{-7}	0.5	H. Fisher, J. Opt. Sci. Amer., 47:981 (1957).
3×10^{-7}	1.4	J. S. T. Looms and R. J. North, Proc. 3rd Int. Cong. on High-Speed Photography, Butterworth & Co., London, 1956.
$1-2 \times 10^{-6}$	50-300	F. Stuhl and K. H. Welge, Z. Naturforschung, 18(a): 900 (1963).
3×10^{-5}	500	G. Porter, M. W. Windsor, Disc. Far. Soc., 17:178 (1958).

6-1.2 Flash Photolysis — Limitations on Observable Reaction Rates

The half life for a first order reaction is proportional to the reciprocal of the rate constant. Therefore, for a flash duration of 1 to 10 μsec one is limited to reactions with rate constants no larger than 10^6.

The half life for a second order reaction is

$$t_{1/2} = \frac{1}{k[C_x]} \tag{6-1}$$

where the reaction is second order in the transient species x, i.e.,

$$\frac{-dC_x}{dt} = k[C_x]^2 \tag{6-2}$$

The half life will have varying values depending upon the concentration of the intermediate. Substituting in Eq. (6-1) for $[C]$ according to Beer's law

$$t_{1/2} = \frac{\varepsilon l}{kD} \tag{6-3}$$

$$k = \frac{\varepsilon l}{D(t_{1/2})} \tag{6-4}$$

In any flash photolysis experiment one usually first determines the spectra of the intermediate.[1] For kinetic or other studies, a predetermined wavelength where the species appears to have a relatively high absorption is selected and relative transmission curves obtained from plate photometry or from photoelectric measurements utilizing an oscilloscope trace of the output from a phototube.

In the photoelectric method as in the plate photometry method the product of the concentration and extinction coefficient is determined. In the photoelectric method the detecting system consists of a photomultiplier with the appropriate electronics coupled to an oscilliscope properly calibrated to give percent transmission versus time. A typical trace is shown in Fig. 6-2. After making appropriate corrections for the scattered light, one can readily obtain the optical density and hence the product of the concentration and extinction coefficient.

The concentration or the extinction coefficient is often very difficult to determine. The usual method is to do a careful kinetic analysis of the reaction and then either relate the intermediate to some product that can be determined by conventional means or determine the concentration of all the species present and make appropriate subtraction. For example, in the photolysis of ClO_2 the only chlorine containing species are ClO and ClO_2. By determining the concentration of ClO_2 (whose extinction coefficient and absorption spectra is known) at any time t, the concentration of ClO is obtained from its absorption spectra because it arises from depletion of ClO_2 and hence is determined by difference. From the usual plot of optical density versus concentration the absolute extinction coefficient of ClO, at the wavelength used, is readily determined. In many cases, however, only upper limits for extinction coefficients can be obtained and hence only approximate concentrations.

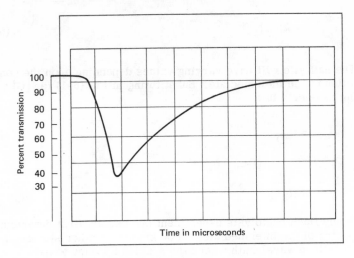

Fig. 6-2. Oscilloscope trace of decay
of absorbing species.

Beer's law, which is used in all spectrophotometric work,
should be tested for linearity in the system under study; however,
for a single substance at a definite wavelength, this law is exactly
true. Deviations occur in practical cases because (1) absorption at
the wavelength used is by more than one species or (2) the wavelengths used are of a finite interval, and the extinction coefficient
changes sharply over this interval. The situation described under
(2) is avoided if optical density at different wavelengths is well
characterized. If this is the case, then a wavelength is chosen where
the optical density has little or no variation over a small wavelength
interval.

6-2 PULSED RADIOLYSIS

The principles involved in pulsed radiolysis are almost exactly
the same as those of flash photolysis. The object here, as in flash
photolysis, is to produce a sufficiently high concentration of reactive intermediates so that they may be observed directly. Spectroscopic means for observing the transients are preferred in most
cases; however, other methods such as conductivity and ESR techniques have been used. Pulsed radiolysis became feasible when
pulsed electron accelerators capable of delivering a sufficient
amount of energy in microsecond pulses became available. Short
pulse times are required because the rate constants for reactions
of many of the intermediates are so very high (10^{10} M^{-1} sec^{-1}) and
therefore the half times for a very large number of these reactions
are in the microsecond region. In addition, G values are usually

low and there is also a large variation in the extinction coefficients of the transients. For example, the extinction coefficient of the hydrated electron is reported to be $15,800\,M^{-1}\,cm^{-1}$ at 7200 Å. To observe an absorption corresponding to an optical density of 0.1 in a cell of 15 cm length, a concentration of hydrated electrons of only 4.1 mM is required; however, with the α-ethanol radical, which has extinction coefficient of only 240 under the same conditions, one would require a concentration of ~28 mM. A typical experimental arrangement for pulsed radiolysis is shown in Fig. 6-3.

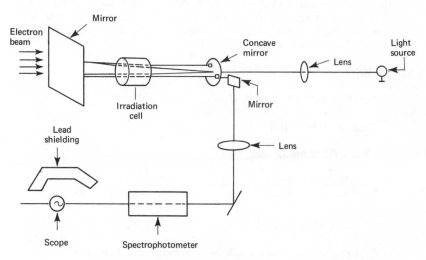

Fig. 6-3. Schematic of pulsed radiolysis setup.

6-2.1 Pulsed Radiolysis – Energy Requirements

The dose necessary to give a detectable concentration of a transient in solution depends upon the G value for the production of the species, the absolute reaction rate constant, and the extinction coefficient.

Several examples can best serve to illustrate the parameters involved.

EXAMPLE 6-2: What concentration of active intermediate will be produced in a 4 cm^3 cell using a 3 Mev accelerator at a current of 20 ma and a 1 μsec pulse? The G value is 2 (cell dimensions 1 cm x 1 cm x 4 cm).

SOLUTION: The energy input is

$$3 \times 10^6 \text{ volts} \times 0.02 \text{ amps} \times 10^{-6} \text{ sec} = 0.06 \text{ joules}$$

2 molec	mole	ev	10^7 ergs	0.06 joule		1000 cm^3
100 ev	6.02×10^{23} molec	1.6×10^{-12}ergs	joule		4 cm^3	liter

$$= 31 \times 10^{-5} \text{ moles/liter}$$

EXAMPLE 6-3: If the extinction coefficient is 1000 and the G value is 2, how much energy must be deposited in a 4 cm^3 cell in 1 μsec to give an optical density of 0.2 (cell dimension 1 cm x 1 cm x 4 cm)? What current is required by a 3 Mev accelerator to produce this energy?

SOLUTION:

optical density $= \varepsilon[C]l$

$0.2 = 1000 \times [C] \times 4$

5×10^{-5} moles/liter $= C$

5×10^{-5} molec	liter	4 cm^3	6.02×10^{23} molec	100 ev	1.6×10^{-12} ergs	joule
liter	1000 cm^3		mole	2 molec	ev	10^7 ergs

$$= 0.96 \text{ joules}$$

the current required by a 3 Mev accelerator would be

$$3 \times 10^6 \text{ volts} \times \text{amps} \times 10^{-6} \text{ sec} = 0.96 \text{ joules}$$

$$\text{amps} = 0.32 \text{ or } 320 \text{ ma}$$

6-2.2 Pulsed Radiolysis — Radiation Sources

Ideally, one would like to have a machine that has variable energies with pulse times of 10^{-3} to 10^{-9} sec. In all cases, the pulse duration should be small compared to the half life of the reaction and should have a short rise and decay time. In these respects pulsed radiolysis experiments are similar to flash photolysis experiments. The principal differences arise from the energy source and the reaction vessels.

The sources currently used in pulsed radiolysis include microwave linear accelerators, Van de Graaff accelerators, and pulsed X-ray machines. Of these the most widely used is the microwave linear accelerator. It is capable of producing stable high current beams at high energies. The higher the energy, the greater the penetration of the beam, hence the longer the path length of the light of the detection system (the optical density is directly proportional to the cell length). Higher energies and currents also allow for very short pulse times. Pulsed X-ray sources capable of delivering between 3000 and 7000 rads per pulse with a 17-20 nanosecond pulse width are readily available. A principal limitation of these sources is the problem of accurate dosimetry.

For many applications, the 3 Mev Van de Graaff accelerator appears to be quite satisfactory (particularly when costs are considered). These accelerators however are inherently limited as regards very high currents and hence very short pulse widths. An enormous amount of energy is stored in the terminal of a Van de Graaff accelerator but only a small amount of this is useful energy. If the terminal voltage drops below that of the accelerating sections, the beam cannot go down the tube. Only a small percentage of the energy stored in the terminal is therefore available for pulsing experiments. There are available 3 Mev Van de Graaff accelerators with currents of 1 amp and pulses of a few tenths to 5 μsec. For pulsed experiments in the nanosecond range, however, the microwave linear accelerator and the pulsed X-ray generator offer the most promise.

6-2.3   Pulsed Radiolysis — Detection of
         Intermediates: Optical Methods

Once the energy has been deposited in the system, a fast optical system similar to that used in flash photolysis is employed. Light from a spectroflash lamp, synchronized with the electron pulse, traverses the irradiation cell and is recorded on a spectrograph. When the spectrum of a transient is known, a particular wavelength can be selected and the change in absorption with time followed photoelectrically. Light from a constant intensity lamp passes through the reaction cell and then through a monochromator; the selected wavelength being picked up by a photomultiplier whose output is brought into an oscilloscope, (Fig. 6-4) calibrated in terms of optical density versus time.

One other important difference between flash photolysis and pulsed radiolysis is that due to radiation effects. There is radiation discoloring of the optical system and, at high energies, induced radioactivity. The latter effect is negligible for most systems, and adequate precautions can protect the optical systems. In addition there is Cerenkov radiation for which appropriate corrections may have to be made.

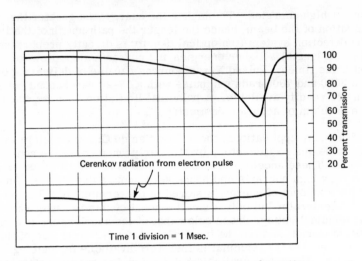

Fig. 6-4. Oscilloscope trace showing absorption of transient. Decay indicates disappearance by reaction.

6-2.3a Kinetics Studies

If a reaction is first order

$$A \xrightarrow{k_r} B \qquad (6\text{-}5)$$

the rate expression is:

$$\frac{-d[A]}{dt} = k_r[A] \qquad (6\text{-}6)$$

integrating between the limits of $t = 0$, $[A] = [A_o]$ and $t = t$, $[A] = [A]$

$$ln \frac{[A_o]}{[A]} = k_r t \qquad (6\text{-}7)$$

under the assumption that the species A is the only absorbing substance at the particular wavelength used, since $D_o = [A_o]\varepsilon l$

$$\frac{ln\, D_o/\varepsilon l}{ln\, D/\varepsilon l} = k_r t \qquad (6\text{-}8)$$

or

$$ln(D_o/D) = k_r t \tag{6-9}$$

where D_o is the optical density at time $t = 0$, and D the optical density at time $t = t$.

Thus, a knowledge of the extinction coefficient is not necessary to determine the rate constant k_r. For the pseudo first order reaction

$$A + C \xrightarrow{k_r} B \ (C_o \ggg A_o) \tag{6-10}$$

and $k_r = k'_r [C_o]$, Eq. (6-9) becomes

$$ln \ \frac{D_o}{D} = k'_r t \tag{6-11}$$

For a bimolecular reaction

$$A + B \longrightarrow C \tag{6-12}$$

If $[A] = [B]$ and only the A species absorbs at the wavelength used then

$$\frac{-d[A]}{dt} = k_r [A]^2 \tag{6-13}$$

and

$$\frac{1}{D_t} - \frac{1}{D_o} = \frac{k_r t}{\varepsilon l} \tag{6-14}$$

It is apparent that a knowledge of the extinction coefficient is necessary to determine the rate constant for a second order reaction.

Most often the extinction coefficient is not known and one must use indirect methods for determining the rate constants. This can be done by determining the G value for production of the particular species under investigation by kinetic studies. For example, good estimates for the G value for hydrated electron have been obtained in this manner.

The oscilliscope trace that one obtains (Fig. 6-4) is calibrated in terms of optical density and time, and therefore one can determine directly the rate of production of species in terms of optical density per unit time. Since the optical density is directly proportional to the concentration one can, given a knowledge of the total dose and optical path, obtain the product of the G value and the extinction coefficient, εG. A knowledge of the G values then yields the extinction coefficient.

EXAMPLE 6-4: Analysis of a trace from a pulsed radiolysis experiment shows that the rate of production of the absorbing species in a medium of unit density at a dose rate of 10^9 rads per second, in terms of optical density units, is 36,000 optical density units per second. If the cell length is 1.2 cm what is the value of $G\varepsilon$?

SOLUTION:

$$\frac{36,000}{\text{sec}} = \varepsilon[C]\,l$$

$$\varepsilon[C] = \left(\frac{36,000}{\text{sec}}\right)\left(\frac{1}{1.2\ \text{cm}}\right)$$

The concentration is in moles per liter, which must be converted to molecules. The product $\varepsilon[C]$ divided by the dose then gives the G value multiplied by the extinction coefficient.

$$\frac{\text{liter}}{1000\ \text{g}}\left|\frac{36,000\,(\text{moles})\,\text{cm}}{\text{sec (liter)}}\right|\frac{1}{1.2\ \text{cm}}\left|\frac{6.02\times10^{23}\ \text{molec}}{\text{mole}}\right|\frac{1\ \text{sec}}{10^9\ \text{rads}}\left|\frac{\text{rad}}{100\ \dfrac{\text{erg}}{\text{g}}}\right|\frac{1.6\times10^{-12}\ \text{ergs}}{\text{ev}}$$

$$= G\varepsilon = 28,000\ \frac{\text{molecules}}{100\ \text{ev}}$$

Another method of determining pseudo first-order rate constants is from the steady-state concentrations of intermediates during a pulse. If one is observing reactions between an absorbing specie reacting with a solute, with rate constants of the order of 5×10^{10} to 10^{11} M^{-1} sec^{-1}, the solute concentration must be kept low in order to have measurable half times. However, at low solute concentrations, there is always the danger of local solute depletion during the measurement period. At very high solute concentrations (millimolar), for a fast reaction, the half time will fall to a few hundredths of a microsecond. For pulsed accelerators with microsecond pulses this time is small compared to the length of the pulse. The concentration of the intermediates then will rapidly reach a steady state, i.e., the rate of the removal of the intermediate by reaction with the solute will be equal to its rate of production.

$$\text{Rate production} = \text{rate of depletion} = k[A][B] \qquad (6\text{-}15)$$

For the reaction

$$A + B \xrightarrow{k_1} C \qquad [B] \ggg [A] \tag{6-16}$$

and if A is the absorbing species then at the steady state

rate of production = rate of disappearance

$$R_p = k_1 [A][B] \tag{6-17}$$

$$[A] = R_p / k_1 [B] \tag{6-18}$$

but $[A] = D_\infty / \varepsilon l$ where D_∞ = equilibrium optical density (at the steady state) and

$$R_p = \left(\frac{dD}{dt}\right)_o \frac{1}{\varepsilon l}$$

where

$$\left(\frac{dD}{dt}\right)_o = \begin{array}{l} \text{the initial rate of production of the inter-} \\ \text{mediate } A \text{ in terms of optical density.} \end{array} \tag{6-19}$$

therefore

$$D_\infty = \left(\frac{dD}{dt}\right)_o \frac{1}{k_1 [B]} \tag{6-20}$$

The quantity D_∞ is measured for several pulse intermediates and $(dD/dt)_o$ is measured from initial slopes (oscillograph trace) in the absence of B.

As indicated earlier most reactions are second order and hence a determination of the extinction coefficient is often necessary. The extinction coefficient also has intrinsic interest since it is important in any complete interpretation of the optical absorption spectrum. As shown previously, a pulsed experiment yields directly the product of the G value and extinction coefficient. For the determination of bimolecular rate constants, the determination of the extinction coefficient most often contributes the largest uncertainty to the measurement.[2]

6-3 ELECTRON SPIN RESONANCE

All molecules that have unpaired electrons are paramagnetic, and thus are drawn from a region of low magnetic field strength to a high one. In most molecules the electrons are paired so that their spins and therefore their magnetic vectors, balance out.

Unpaired electrons are detected by magnetic susceptibilities and by electron spin resonance (ESR). Rather high concentrations of radicals are required for measurement of magnetic susceptibilities and this method is of little value in studying reactive free radicals. The most satisfactory method is that of electron spin resonance.

The magnetic moment and the spin of an unpaired electron which is not coupled to any nuclei in the molecule is oriented in a random fashion. If a dc magnetic field is applied, the spins of the unpaired electron will be aligned either parallel or antiparallel and there will be a net magnetic moment. Those that are parallel to the applied magnetic field will have an energy $1/2$ gBH less than the zero field value and those electrons aligned antiparallel, $1/2$ gBH greater than the zero field value. The difference in energy $\Delta E = h\nu$ between the two states is:

$$\Delta E = gBH = h\nu \tag{6-21}$$

where g = the spectroscopic splitting factor or gyromagnetic ratio for a free electron. It is a measure of the contribution of the spin and orbital motion of the electron to its total angular momentum. For a free electron $g = 2.0023$

H = the applied field strength

B = the Bohr magneton and converts the angular momentum to magnetic moment in electromagnetic cgs units.

For a particular magnetic field there is a unique frequency, ν, which can raise the electrons from the lower state to the upper state. For most electron spin resonance studies the magnetic fields are in the kilogauss region, and the radiation frequency in the microwave region.

In order to observe an absorption of radiation there must be a net effect, i.e., an electron in the lower state absorbs energy and is raised to an upper state; those in the upper state in turn are stimulated to emit radiation and fall to a lower state. For the net absorption to be observable, there must be more electrons in the one state than in the other. For a system in thermal equilibrium this is true; there are more unpaired electrons in the lower states than in the upper. For practical purposes the distribution of the spins, S, between the two states in thermal equilibrium is given by

$$\frac{S_1}{S_2} = e^{-\Delta E/kT} \tag{6-22}$$

where S_1 = upper (higher energy) state

S_2 = lower energy state

ΔE = the energy of separation between the two levels and

k = the Boltzmann constant.

At any given energy level the ratio of S_1/S_2 decreases with decreasing temperatures and hence one always attempts to do ESR experiments at low temperatures. Additional sensitivity is also obtained by increasing the magnetic field strength and the resonant frequency.

6-3.1   Electron Spin Resonance — Spectra

The mechanisms whereby electrons in an upper state lose energy and return to a lower state are called relaxation processes. When the energy of the spins is being shared with the thermal vibrations of the system as a whole, as in a solid, it is called *spin lattice interaction*. The strength of this interaction is measured by a *spin lattice relaxation time* which is the time it takes for an initial excess of energy given to the spins to fall to $1/e$ of its value. A strong spin lattice interaction produces a short relaxation time; a weak interaction produces a long relaxation time.

If the orbit of an unpaired electron is associated with a nucleus having a magnetic moment and spin, there will be an interaction between the nucleus and the electron. The magnetic moment of the nucleus will produce a small additional field which will either add to or subtract from the applied field, thus causing a splitting of the energy levels. For example, interaction of an unpaired electron with a proton of spin $\pm 1/2$ will result in two possible orientations, with components along the field of $\pm 1/2$. If the magnetic field is varied at a fixed frequency, we would observe two absorption peaks, one higher than the single unperturbed electron transition, and one lower (Fig. 6-5). The greater the nuclear spin, in general, the greater the splitting. For a nuclear spin I there will be $(2I + 1)$ component lines with equal spacing. This nuclear interaction, which causes a splitting of the single electron transition, is called *hyperfine interaction* and the separation between the lines, *hyperfine splitting*. The magnitude of this splitting of the single electron transition is taken as a direct measure of the interaction of the nucleus and the electron.

Most often the unpaired electron is perturbed by many nuclei, in which case hyperfine splitting becomes very complicated and the spectra becomes difficult to resolve. Free radical spectra can be resolved, however, because the spectrum observed arises from:

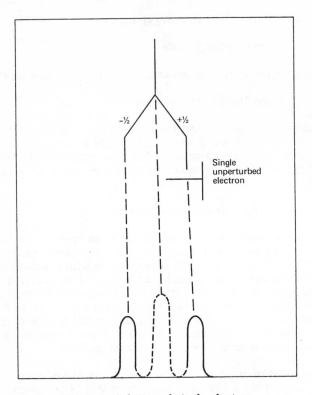

Fig. 6-5. Splitting of single electron.

(1) A strong interaction with nuclei coupled with a weak interaction. (The strong interaction $\bar{I}_s$ will split the single electronic absorption line into $(2\,\bar{I}_s + 1)$ well separated lines, the weaker interaction $\bar{I}_w$ will further split these well separated lines into $(2\,\bar{I}_w + 1)$ lines.) (2) The unpaired electron is coupled to several identical nuclei. If there are n identical nuclei there will be $(2n\,\bar{I} + 1)$ lines. For an interaction, therefore, of an unpaired electron with 3 protons (as in a methyl radical) there will be $(2 \times 3 \times 1/2 + 1) = 4$ lines. These lines will have varying intensities. The maximum intensity will occur in the center, with a symmetrical distribution on both sides. Figure 6-6 shows the hyperfine interaction with three identical protons. The first proton will split the original electronic levels into two components of $\pm 1/2$ each. The interaction of the next proton will split these levels into another two components of $\pm 1/2$ each and, finally, the interaction of the third proton would split each of these levels in two components of $\pm 1/2$ each. However, since the

interaction with the protons is equal, the -1/2 split of the second proton of the +1/2 part of the interaction of the first proton will be coincident with the +1/2 split of the second proton of the -1/2 part of the interaction of the first proton. Thus, the original line is split into four lines with the relative intensities of 1:3:3:1.

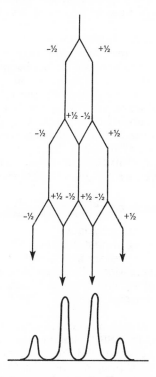

Fig. 6-6. Hyperfine interaction
with three identical protons.

In performing an ESR experiment it is customary to scan at fixed frequency and varying magnetic field, hence the energy transitions are reported in Gauss. The hyperfine structure of isolated H atoms will show a splitting of 504 gauss whereas the splitting of the unpaired electron by the protons on the methyl radical are about 26 gauss or only about 5% of that of the free H atom. The reason for this is that the unpaired electron is primarily on the carbon atom of the methyl radical, whereas it is all concentrated in the 1s orbital in the hydrogen atom radical. The energetics of the splitting therefore tells us considerably about the nature of the interacting spins.

Although we have only considered the interaction of protons with the unpaired electron, any nucleus with a net magnetic moment will interact ^{13}C, ^{14}N, ^{17}O, ^{19}F, and ^{33}S are common isotopes that have net magnetic moments and cause hyperfine splitting.

In solids, where there is restricted motion, the ESR spectrum of the same specie can be different from that in a liquid. In the solid, the orientation of the species in the magnetic field will affect the ESR spectra because bonds have direction. For example, for the unpaired electron in an ethyl radical, the most stable configuration is one in which the three remaining bonds of the CH_2 carbon in CH_3CH_2 are not tetrahedral but planar (sp_2 hybridization) and the unpaired electron is in a π orbital perpendicular to the plane. In the solid, for certain orientations, the coupling of the CH_2 and CH_3 groups will appear equivalent, however in the liquid, the splitting of CH_3 and CH_2 groups can be distinguished.

6-3.2   ESR Application to Radiation Chemistry

The application of ESR techniques to the study of transient intermediates is becoming almost routine. The principal difficulties lie in obtaining a sufficiently high concentration of radicals, consistent with good resolution. This has been achieved for the liquid phase reaction of various alkyl radicals, and for numerous solid state polymer reactions.

Aside from the problems of instrumentation, in the study of transient intermediates by ESR techniques one needs to know the relationship between the signal and the concentrations of radicals. This is accomplished by placing a reference sample of known spin concentration in the cavity. This, in effect, permits the calibration of the detection circuit. There are several such reference materials, including 2,6-di-tert-butyl-(3,5-di-tert-butyl-4-oxo-2,5-cyclohexadiene-1-ylidene)-p-tolyloxy, commonly called galvinoxyl.

The concentration of galvinoxyl is first determined by spectrophotometric absorption (extinction coefficient = $180,000M$ cm^{-1} at 4280 Å) of an appropriate solution in cyclohexane. The concentration of spins in the reference sample in terms of the measuring system of the ESR spectrometer is then determined. The concentration of electron spins produced during irradiation in the unknown is then obtained by comparing the area under the absorption curve with that of the reference solution.

In order to study the kinetics of the radical decay, it is necessary to know (as in pulsed radiolysis) the dosimetry, and the G value for radical formation. The rate at which the radicals are produced is:

Rate of radical production = dose rate $\times$ G value

$$\text{Rate} = D_r \times G \tag{6-23}$$

At the steady state (during continuous irradiation) the rate of production of radicals is equal to the rate of disappearance. For the reaction between like radicals (for instance ethyl radicals)

$$R_a + R_a \xrightarrow{k_r} R_a R_a \tag{6-24}$$

the rate of disappearance is

$$\frac{-d(R_a)}{dt} = k_r [R_a]^2 \tag{6-25}$$

$$\frac{(D_r \times G)}{[R_a]^2} = k_r \tag{6-26}$$

For reactions between unlike radicals, Eq. (6-26) becomes

$$\frac{D_r(G_a + G_b)}{[R_a][R_b]} = k_r \tag{6-27}$$

In an experiment, the situation corresponding to Eq. (6-26) or Eq. (6-27) can be readily resolved by noting that in the reaction between like radicals the radical concentration is proportional to the square root of the dose rate, whereas for reactions between unlike radicals, the radical concentration is a linear function of D_r. From a knowledge therefore of the dose rate, G value, and radical concentration, one can determine the absolute rate constant.

The ESR method is not applicable to the study of fast radical decay, the best time resolution being about 200 μsec. Much better time resolution could be achieved at higher radical concentrations, however a limitation is imposed by the radiation intensity; large currents in the cavity will cause a dielectric loss which places a severe restriction on the sensitivity since the minimum detectable susceptibility of a sample in a cavity is a very sensitive function of the Q factor of the cavity (Q = energy stored in cavity/energy lost). Despite the limitations imposed by time resolution however, the method is applicable to the study of many systems.

6-4 MASS SPECTROMETRY

The essentials of any mass spectrometer* are a beam of electrons of known energy which are allowed to interact with gaseous molecules, a device for quantitative detection of the ions produced, and a device for separating the ions by mass in either time or space.

Mass spectrometers of great versatility are readily available today. Because of this, their use is very widespread. Indeed, uses of mass spectrometers are so diverse that we can only discuss the basic instrument here.

6-4.1 Mass Spectrometry — General

The ion source in a mass spectrometer is that part which is concerned with producing the ions. A typical source is shown in Fig. 6-7. The source of electrons may be a heated filament, usually made of tungsten ribbon about 0.001- to 0.002 in. thickness. The electrons essentially "boil out" of the filament and are accelerated by means of an applied voltage between the filament and the plates P_1, P_2 (Fig. 6-7). The electrons in the beam have a small but finite energy spread, the magnitude of the energy spread depending in part upon filament temperature. Various techniques are used to minimize this spread. The electron beam is focused, usually by a magnetic field directed along the beam. The source of this magnetic field for $60°$ instruments is a permanent magnet of a few hundred gauss.

The electron beam enters the ionization chamber through small slits in plates P_1, P_2. In the ionization chamber there is essentially no electric field because the plate P_3 is at the same potential as P_2. The electron beam is collected by the trap T.

The gas enters the ionization chamber (Fig. 6-7) perpendicular to the electron beam and the ions formed by impact with the electron beam are drawn out through the exit slit in the grid F_1 by a small potential difference between F_1 and the ion repeller plate, R. Having passed through the exit slit, the ions are then accelerated by an applied potential between the grids F_2 and F_3 which are usually held constant at 1000 to 2000 V. The accelerated ion beam then may pass through narrow slits which further focus the ion beam by reducing its width and angular spread. Other slits may be added to aid in beam alignment.

---

*Mass spectrograph and mass spectrometer are often synonomous in the literature. The mass spectrograph however is an instrument that produces a focused mass spectrum on a photographic plate. The mass spectrometer brings a focused beam of ions to a collector which are then detected electrically.

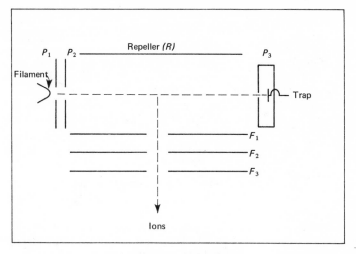

Fig. 6-7. Ion source.

The ion beam emerging from the source is then subjected to a transverse magnetic field (see Fig. 6-8). The ions will then have a kinetic energy expressed in electron volts (eV), where e is the charge (in emu) and V the voltage. Ions having the same charge have equal energy, but not necessarily momentum, since this depends on the mass. The energy is

$$eV = 1/2 \ m\overline{V}^2 \tag{6-28}$$

The ion in the magnetic field experiences a force $e\overline{V}H$ normal to the direction of magnetic field and to the direction of motion. This results in a circular orbit such that the centrifugal force balances the deflecting force.

$$e\overline{V}H = \frac{m\overline{V}^2}{r} \tag{6-29}$$

where H = magnetic field strength

r = radius of orbit

substituting for the velocity from Eq. (6-28) into Eq. (6-29)

$$r = \sqrt{\frac{2 \ mV}{eH^2}} \tag{6-30}$$

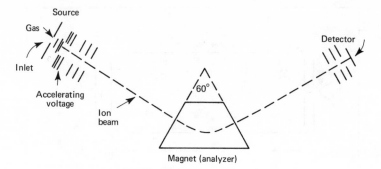

Fig. 6-8. Schematic of mass spectrometer.

It is clear, therefore, that by adjusting the magnetic field strength and the ion energy, one can collect ions of a given mass.

The ions, after passing through the magnetic analyzer, pass again through a series of defining slits to a collector, and are collected as a current. Ion currents in mass spectrometers are usually very small, and therefore require very sensitive detecting devices. The ion currents which are collected are amplified and then recorded on chart paper as relative currents versus mass.

The mass spectral *pattern* of a molecule is unique and distinguishing, allowing the instrument to be used, under carefully controlled conditions, as an analytical tool. For instance, the mass pattern for isobutane is about the same as that for *n*-butane, but the relative intensity of some of the mass peaks are different permitting the two patterns to be distinguished.

High resolution in mass spectrographs has been achieved by various devices, the most common of which is a double focusing instrument. High resolution is accomplished by a combination of electrostatic and magnetic focusing.

Mass spectrometers are usually operated at low pressures 10^{-6} torr but experiments with pressure as high as 1 to 10 torr have been done. At high pressures collisional processes occur between ions making identification and subsequent resolution extremely difficult. High pressure experiments are usually performed specifically to study ion-molecule reactions which are discussed in Sec. 6-5.1 and Chap. 5.

6-4.2   Mass Spectrometry — Special Types of
        Mass Spectrometers

There are several types of mass spectrometers such as the
quadropole spectrometer, omegatron, coincidence mass spectrometer and the time-of-flight mass spectrometer. The last instrument is especially valuable for studying the growth and decay of
substances taking part in fast gas phase reactions such as reactions
initiated by shock waves, and special radiation chemistry experiments. The sampling times are of the order of tenths of a microsecond, and complete mass spectra are available at intervals of
10 to 20 μsec.

The salient features of the time-of-flight mass spectrometer are
shown in Fig. 6-9. A pulsed electron beam is passed through an
ionization chamber, thereby generating a 'bunch' of ions. The ions
are swept out of the ionization chamber by an electric field applied
across the ionization chamber for a few microseconds. This accel-
erates the ions through a grid and they then are further accelerated
by the application of a continuous field. The ion bunch then enters
a drift space and proceeds to a detector.

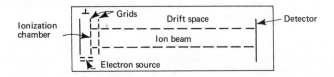

Fig. 6-9. Schematic of time-of-flight
mass spectrometer.

Flight time for the case where the initial kinetic energy of the
ions is zero is given by:

$$ t = \left(\frac{m}{2e(aV_1 + bV_2)} \right)^{1/2} \times \bar{K} \qquad (6\text{-}31) $$

where e = charge and V_1 and V_2 are the accelerating voltages
applied to the ions. The constant $\bar{K}$ is essentially a constant of the
instrument and experiment.

In actual practice the ions have a spread in kinetic energies,
causing a spread in flight times. This effect is minimized by having
short acceleration periods so that the ions move at their terminal
velocity during most of their flight.

The mass spectrometer is an extremely valuable tool for the radiation chemist who is intimately concerned with electron impact phenomenon and reactions of ions in the gas phase. Aside from the identification of various masses of the ions produced by electron impact on a molecule, the reactions of ions are exceptionally important; their unimolecular decay, their reactions with other ions and molecules, and also the phenomenon of electron impact itself constitute important fields of research.

6-5 APPLICATIONS OF MASS SPECTROMETRY

6-5.1 Ionization Potential and Appearance Potential

The *appearance potential* is the minimum energy required to produce a given ion (and accompanying neutral fragments if there are any) from a given molecule, ion or radical. Both reactants and products are in their ground states and the products have no excess kinetic energy. The *ionization potential* of a molecule is a special case of the appearance potential and is defined as the minimum energy required to remove an electron from the neutral molecule, atom, or radical (in the ground state) to form the molecule-ion in the ground state. The *true* or *adiabatic* ionization potential (first) of a molecule is the energy difference between the ground vibrational level of the lowest electronic state of the molecule and the ground vibrational level of the molecule-ion.

Ionization potentials may also be determined spectroscopically, and by photoionization. The latter method employs a light source in conjunction with the analyzer of a mass spectrometer. Ionization potentials as determined by electron impact are often higher than those determined by spectroscopic means because if the potential energy curves for the molecule and the molecule-ion have minimums at appreciably different internuclear distances, the 0-0 vibration transition would not generally be observed and the transition would be nonadiabatic. This can occur with even relatively small displacements of the potential energy curves.

Appearance potentials (by electron impact) are usually determined through the interpretation of *ionization efficiency curves*. An ionization efficiency curve is a plot of the ion current of a particular ion as a function of the energy of the electron beam. Such a curve is shown in Fig. 6-10. A variety of methods are available for obtaining the ionization potential from these curves, none of which is completely satisfactory. Ionization potentials for a particular molecule may be determined from appearance potential data providing that sufficient information is available.

The appearance potential (AP) of the ion M^+ may be expressed in a thermodynamic equation (assuming no excess kinetic energy)

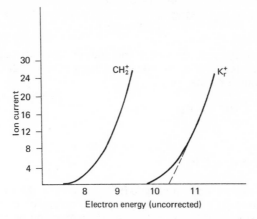

Fig. 6-10. Ionization efficiency curves.

$$AP\ (M^+)\ =\ \Delta H_f\ (M^+)\ +\ \Sigma \Delta H_f (N_i)\ -\ \Delta H_f(M) \qquad (6\text{-}32)$$

where $\Sigma \Delta H\ (N_i)$ = sum of the standard heats of formation of the neutral fragments

$\Delta H_f(M^+)$ = standard heat of formation of the parent ion

$\Delta H_f(M)$ = standard heat of formation of the parent molecule

Knowing the appearance potential and the standard heats of formation of the parent molecule and neutral fragments (if any), the standard heat of formation of the parent ion may be determined, and from this the ionization potential (IP), viz.

$$M + e^- \longrightarrow M^+ + 2e^- \quad \Delta H = IP \qquad (6\text{-}33)$$

$$IP\,(M^+)\ =\ \Delta H_f(M)\ -\ \Delta H_f(M^+) \qquad (6\text{-}34)$$

The interpretation of the ionization efficiency curves is facilitated by comparison with a calibrating gas such as krypton whose ionization potential has been accurately determined by other methods.

6-5.2 Ion-Molecule Reactions

Ion-molecule reactions are studied by operating the spectrometer in such a manner as to cause bimolecular collisions of the primary ions formed in the source with neutral molecules. This is accomplished by operating the source at relatively high pressures ($> 10^{-4}$ torr).

The primary ions formed in the source undergo collisions with neutral gas molecules in the source, giving rise to reactions which produce secondary ions

$$CH_4^+ + CH_4 \rightarrow CH_5^+ + CH_3 \qquad (6\text{-}35)$$

or generally

$$X^+ + YH \rightarrow XH^+ + Y \qquad (6\text{-}36)$$

The secondary ion current (XH^+) is equal to the concentration of primary ions (i_p) multiplied by the concentration of neutral molecules in the source (n), the distance, d, traversed by the primary ions between point of origin and the exit slit, and the cross section, Q, for the reaction:

$$i_s = i_p \, ndQ \qquad (6\text{-}37)$$

Assuming that Q is inversely proportional to the square root of the repeller voltage (V_r) (this assumption will be discussed in Chap. 7), and independent of the temperature of the gas in the source, Q is then given by

$$Q = \frac{B}{\sqrt{V_r}} \qquad (6\text{-}38)$$

where B = a constant

The kinetic energy (KE) of the primary ions is the product of charge e, and the distance the ions travel under the repeller voltage gradient, V_r

$$KE = \frac{1}{2} \, m\bar{V}^2 = de V_r \qquad (6\text{-}39)$$

$$V_r = \frac{1}{2} \, \frac{m\bar{V}^2}{de} \qquad (6\text{-}40)$$

substituting for V_r in Eq. (6-38) and combining with Eq. (6-37)

$$i_s = i_p \, \frac{d}{\bar{V}} \, nB \left(\frac{m}{2de} \right)^{-1/2} \qquad (6\text{-}41)$$

The current of secondary ions (i_s) is directly related to the rate of formation of the secondary ions [Eq. (6-36)]. The distance, *d*, divided by the velocity is the time the primary ions spend in the source and this multiplied by the primary ion current (i_p) is the concentration of primary ions in the source.

$$i_s = \frac{d(XH^+)}{dt} = [X^+][n]B \frac{(m)^{-1/2}}{(2de)} \tag{6-42}$$

Since *B* is a constant as are the remaining terms we may write Eq. (6-42) as

$$\frac{d(XH^+)}{dt} = k_r[X^+][n] \tag{6-43}$$

where k_r is the bimolecular rate constant for Reaction (6-36).

The above arguments, though not rigorous, show qualitatively how the rate constant is obtained. In terms of the measurable quantities in the mass spectrometer it can readily be seen from the preceding discussion that Eq. (6-41) can be rewritten in the notation of Eq. (6-36) as

$$\frac{{}^iXH^+}{{}^iX^+} = k_r[X]R_t[XH^+] \tag{6-44}$$

where $R_t(XH^+)$ is the residence time of the species XH^+ in the source. The currents of the primary and secondary ions are directly determined, as is the concentration of gas molecules in the source. The residence time for the secondary ions in the source may be calculated from the dimensions of the ion source, the voltage gradient, and the mass of the ion.

Of great interest to radiation chemists are the rate constants for ion-molecule reactions. Their high values 10^{-9} to 10^{-10} cm^3 per molecule-sec indicates the readiness with which they occur.

There are several types of ion-molecule reactions which are amenable to study by the mass spectrometer. Complex reactions such as

$$CH_3^+ + CH_4 \rightarrow C_2H_5^+ + H_2 \tag{6-45}$$

$$C_2H_4^+ + C_2H_4 \rightarrow C_3H_5^+ + CH_3 \tag{6-46}$$

$$C_2H_4^+ + C_2H_4 \rightarrow C_4H_7^+ + H \tag{6-47}$$

and decomposition reactions as

$$CH_3CN^+ \rightarrow CH_3^+ + CN \tag{6-48}$$

$$C_2 H_5^+ \rightarrow C_2 H_3^+ + H_2 \tag{6-49}$$

have all been studied in great detail. The mass spectrometer has also been invaluable in determining bond dissociation energies, ionization potentials of radicals and decomposition kinetics of ions.

Special high pressure mass spectrometers employing proton beams, alpha particles and photoionization sources have been developed for the study of secondary and higher order ion reactions and ion clustering.[3,4]

6-6 NEGATIVE IONS

The mass spectrometer may be used to study negative ion mass spectra and appearance potentials of negative ions. Negative ions may be formed by

$$\text{resonance capture } M + e^- \rightarrow M^- \tag{6-50}$$

$$SF_6 + e^- \rightarrow SF_6^- \tag{6-50a}$$

$$\text{dissociative attachment } AB + e^- \rightarrow A + B^- \tag{6-51}$$

$$C_2 N_2 + e^- \rightarrow CN + CN^- \tag{6-51a}$$

$$\text{ion pair formation } AB + e^- \rightarrow A^+ + B^- + e^- \tag{6-52}$$

$$NO + e^- \rightarrow N^+ + O^- + e^- \tag{6-52a}$$

REFERENCES

1.   G. Porter, "Techniques of Organic Chemistry," 2nd ed., vol. VIII, part 2, p. 1055, Interscience Publishers, 1965.

2.   L. M. Dorfman and M. S. Matheson "Progress in Reaction Kinetics" vol. 3, p. 239-301, G. Porter (ed.), Pergamon Press, New York, 1965.

3.   P. Kebarle, R. M. Haynes, and S. Searles, *Adv. Chem. Series*, 58:210 (1966).

4.   S. Wexler, A. Lifshitz, A. Quattrochi, *Adv. Chem. Series*, 58:193 (1966).

7

RADIATION CHEMISTRY
OF GASES

7-1 INTRODUCTION

The radiation chemistry of gases developed in three broad phases. The first was dominated by the ion "cluster theory" of S. C. Lind. This theory was gradually displaced as the emphasis shifted to free radicals as the principal species responsible for radiation-induced reactions. The third phase evolved with the experimental measurement of the rate constants for ion-molecule reactions. The rate constants for these reactions were found to be extremely high and consequently emphasis on the reactions of unclustered ions as the principal reacting species overshadowed that of radicals.

As a consequence of recent research it is now commonly accepted that the kinetics of the radiation chemistry of gases involves all three types of reactions in some degree, plus various energy transfer mechanisms.

The radiation chemistry of gases is very complex, as is the radiation chemistry of most systems. To treat any particular gas reaction in detail is beyond the scope of this text; what is attempted is to develop those aspects which are common to any radiation-induced gas reaction. In many cases the available information is at best qualitative and the treatment in all cases should be considered as introductory.

7-2 CLUSTER THEORY OF LIND

The first summary and review of the effects of alpha particles and electrons on gases was published by S. C. Lind as *ACS Monograph No. 2* in 1921. It was revised in 1928 and again in 1961. The original volume remained for many years as an outstanding contribution to our knowledge of the radiation chemistry of gases.

The cluster theory was postulated to account for the observed fact that some M/N yields were > 1. To account for these large M/N yields found in certain reactions, Lind postulated that the ions produced during radiation induced an electric dipole in neighboring molecules, forming a cluster (Fig. 7-1). On neutralization of the parent ion, sufficient energy was presumed to be released to cause

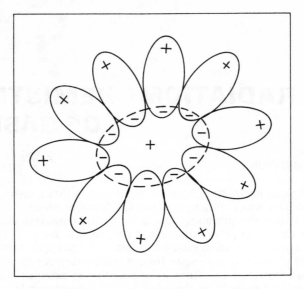

Fig. 7-1. Typical ion cluster.

chemical reaction between the ion and the neutral molecules in the cluster. For example, the average M/N yield for the alpha particle radiolysis of C_2N_2 was found to be somewhat greater than 7. The principal product of this radiolysis was a solid polymer and the reaction was presumed to go as follows:

$$n\,(C_2N_2) \xrightarrow{} (C_2N_2)_n \text{ solid } (n = 7) \tag{7-1}$$

The ion cluster, in this case, would consist on the average of 6 C_2N_2 molecules clustered about an ion; on neutralization of the ion, sufficient energy was liberated to affect the polymerization.

Another example is the radiation induced reaction of acetylene which was found to have an M/N yield of about 21. The sole product was thought to be cuprene, a solid polymer. The cluster theory predicted a central acetylene ion surrounded by a cluster of about 20 neutral acetylene molecules. Upon neutralization of the parent ion, sufficient energy was presumed liberated to form the polymer.

Several reactions, however, were known where the cluster theory appeared to be incompatible with experimental facts. The conversion of para to ortho hydrogen was found to have an M/N yield > 1000 and appeared best explained by a chain mechanism induced by H atoms. The decomposition of ozone by alpha rays was found to have an M/N yield of about $5\text{--}15 \times 10^3$ depending on the pressure; this also suggests a chain mechanism.

Despite the experimental evidence indicating the importance of free radicals in these and related systems, the cluster theory persisted up into the middle or late 1940s. A re-examination of the radiolysis of acetylene in 1948 was one of several factors which emphasized the untenable position of the cluster theory.[1] Careful analysis of the products of this reaction revealed that cuprene formation only accounted for 80 percent of the product yield and benzene for the remaining 20 percent. According to the cluster theory one would have to assume that two types of clusters were formed, one consisting of 3 molecules of acetylene and the other consisting of 18 molecules of acetylene. This was necessary to give the observed M/N yield of 21. Also, since benzene formation accounts for 20 percent of the acetylene disappearing, it would have an M/N yield (of C_2H_2 disappearance) of $0.2 \times 21 = 4.2$; not 3 as predicted by the cluster theory. An explanation advanced to account for these products appears best explained in part by a free radical mechanism, [2]

$$C_2H_2 \xrightarrow{\text{\tiny\rawnl}} C_2H + H \qquad\qquad (7\text{-}2)$$

$$C_2H + 2\, C_2H_2 \longrightarrow C_6H_5 \qquad\qquad (7\text{-}3)$$

$$C_6H_5 \longrightarrow \text{cyclization} \qquad\qquad (7\text{-}4)$$

$$\Phi\cdot + C_2H_2 \longrightarrow C_6H_6 + C_2H \qquad\qquad (7\text{-}5)$$

$$C_6H_5 \text{ or } \Phi\cdot + n C_2H_2 \longrightarrow R' \qquad\qquad (7\text{-}6)$$

$$C_6H_5 \text{ or } \Phi\cdot + R' \longrightarrow \text{polymer} \qquad\qquad (7\text{-}7)$$

Ion clusters are known to form in gases; theoretically calculated mobilities of gaseous ions have been found to be three to five times greater than observed values, a fact which can be explained by clustering of ions with neutral molecules. The size of the clusters is a function of the pressure, the polarizability, and the intermolecular forces. In water vapor, for example, a rare gas ion can cluster up to six molecules of water. Also, ion clusters such as $NH_4^+(NH_3)_{4\text{-}20}$ and $H_3O^+(H_2O)_{1\text{-}18}$ have recently been observed.[3] The ultimate fate of the cluster upon neutralization of the parent ion, however, is open to question. It is doubtful that molecules held together by secondary valence forces would stay together on ion recombination.

Clustering may prevent the completion of reactions which might occur in its absence. Magee and Funabashi[4] have re-examined the role of clusters in the radiation chemistry of gases and point out that large clusters only occur near saturation pressures of a gas

---

*This reaction scheme is not intended as a summary of the radiolysis of C_2H_2.

and that "interesting possibilities exist for the induction of chemical reaction in small components of a mixture through the mechanism of clustering." By this it is meant that a component in small concentration, by preferential clustering, could be involved in preferred reaction. The effect of small amounts of a particular component on a radiation induced reaction is more usually attributed, however, to charge or excitation energy transfer, or hydride ion formation.

Mass spectra studies[5] have established the existence of ion complexes such as $(C_4H_{10}I_2)^+$ and $(C_6H_{14}I_2)^+$ from the reactions

$$(C_2H_5I)^+ + C_2H_5I \longrightarrow (C_4H_{10}I_2)^+ \tag{7-8}$$

and

$$(C_3H_7I)^+ + C_3H_7I \longrightarrow (C_6H_{14}I_2)^+ \tag{7-8a}$$

Such complexes are called "sticky collision complexes"[6] and have half lives that are much longer than 10^{-12} sec. In order for a sticky collision to occur, the energy of the colliding pair must be distributed throughout the complex. The lifetime of the complex is proportional to the binding energy of the complex and to the number of degrees of vibrational freedom. The relative lifetime of the complex depends upon competing processes such as charge neutralization and internal conversion processes. These complexes can be stabilized by collision and may possibly enter into other reactions.

7-3 SUMMARY OF CLUSTER MECHANISM

Clusters exist in gases and are most likely to occur in systems containing molecules with high polarizabilities and at saturation pressure.

There is no evidence that neutralization of a cluster will produce chemical reaction in the sense of Lind's hypothesis.

Ion complexes have been identified directly in some systems, however, the reactions of these complexes are still speculative.

7-4 REACTIONS OF IONS —
ION-MOLECULE REACTIONS

In the decade following Lind's revised monograph, experimental and theoretical results shifted the emphasis from ion clusters toward free radicals as the principal reactive species. The outstanding theoretical advance was that by Eyring, Hirshfelder, and Taylor[7] who introduced the concept of ion-molecule reactions which produced free radicals. It was these free radicals which were thought to be largely responsible for the observed gas phase decompositions.

7-4.1   EHT Theory

To explain the mechanism of the alpha radiolysis of para-ortho hydrogen exchange, a detailed analysis of the reaction was made. The mass spectra of hydrogen indicated the presence of the ions H_2^+, H^+ and H_3^+; the latter ion was more abundant at higher pressures. Hydrogen atoms can arise from several sources; direct dissociation (from excited states), neutralization of H_2^+ and secondary reactions

$$H_2^+ + H_2 = H_3^+ + H \tag{7-9}$$

$$H_2^+ + H_2 = H^+ + H + H_2 \tag{7-10}$$

Reaction (7-10) requires an activation energy of more than 2.5 ev and is not too probable. The rate of Reaction (7-9), is extremely high, which makes it the most probable source of H atoms. To determine the rate of Reaction (7-9) EHT used the activated state theory and determined the specific rate of the reaction

$$H_2^+ + H_2 \rightleftarrows H_4^+ \longrightarrow H_3^+ + H \tag{7-11}$$

where H_4^+ is the activated complex.

Assuming a transmission coefficient of unity

$$k_r = \frac{kT}{h} K^* \tag{7-12}$$

where k = Boltzman constant

k_r = reaction rate constant

h = Planck's constant

K^* = equilibrium constant for the reaction between reactants and the activated complex.

The equilibrium constant may be written as

$$K^* = \frac{f^*_{H_4^+}}{f_{H_2} f_{H_2^+}} e^{-\Delta E_0 / RT} \tag{7-13}$$

where $f^*_{H_4^+}$ is the total partition function per unit volume of the activated complex and f_{H_2} and $f_{H_2^+}$ the total partition function per unit volume of the reacting molecules. ΔE_o is the activation energy of the reaction at absolute zero; it is the difference in energies E_o of the reactants and complex

$$\Delta E_o = E_{oH_4^+}^* - E_{oH_2} + E_{oH_2^+} \tag{7-14}$$

For the reaction expressed by Eq. (7-11) the rate constant is

$$k_r = \frac{kT}{h} \frac{f_{H_4^+}^*}{f_{H_2} f_{H_2^+}} e^{-\Delta E_o/RT} \tag{7-15}$$

In evaluating the total partition function for the activated state it is argued in this case, that the separation between the molecule (H_2) and the ion (H_2^+) is sufficiently large so that the vibrational and rotational partition functions in this state are the same as in the separated molecule and ion. These will then cancel in the expression for the rate constant leaving only the translational partition functions

$$k_r = \frac{kT}{h} \frac{\dfrac{\left(2\pi m_{H_4^+} kT\right)^{3/2}}{h^3}}{\dfrac{\left(2\pi m_{H_2} kT\right)^{3/2}}{h^3} \dfrac{\left(2\pi m_{H_2} kT\right)^{3/2}}{h^3}} \left[1 + \Sigma (2J+1) e^{-\Delta E_o/kT}\right] \tag{7-16}$$

or

$$k_r = \frac{kT}{h} \left(\frac{m_{H_4^+}}{m_{H_2} m_{H_2^+}}\right)^{3/2} \frac{h^3}{(2\pi kT)^{3/2}} \left[1 + \Sigma (2J+1) e^{-\Delta E_o/kT}\right] \tag{7-16a}$$

The factor $\left(1 + \Sigma (2J + 1) e^{\Delta E_o/kT}\right)$ is the rotational partition function of the complex itself; it is the rotation of this complex which gives rise to a centrifugal force which opposes the attractive polarization forces which hold the complex together.

The activation energy then consists of the superposition of the centrifugal force of rotation of the complex E_{rot}^* , and the polarization energy, E_{pol}^* , between the molecules and the ion, acting in opposing direction.

$$\Delta E_o = E_{rot}^* - E_{pol}^* \tag{7-17}$$

$$E^*_{pol} = \frac{\alpha e^2}{2r^4} \tag{7-18}$$

where e = electronic charge

α = polarizability

r = distance between centers of the molecule and ion

$$E^*_{rot} = \frac{J(J+1) h^2}{8\pi^2 \mu r^2} \tag{7-19}$$

where μ = reduced mass of the system = $\dfrac{m_{H_4^+}}{m_{H_2^+} m_{H_2^+}}$

J = rotational quantum number

Subtracting Eq. (7-18) from (7-19) gives the total energy; differentiating this with respect to r and equating the derivative to zero, one obtains the maximum value of r . Appropriate substitution then yields for the activation energy:

$$\Delta E_o = \frac{J^2(J+1)^2 h^4}{128\pi^4 (m_H)^2 \alpha e^2} \tag{7-20}$$

Substituting (7-20) for the activation energy in (7-16a) and replacing the summation by an integral gives for this term:

$$\int_0^\infty (2J+1) \exp\left[\frac{J^2(J+1) h^4}{128\pi^4 (m_H)^2 \alpha e^2}\right] dJ = \frac{(2\pi\alpha kT)^{1/2} 4\pi (m_H) e}{h^2} \tag{7-21}$$

Combining Eq. (7-21) with (7-16a) gives:

$$k_r = \frac{kT}{h} \left(\frac{m_{H_4^+}}{m_{H_2} m_{H_2^+}}\right)^{3/2} \frac{(2\pi\alpha kT)^{1/2} 4\pi^2 (m_H) e}{\dfrac{(2\pi kT)^{3/2} h^2}{h^3}} \tag{7-22}$$

or

$$k_r = \left(\frac{m_{H_4^+}}{m_{H_2} m_{H_2^+}}\right)^{3/2} 2\pi m_H (\alpha)^{1/2} e$$

For hydrogen

$$\alpha = 0.8 \times 10^{-24} \text{ cm}^3$$

$$e = 4.8 \times 10^{-10} \text{ esu}$$

$$m_H = 1.673 \times 10^{-24} \text{ g}$$

$$k_r = \left[\frac{6.68 \times 10^{-24}}{11.16 \times 10^{-48}}\right]^{3/2} g^{-3/2} \left[\left(6.28 \times \frac{1.67 \times 10^{-24} g}{\text{molecule}}\right) \times \right.$$

$$\left. \left(0.8 \times 10^{-24}\right)^{1/2} \text{cm}^{3/2} \left(4.8 \times 10^{-10} \text{ esu}\right)\right]$$

$$k_r = 2.66 \times \frac{10^{-9} \text{ cm}^3}{\text{molecule-sec}}$$

$$= 1.6 \times 10^{15} \text{ cm}^3 \text{ mol}^{-1} \text{ sec}^{-1}$$

The rate constant for this reaction may be compared with that for a few familiar fast gas reactions to give a better idea of its magnitude.

$$M + H + H \longrightarrow H_2 + M, \quad k_r = 3 \times 10^{13} \text{ cm}^3 \text{ mol}^{-1} \text{ sec}^{-1}$$

$$CH_3 + CH_3 \longrightarrow C_2H_6, \quad k_r = 3.8 \times 10^{13} \text{ cm}^3 \text{ mol}^{-1} \text{ sec}^{-1}$$

The rate constant for the ion-molecule reaction, Eq. (7-9), is seen to be an order of magnitude larger than the fastest measured gas reactions.

Eyring, Hirshfelder, and Taylor[7] were able, after a careful consideration of vessel size, wall effects, rates of elemental reactions, etc., to calculate M/N yields in excellent agreement with experiment. The principal point in their paper was to show that the free radicals that took part in the reaction had their origin in an ion-molecule reaction which occurred with a rate faster than that of any reaction which had been measured up until that time. It is now believed that the exchange reaction probably occurs primarily by an

---

*The units of e in the CGS system are $g^{1/2}$ $cm^{3/2}$ $time^{-1}$. This is obtained by considering the following:

$$\text{energy} = \frac{e^2}{\text{cm}} = \frac{\text{mass cm}^2}{\text{time}^2}, \quad e = \frac{1}{\text{time}} \sqrt{\text{mass cm}^3}$$

ion chain (see Sec. 7-9.2) as with hydrogen-deuterium exchange, the free radical mechanism viz.: $H + H_2 \longrightarrow H_2 + H$ contributing slightly.

Despite the success of EHT in providing an explanation for alpha-induced exchange reaction, it was not until some twenty years later when an experimental measurement[8] of the rates of these ion-molecule reactions verified the calculations of EHT, that emphasis was placed on the role of ions and reactions of ions in gas phase radiolysis.

7-4.2 Rates of Ion-Molecule Reactions as Determined by Mass Spectrometry

Equation (6-44) gives the expression for ion-molecule reactions in terms of the measurable quantities in the mass spectrometer,

$$\frac{i_{XH^+}}{i_{Y^+}} = k_r \, [X] \, R_t \, [X^+] \tag{7-23}$$

where $[X]$ = concentration of neutral molecules.

For the reaction

$$X^+ + YH = XH^+ + Y \tag{7-23a}$$

The residence time in the source is given by:

$$R_t = \left(\frac{2 S m_1}{e R_v} \right)^{1/2} \tag{7-24}$$

where $\quad S$ = distance from the electron beam to the exit slit

$\quad m_1$ = mass of the primary ion

$\quad e$ = the electronic charge

$\quad R_v$ = the repeller voltage gradient in the source

The concentration of the neutral specie in the source is obtained by determining the total number of ions collected by the ion repeller when it is at a negative potential, and from the known ionization cross section of the gas.

EXAMPLE 7-1: Calculate the rate constant for the reaction

$$CH_4^+ + CH_4 \longrightarrow CH_5^+ + CH_3$$

if the concentration of CH_4 in the source is 2.5×10^{11} molecules per cm^3. Assume $S = 0.2$ cm and $R_v = 12.5$ V per centimeter and

$$\frac{i_{CH_5^+}}{i_{CH_4^+}} = 0.68 \times 10^{-3}$$

SOLUTION

$$\frac{i_{XH^+}}{i_{X^+}} = k_r \, [X] \left(\frac{2Sm}{eR_v}\right)^{1/2}$$

$$\frac{0.68 \times 10^{-3} \; cm^3}{2.5 \times 10^{11} \; molecules} =$$

$$k_r \times \left[\frac{(2) \, (0.2 \; cm) \, (2.67 \times 10^{-23} \; g)}{\left(4.8 \times 10^{-10} \; \dfrac{esu}{molecule}\right) \left(12.5 \; \dfrac{V}{cm} \; molecule\right)}\right]^{1/2}$$

dividing by 300 to convert practical volts to the esu system

$$\frac{0.68 \times 10^{-3} \; cm^3}{2.5 \times 10^{11} \; molecules} = k_r \left[\frac{1.068 \times 10^{-23} \, g \, cm^2 \times 300}{60 \times 10^{-10} g \; \dfrac{cm^2}{sec^2}}\right]^{1/2}$$

$$3.8 \times \frac{10^{-9} \; cm^3}{molecules\text{-}sec} = k_r$$

Ion-molecule reactions can be observed and measured in a mass spectrometer operated at high pressures, however, the fact that a reaction is not observed merely places an upper limit of the order of 10^{-11} cm^3 per molecule-sec on the rate constant.

The possibility of a particular ion-molecule reaction may be determined by thermodynamic techniques; a necessary but not sufficient condition for an ion-molecule reaction to occur in a closed system is that it be exothermic.

EXAMPLE 7-2: Calculate ΔH for the reaction

$$C_2H_5^+ + CH_4 \longrightarrow i\,C_3H_7^+ + H_2$$

SOLUTION:

$$\Delta H_f \text{ (Products)} - \Delta H_f \text{ (Reactants)} = \Delta H \text{ Reaction}$$

For an ion-molecule reaction ΔH reaction $\Delta H < 0$.

The heats of formation* of the ions ΔH_f are obtained as follows:

$$e^- + C_2H_6 \longrightarrow C_2H_5^+ + H + 2e^-$$

Appearance potential for the ethyl ion = 12.88 ev = 297.23 kcal

$$[\Delta H_f (C_2H_5^+) + \Delta H_f (H)] - \Delta H_f (C_2H_6) = 297.23 \text{ kcal}$$

$$\Delta H_f (C_2H_5^+) = 297.23 - 52.1 - 20.1 = 225 \text{ kcal}$$

Similarly:

$$\Delta C_3H_8 \longrightarrow iC_3H_7^+ + H + e^-$$

$$[\text{A.P.} = 11.57 \text{ ev} = 206.9 \text{ kcal}]$$

$$\Delta H_f (C_3H_7^+) = 190 \text{ kcal}$$

Therefore

$$\Delta H_f (C_3H_7^+) + \Delta H_f (H_2) - \Delta H_f (C_2H_5^+) - \Delta H_f (CH_4) = \Delta H$$

$$(190) + (0) - (225) - (-17.88) = \Delta H$$

$$-17.1 \text{ kcal} = \Delta H$$

The heats of formation of the ions may also be calculated from proton affinity data. The proton affinity of a molecule is defined as the *negative* of the enthalpy change of the reaction

$$M + H^+ \longrightarrow MH^+ \qquad\qquad -(\Delta H)$$

$$-(\Delta H) = \text{Proton affinity} = \Delta H_f (H^+) + \Delta H_f (M) - \Delta H_f (MH^+)$$

Some values for proton affinities are given in Table 7-1.

7-4.3   Ion-Molecule Reactions — Theory

Gioumousis and Stevenson[9] have derived an expression for the specific rate constant for ion-molecule reactions† which is given by

---

*Note: Heats of formation of neutral molecules may be obtained from the Handbook of Chemistry and Physics.
†This theory gives at best an order of magnitude value; for a more general discussion see Ref. 10.

Table 7-1. PROTON AFFINITY

Substance	Proton affinity, ev
H_2	3.0
CH	5.1
CH_2	5.2
CH_3	5.1
CH_4	5.3
C_2H_4	6.8
$n-C_3H_6$	6.6
C_6H_6	6.3
F	3.7
Cl	5.4
Br	5.8
I	6.3
O	4.8
OH	6.2
H_2O	8.2
CH_3OH	9.1
NH_3	9.15
C_2H_5OH	9.4
CH_3NH_2	9.35
$(CH_3)_2NH$	9.3
H_2S	7.6

$$k_r = \left(\frac{eR_vS}{2m_1}\right)^{1/2} Q \qquad (7\text{-}25)$$

where Q is the cross section for Reaction (7-23a) and is given by:

$$Q = \eta \left(\frac{4\pi^2 e^2 \alpha}{\mu}\right)^{1/2} \left[\frac{2m_1}{eR_vS}\right]^{1/2} \qquad (7\text{-}26)$$

where η = probability that a collision leads to reaction

α = polarizability

μ = reduced mass

m_1 = mass of the primary ion

Equation (7-25) is correct providing Q has an inverse square root dependence on the repeller voltage gradient. Generally for complicated molecules, experimentally determined reaction cross sections are not simple functions of $(R_v)^{-1/2}$ but have some complicated dependence on the inverse power of R_v. This is believed to be due to the complex manner in which the internal coordinates of the reacting species enter into the reactions.[11] The $(R_\nu)^{-1/2}$ dependence on cross sections holds, however, for many reactions. It is also seen from Eq. (7-26) that Q is independent of temperature. This fact and the inverse dependence on $(R_\nu)^{1/2}$ are summarized in Table 7-2.

Table 7-2. EFFECT OF TEMPERATURE ON
REACTION CROSS SECTIONS*

Temperature ($°K$)	$Q(\text{Å})^2$		
	$R_\nu = 2.57$ V/cm	$R_\nu = 5.14$ V/cm	$R_\nu = 10.3$ V/cm
333	181	130	97.5
377	179	133	97.0
425	177	132	96.7
537	176	131	98.5
614	185	140	108

*Data from D. P. Stevenson and D. O. Shissler, *J. Chem. Phys.*, **29**, 2822 (1958).
For the reaction A^+ (or K_2^+ or D_2^+) + H_2 (or D_2 or HD) $\rightarrow$ AH^+ (or KH^+ or D_2H^+) + H (or D).

Substitution of Eq. (7-26) into (7-25) assuming η is unity gives

$$k_r = 2\pi \, e \left(\frac{\alpha}{\mu}\right)^{1/2} \tag{7-27}$$

It will be shown in Example 7-3 that Eq. (7-27) is identical with Eq. (7-22). The EHT calculation therefore not only gave the correct order of magnitude for the rate constants of the particular ion-molecule reaction but also the correct dependence on mass and temperature. It must be borne in mind however that neither the "activated complex theory" or that referred to in Sec. 7-4.3 are completely adequate to describe all ion-molecule reactions.

EXAMPLE 7-3: Show that Eq. (7-27) is identical with that obtained by EHT [Eq. (7-22)] assuming η is unity.

SOLUTION

Examining Eq. (7-22) we note that

$$\mu = \frac{m_1 \, m_2}{m_1 + m_2} = \frac{m_{H_2} \, m_{H_2^+}}{m_{H_2} + m_{H_2^+}} = \frac{m_{H_2} \, m_{H_2^+}}{m_{H_4^+}}$$

Equating (7-22) and (7-27)

$$\left(\frac{m_{H_4^+}}{m_{H_2}\,m_{H_4^+}}\right)^{3/2} m_H(2\pi\alpha^{1/2}\,e) = 2e\pi\left(\frac{\alpha}{\mu}\right)^{1/2}$$

$$m_H\left(\frac{m_{H_4^+}}{m_{H_2}\,m_{H_2^+}}\right)\left(\frac{m_{H_4^+}}{m_{H_2}\,m_{H_2^+}}\right)^{1/2} = \left(\frac{1}{\mu}\right)^{1/2} = \left(\frac{m_{H_4^+}}{m_{H_2}\,m_{H_2^+}}\right)^{1/2}$$

$$m_H\left(\frac{m_{H_4^+}}{m_{H_2}\,m_{H_2^+}}\right) = m_H\left(\frac{m_{H_2^+}\,m_{H_2^+}}{m_{H_2}\,m_{H_2^+}}\right) \cong m_H\left(\frac{2m_{H_2}}{\left(m_{H_2}\right)^2}\right)$$

$$= m_H\left(\frac{2}{2m_H}\right) = m_H\left(\frac{1}{m_H}\right) = 1$$

completes the proof.

The specific reaction rates of most ion-molecule reactions are so high one could expect that little or no thermal activation is required. This is borne out by the experimental data shown in Table 7-2. Theoretical arguments have also been advanced to support this thesis.[11]

Equation (7-25) is the bimolecular rate constant for reactions of ions with molecules with Maxwellian velocity distributions. Appropriate substitution into Eq. (7-25) yields the value for the cross section, as will be shown in the next example.

EXAMPLE 7-4: Using the data in Example 7-1, calculate the cross section for the reaction: $CH_4^+ + CH_4 \longrightarrow CH_5^+ + CH_3$

SOLUTION:

By Eq. (7-25)

$$k_r = \left(\frac{eR_v S}{2m_1}\right)^{1/2} Q$$

Substituting the values of Example 7-1

$$3.8\times10^{-9}\ \frac{cm^3}{molecules\text{-}sec} = \left(\frac{4.8\times10^{-10}\times12.5\ V\times molec\times0.2\ cm}{molec\times2\times2.67\times10^{-23}\,g\times cm\times300}\right)^{1/2} Q$$

Making the appropriate conversions

$$61.7 \; \frac{\overset{\circ}{\mathrm{A}}{}^2}{\text{molecule}} = Q$$

7-4.4 Importance of Ion-Molecule Reactions in Radiation Chemistry

Experiment has shown that the rate constants for most ion-molecule reactions are very high. Stevenson[12] has made calculations that show an exact correspondence between the empirical reaction cross section Q and the classical geometric cross section, πd^2, which is interpreted to mean that reaction occurs on every collision. This is not strictly true since relatively slow ion-molecule reactions have been measured; however the calculation does establish the fact that these reactions have rate constants approaching the maximum for bimolecular reactions. Some idea of the significance of ion-molecule reactions in radiation chemistry of gases may be seen from the following example.

EXAMPLE 7-5: Calculate the number of collisions H_2^+ will undergo before neutralization at a gas pressure of 1 atm. The dose rate is 300 r per second and the specific rate of recombination of ions with electrons is 10^{-6} cm^3 per molecule-sec. The ion concentration is C_o at steady state.*

SOLUTION:

By definition 1 r = 2.08×10^9 ions/cm^3

300 r/sec $\cong$ 6×10^{11} ions/cm^3 sec

The mean life of an ion (τ) with respect to neutralization by an electron in a bimolecular reaction is

$$\tau = \frac{2.718}{k_r \, C_o} \tag{7-28}$$

Since the ions (charges) are produced at a steady rate (300 r/sec), C_o is the steady state concentration with respect to neutralization. At the steady state

Rate of formation = rate of disappearance

---

*In the calculation in Prob. 7-5 no correction for the difference in mass absorption coefficients and W for air and hydrogen was made because it was felt that this correction would be small compared to the other approximations.

$$\frac{6 \times 10^{11} \text{ ions}}{\text{cm}^3 \text{ sec}} = k_r \, (C_o)^2$$

$$\frac{6 \times 10^{11} \text{ ions}}{\text{cm}^3 \text{ sec}} = \frac{10^{-6} \text{ cm}^3 \, (C_o)^2}{\text{ions-sec}}$$

$$C_o \cong 10^9 \, \frac{\text{ions}}{\text{cm}^3}$$

Substituting we obtain

$$\tau = \frac{2.718}{10^{-6} \, \dfrac{\text{cm}^3}{\text{ions-sec}} \, 10^9 \, \dfrac{\text{ions}}{\text{cm}^3}} = 2.718 \times 10^{-3} \text{ sec}$$

The number of collisions that a particular molecule will make per second is given by

$$\text{No collisions/sec} = z = \pi d^2 n \overline{V}$$

where d = molecule diameter

n = no molecules/cm^3

$\overline{V}$ = average speed

The cross section is πd^2; the value given in Table 7-3 is 27 $\mathring{A}^2$. The average speed $\overline{V}$ for any molecule at 300°K is

$$\sqrt{\frac{8kT}{\pi m}} = \overline{V} = \left(\frac{8 \times 1.38 \times 10^{-16} \, \dfrac{\text{ergs}}{°K} \, 300°K}{3.14 \times 3.3 \times 10^{-24} g} \right)^{1/2} \cong 1.8 \times 10^5 \, \frac{\text{cm}}{\text{sec}}$$

The number of collisions per second are:

$$Z = 0.27 \times 10^{-14} \text{ cm}^2 \times 0.27 \times 10^{20} \, \frac{\text{molecules}}{\text{cm}^3} \times 1.8 \times 10^5 \, \frac{\text{cm}}{\text{sec}}$$

$$Z = 0.12 \times 10^{11} \, \frac{\text{collisions}}{\text{sec}}$$

The mean life of the ion with respect to neutralization by an electron is 2.718×10^{-3} sec. In this time the ion will undergo $0.12 \times 10^{11} \times 1.7 \times 10^{-3} \cong 0.2 \times 10^8$ collisions. Since in most cases the probability for reaction on each collision is very high (Table 7-3) we see that ion-molecule reactions are indeed important in any consideration of gas phase radiolysis.

Parent ions undergo other fast reactions such as neutralization and unimolecular decomposition in the gas phase which under certain conditions are competitive with ion-molecule reactions and the relative rates therefore of all these reactions must be considered under different experimental conditions. These aspects of reactions of ions are now considered.

Table 7-3. CROSS SECTIONS AND RATE CONSTANTS
FOR ION-MOLECULE REACTIONS

Reaction	$Q\ (10^{16}\ cm^2)$	$k\ [l\ mole^{-1}\ sec^{-1}]$
$H_2^+ + H_2 \rightarrow H_3^+ + H$	27.4	126×10^{10}
$H_2 + O_2 \rightarrow HO_2 + H$	126	580
$D_2^+ + D_2 \rightarrow D_3^+ + D$	26.8	86.8×10^{10}
$D_2^+ + O_2 \rightarrow DO_2^+ + D$	88	280
$H_2O^+ + H_2O \rightarrow H_3O^+ + OH$	95.0	76×10^{10}
$D_2O^+ + D_2O \rightarrow D_3O^+ + OD$	105	61.5×10^{10}
$D_2O^+ + H_2 \rightarrow HD_2O^+ + H$	63	38.7
$C_2H_6^+ + D_2O \rightarrow HD_2O^+ + C_2H_5$	440	445×10^{10}
$C_3H_8^+ + D_2O \rightarrow HD_2O^+ + C_2H_2$	440	540×10^{10}
$CH_4^+ + CH_4 \rightarrow CH_5^+ + CH_3$		57.4
$CD_4^+ + CD_4 \rightarrow CD_5^+ + CD_3$	57.2	47.5×10^{10}
$CD_4^+ + C_2H_6 \rightarrow CD_4H^+ + C_2H_5$	8.1	6×10^{10}
$CD_4^+ + C_3H_8 \rightarrow CD_4H^+ + C_3H_7$	4	3×10^{10}
$CD_4^+ + H_2S \rightarrow CD_4H^+ + SH$	12	8.4×10^{10}
$C_2H_3^+ + C_2H_4 - C_2H_5^+ + C_2H_2$	32	18×10^{10}
$CH_3^+ + CH_4 \rightarrow C_2H_5^+ + H_2$		48×10^{10}
$CH_2^+ + CH_4 \rightarrow C_2H_4^+ + H_2$		12.4×10^{10}
$CH^+ + C_2H_2 \rightarrow C_3H^+ + H_2$	39	36×10^{10}
$CH^+ + CH_4 \rightarrow C_2H_2^+ + H_2 + H$	54	16×10^{10}
$CH^+ + C_2H_2 \rightarrow C_3H_2^+ + H$	19	18×10^{10}
$CH_2^+ + CH_4 \rightarrow C_2H_3^+ + H_2 + H$	25	
$C_2H_2^+ + C_2H_4 \rightarrow C_3H_3^+ + CH_3$	22	14×10^{10}
$C_2H_2^+ + C_2H_2 \rightarrow C_4H_2^+ + H_2$	35	22
$C_2H_2^+ + C_2H_2 \rightarrow C_4H_3^+ + H$	42	27
$C_2H^+ + C_2H_4 \rightarrow C_4H_3^+ + H_2$	34	23
$C_2H_2^+ + C_2H_4 \rightarrow C_4H_5^+ + H$	14	9.6

Table continues

Table 7-3. CROSS SECTIONS AND RATE CONSTANTS
FOR ION-MOLECULE REACTIONS (Continued)

Reaction	Q (10^{16} cm^2)	k [l mole^{-1} sec^{-1}]
$C_2H_4^+ + C_2H_4 \rightarrow C_4H_7^+ + H$	4	3
$C_3H_5^+ + C_3H_6 \rightarrow C_4H_7^+ + C_2H_4$	140	127
$C_3H_6^+ + C_3H_6 \rightarrow C_4H_8^+ + C_2H_4$	74	66
$CH_4^+ + D_2 \rightarrow CH_4D^+ + D$		15×10^8
$CH_4^+ + H_2 \rightarrow CH_5^+ + H$		4×10^8
$CH_3^+ + D_2 \rightarrow CH_2D^+ + H_2$		10.2×10^{10}
$CH_3^+ + D_2 \rightarrow CH_3D_2^+$		10.2×10^{10}
$CH_2^+ + H_2 \rightarrow CH_3^+ + H$		13.8×10^{10}
$CH^+ + H_2 \rightarrow CH_2^+ + H$		35×10^{10}
$C_2H_3^+ + C_2H_6 \rightarrow C_3H_5^+ + CH_4$	16	
$C_2H^+ + C_2H_6 \rightarrow C_3H_3^+ + CH_4$	30	
$C_2H^+ + C_2H_6 \rightarrow C_4H_4^+ + H_2 + H$	1	
$I^+ + C_2H_5I \rightarrow HI_2^+ + C_2H_4$	2.2	0.93×10^{10}
$CH_3I^+ + CH_3I \rightarrow C_2H_6I^+ + I$	3.4	1.6×10^{10}

From the data of F. W. Lampe, J. L. Franklin, and F. A. Field, "Progress
in Reaction Kinetics," G. Porter (ed.), Pergamon Press, New York, 1961.

7-5 ION RECOMBINATION REACTIONS —
ELECTRONS AND POSITIVE IONS

The recombination of positive ions with electrons occurs in all
radiation chemistry systems providing the electrons are not consumed in forming negative ions. As indicated in Chap. 6 reactions
of the type

$$\text{Radiative recombination} \quad M^+ + e \longrightarrow M^* \qquad (7\text{-}28a)$$

$$M^* \longrightarrow M + h\nu \qquad (7\text{-}28b)$$

$$\text{Dissociative recombination} \quad M^+ + e \longrightarrow A + B \qquad (7\text{-}29a)$$

$$\text{Three-body recombination} \quad M^+ + e + X \longrightarrow A + Y \qquad (7\text{-}29b)$$

are all possible and their relative importance can be obtained from
a knowledge of their rate constants. Unfortunately, there is very
little information available; however, it is known that only Reactions
(7-29a) and (7-29b) appear to be significant. For these it is estimated that rate constants are of the order 10^{-5} to 10^{-7} cm^3/
molecule-sec.[13,14] These rate constants are several orders of

magnitude greater than those of ion-molecule reactions; the *rates* however are dependent on concentration. The example given in Prob. 7-5 provides reasonable criteria for the competition between ion-molecule reactions and neutralization.

7-5.1 Recombination of Positive and Negative Ions

It is fairly well established that the negative ion concentration is generally significantly less than the positive ion concentration in closed systems which do not contain appreciable quantities of substances that have high electron affinities. In the usual low pressure mass spectrometric conditions[15] the ratio of positive ions to negative ions is greater than 10^3. However, at high pressures, molecules or fragments with high electron affinities may capture low-energy secondary electrons with high efficiencies. For example, the alkyl halides, halogens, hydrogen halides, NO, O_2, H_2O, and alcohols would be expected to form negative ions readily. In the presence of such substances, the principal neutralization reaction will be between positive and negative ions.[16]

For the combination of negative and positive ions only the following processes appear to be important:

Charge exchange $\quad A^- + B^+ \longrightarrow A + B \qquad$ (7-30a)

and

Three body combination $\quad A^+ + B^- + Z \longrightarrow AB + Z \quad$ (7-30b)

The rate constant[13a, b] for Reaction (7-30a) is estimated to be about 10^{-8} cm^3 per molecule-sec whereas at ordinary temperatures and pressure, Reaction (7-30b) is estimated to be about 10^{-4} to 10^{-5} cm^3 per molecule per second.

Although the rate constants for Reactions (7-29) and (7-30) are very high, the concentration of ions is usually sufficiently low so that the rates of these reactions are in general not too competitive with the ion-molecule reactions of the primary ions.

All the ions formed during radiolysis are eventually neutralized by one process or another, however the ions that are neutralized by combination with electrons or negative ions may not necessarily be the ions formed in the initial act. For the neutralization process there will be competition between the different processes depending on the particular system. At extremely high dose rates (see Example 7-5) neutralization reactions must be considered competitive with ion-molecule reactions.

7-6 UNIMOLECULAR DECOMPOSITION OF IONS

Another process which is competitive with ion-molecule reactions of the primary ions is unimolecular decomposition. The usual gas phase radiolysis experiment takes place in a closed system; the ions are not under any gradients nor is the system under flow. In a mass spectrometer the system is essentially a flow (constantly pumped) system and the ions are formed in the presence of electric and magnetic fields. Ions undergo unimolecular decomposition, and it is this process which gives rise to the usual mass spectrum. The question that arises as far as the decomposition of ions is concerned is the relative importance of this event compared to other reactions of the primary ions, such as neutralization and ion-molecule reactions (i.e., to what extent is the low pressure mass spectrum representative of the primary ion species in any gas phase radiolysis).

The collision frequency of an ion can be calculated and since most ion-molecule reactions appear to occur at almost each collision, we are interested in knowing if the rates of ion decompositions are comparable to the collision frequency. For a gas at 1 atm pressure this would be 10^{10} collisions per second, whereas for a high-pressure gas the number of collisions $> 10^{10}$ per second.

The only theory that is available to treat this problem is the quasi-equilibrium theory of mass spectra.[17-19]

The theory states that the decomposition of an ion may be treated by means of the absolute reaction rate theory assuming that the observed mass spectrum consists of a number of competing unimolecular decomposition reactions of the excited ion. In principle one would take an energy-rich ion with all its vibrational and rotational degrees of freedom and attempt an *a priori* calculation of the mass spectra. The theory has not been too successful, but it has established qualitatively the correct dependence of mass spectra on temperature, energy, and isotope effects.

A very simplified form of this theory reduces to the classical unimolecular decomposition law

$$k_r = A \left(\frac{E - \Delta E_o}{E} \right)^{F-1} \tag{7-31}$$

where A = pre-exponential factor $\cong 10^{14}/\text{sec}$

E = total internal energy (excitation energy)

ΔE_o = activation energy for the particular reaction

F = $3N - 6$ is the number of degrees of vibrational freedom for a molecule containing N atoms

This equation is only approximately in agreement with experiment, and is useful only in estimating relative rates when some knowledge of the activation and excitation energies are known. Some knowledge of excitation and activation energies may be obtained from appearance potentials.[20]

7-6.1 Approximate Calculation of Relative Rates

The fraction of ions remaining undecomposed after a time t is given approximately by*

$$f = \int_0^{E'} D(E) \, dE \qquad (7\text{-}32)$$

where $D(E)$ = excitation energy distribution function and E' = an energy greater than the lowest amount necessary for dissociation (greater than the activation energy). A distribution function $D(E)$ suitable for this equation is

$$D(E) = \frac{1}{2\overline{\overline{E}}} \qquad (7\text{-}33)$$

where $\overline{E}$ = average excitation energy, hence

$$f = \frac{E'}{2\overline{\overline{E}}} \qquad (7\text{-}34)$$

The time for an ion to reach the detector in a mass spectrometer operating at low pressures is about 10^{-5} sec. Therefore ions with this amount of excitation energy have a rate constant of at least 10^5 sec^{-1}. From Eq. (7-31)

$$k_r(E') = 10^5 \text{ sec}^{-1} = A \left(\frac{E' - \Delta E_o}{E'} \right)^{F-1} \qquad (7\text{-}35)$$

$$E' = \frac{\Delta E_o}{1 - \left(\dfrac{10^5}{A} \right)^{F-1}} \qquad (7\text{-}36)$$

---

*The treatment of the quasi-unimolecular theory used here is at best qualitative, and more rigorous treatments may be obtained by reference to the literature (see Ref. 16). The approach used is however sufficiently satisfactory to give "order-of-magnitude" results.

The fraction of parent ions that remain undecomposed after 10 sec is simply

$$f_i = \frac{P_i}{\Sigma_i} \qquad (7\text{-}37)$$

where P_i = parent ion

Σ_i = sum of all the ions present.

This assumes that all the ions seen in the mass spectral pattern arise from a unimolecular decay of the parent ion. This is not strictly true, since an ion may be formed directly, for example $CH_3CH_2SSCH_2CH_3 \xrightarrow{\hspace{0.5cm}} HSSH^+ + 2H_2C{=}CH_2$. It is known, however, that parent ion intensities in mass spectral studies are relatively constant for bombarding electron energies more than twice that of the ionization potential. As a first approximation, f_i can be experimentally determined for a particular ion by determining the relative intensities of the ions in the mass spectral pattern.

As seen in Example 7-5, a molecule makes about 10^{10} collisions per second at ordinary pressures. It is necessary to know, for a given excitation energy, what fraction of the ions decompose in 10^{-10} sec, since ion decomposition reaction may be competitive with the ion-molecule reactions of the primary ions. By analogy with Reaction (7-38) one may assume a different excitation E'' such that

$$E'' = \frac{\Delta E_o}{1 - \left(\dfrac{10^{10}}{A}\right)^{1/(F-1)}} \qquad (7\text{-}38)$$

where E'' is the excitation energy which is obtained as the solution to Eq. (7-35) for

$$k_r(E'') = 10^{10} \text{ sec}^{-1} \qquad (7\text{-}39)$$

Since the calculation involves the same reaction (bond dissociation, for example, in a parent ion) we may equate Reactions (7-36) and (7-38) because ΔE_o is identical in both equations and obtain

$$E'' = \left[\frac{1 - \left(\dfrac{10^5}{A}\right)^{1/F-1}}{1 - \left(\dfrac{10^{10}}{A}\right)^{1/F-1}} \right] E' \qquad (7\text{-}40)$$

If E' can be determined, a value for E'' can be obtained by analogy to Eq. (7-34). The expression for the fraction of parent ions remaining undecomposed after 10^{-10} sec would be

$$f = \frac{E''}{2\overline{\overline{E}}} \tag{7-41}$$

Some knowledge of the average excitation energy $\overline{E}$ in Eq. (7-41) may be obtained from mass spectral data[13, 21, 22] by suitable interpolation of appearance potential curves. These average excitation energies may also be calculated from the quasi-equilibrium theory.

Stevenson[20] has calculated the portion of parent ions remaining undecomposed at 10^{-10} sec and finds the rate of decomposition of complex alkane and alkene parent ions to be competitive with the rates of ion-molecule reactions from these ions. The importance of this finding is that the reactions of the fragment ions must be considered along with those of the primary ions (i.e., the parent ion can decompose before undergoing an ion-molecule reaction). For most cases it appears that the low pressure mass spectrum is representative of the primary ion species in gas phase radiolysis and may be used as a first approximation for the initial ion distribution.

EXAMPLE 7-6: Calculate the fraction of parent propylene ions remaining after 10^{-10} sec given that the parent ion fraction is 19 percent of the total ions (as observed in the mass spectrometer at 10^{-3} torr) and the average excitation energy is 6.1 ev. Assume the pre-exponential factors are 10^{14} sec^{-1}.

SOLUTION: From Eq. (7-40)

$$E'' = \left[\frac{1 - \left(\dfrac{10^5}{10^{14}} \right)^{1/F-1}}{1 - \left(\dfrac{10^{10}}{10^{14}} \right)^{1/F-1}} \right] E'$$

$$F = 3N - 6 = 27 - 6 = 21$$

$$E'' = \left(\frac{1 - 10^{-9/20}}{1 - 10^{-1/5}} \right) E'$$

From Eq. (7-34)

$$f(10^5) = \frac{E'}{2\bar{\bar{E}}}$$

$$0.190 = \frac{E'}{12.2}$$

$$E' = 2.3$$

$$E'' = \left(\frac{1 - \dfrac{1}{2.82}}{1 - \dfrac{1}{1.585}} \right) 2.3 = 4.02$$

$$f(10^{10}) = \frac{4.02}{12.2}$$

$$f(10^{10}) = 0.33$$

Therefore only 33 percent of the parent propylene ion remains undecomposed after 10^{-10} sec and ion-molecule reactions of the fragment ions must be considered in a kinetic reaction scheme for the radiolysis of propylene.

This type of calculation is useful for estimating to what extent reaction of the fragment ions must be considered at high pressures. At sufficiently high pressures the *rate* of a particular ion-molecule reaction may be such that unimolecular decomposition of the parent ion does not occur. An effect of pressure (density) on the radiolysis of methane and ethane and propane[23] has been observed, indicating the importance of these considerations.

7-7 EFFECT OF TEMPERATURE ON PRIMARY ION PRODUCTION

The only direct evidence for the change in primary ion production as a function of temperature is from mass spectrometry. There are two effects of increasing the temperature in the ion source. There is a decrease in the specific intensity of all the ions due to the increased kinetic energy of the molecules and ions, hence lower ion currents are detected in the collector. The second effect is a possibility of a change in the relative intensity of the initial ion distribution. This is believed due to an increase in the vibrational energies of the parent ion with subsequent increase in the rate of decomposition of these ions.[24, 25]

Figure 7-2 shows the relative intensity of the $C_3H_8^+$ ion as a function of temperature. It is apparent from Fig. 7-2 that in the radiation chemistry of gases the possible change in initial ion distribution as a function of temperature must be considered. Some molecule ions will, of course, be less sensitive to temperature changes than others.

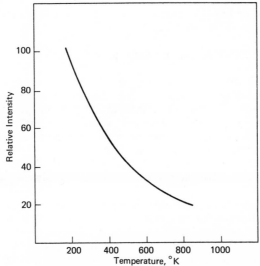

Fig. 7-2. Relative intensity of $C_3H_8^+$ as a function of temperature. [From Von H. Ehrhardt and O. Osberghaus, Z. Naturforschung, **15**, 575 (1960).]

7-8 SUMMARY OF ION-MOLECULE REACTIONS

There is considerable evidence indicating that the reactions of ions are significant chemical events in systems exposed to ionizing radiation. It has been found that:

(1) Rate constants for most ion-molecule reactions are exceptionally high, so these reactions may be expected to occur readily.

(2) A necessary but not sufficient criterion for an ion-molecule reaction to occur in a closed system is that the reaction be exothermic.

(3) The low pressure mass spectrum may be used as an approximation of the initial ion distribution.

(4) The unimolecular decomposition of the parent ion is a sensitive function of the excess energy and may also be a function of the pressure.

(5) Initial ion distribution may be sensitive to temperature.

A listing of cross sections and rate constants for ion-molecule reactions is given in Table 7-3.

7-9 SPECIAL TECHNIQUES IN GAS RADIOLYSIS

Radiation chemists have employed a variety of techniques in an effort to determine the relative contribution of ion and free radical reactions in gases. These are: the addition of rare gases to effect charge exchange (or energy exchange); scavengers such as I_2, HI, N_2O, NO, and O_2; tagging by means of isotopes; and removal of ions by the application of electric fields.

7-9.1 Application of Electric Fields During Radiolysis

This technique was practiced by Essex[26] and co-workers who attempted to delineate the reactions of ions from other chemically active species by removal of the ions by an applied field. Removal of the ions by an applied field from the reaction does not, of course, prevent the reactions of ions, but it does decrease homogeneous neutralization in the reaction medium by making this process occur principally at the electrodes. The apparatus employed by Essex is shown in Fig. 7-3.

This technique utilizes an applied field to remove the electrons and ions from the gas. The field is applied until a point is reached where no further increase in current is observed (saturation current). At this point the ions have been completely removed from the system. At very high fields, cascading will occur with resulting electron and ion multiplication.

It was originally believed by Essex et al. that the application of the field removed the ions from the gas and, therefore, prevented "ion reactions." We now know this to be untrue because the rates of ion molecule reactions are very high, hence, before a positive ion is collected, it will have undergone many thousands of collisions. The ions that are actually collected, therefore, are relatively unreactive ions.

The principal advantage of the technique may be that it aids in distinguishing between products formed by fast ion-molecule reactions, which remain constant despite the application of the applied

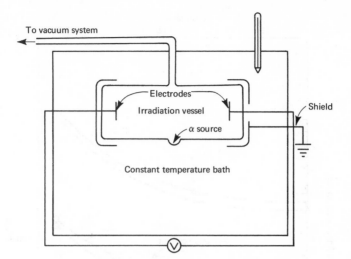

To vacuum system

Electrodes

Irradiation vessel

Shield

α source

Constant temperature bath

Fig. 7-3. Schematic diagram of radiation vessel
as used by Essex.

field, and the contribution of excited states to the overall decomposition. Figure 7-4 shows that when mixtures of C_2H_6 and C_2D_6 are irradiated, products such as C_2D_3H and CD_3H show no increase during the application of a field whereas products such as CD_4 show a three- to fourfold increase.

The positive ions and electrons, as they are drawn to their respective electrodes, will not be accelerated to the degree indicated by the applied voltage because of the numerous collisions they will make en route. The electrons, it is estimated, have the highest energies; however, these will not exceed about 15–25 ev. At these energies the electrons will primarily excite, not ionize, the molecules they encounter. This can be seen by observing that the saturation current is constant even though the yields of certain molecules change (Fig. 7-4). If ionization were occurring to any appreciable extent, one would expect a change in the collected current with applied voltage. Examination of the product yields under these conditions can give some clue, therefore, as to those products which are formed as a result of the excitation of the parent molecule.

One must however be very cautious in interpreting the results obtained with this technique. For example, in ethylene radiolysis a primary process leading to vinyl radical formation is important when applied fields are present, but is virtually absent when they are absent.[27]

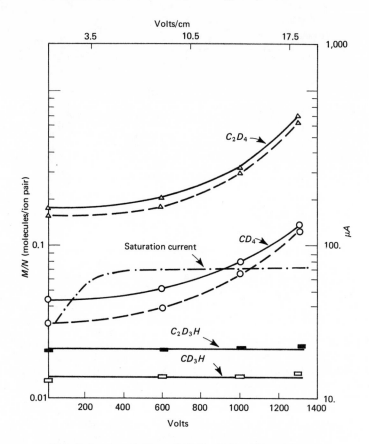

Fig. 7-4. Irradiation of C_2H_6-C_2D_6-NO mixtures (1:1:0.05) in the presence of electric fields. [From H. H. Carmichael, R. Gorden, and P. Ausloos, J. Chem. Phys., **42**, 343 (1965).]

7-9.2 Addition of Rare Gases

The addition of rare gases during radiolysis can affect the course of a variety of ionic reactions by inducing charge or excitation exchange or participating in hydride ion formation, or other ion-molecule reactions. An outstanding example is the radiation induced exchange of hydrogen and deuterium.[28,29]

In this reaction a mixture of H_2 and D_2 is irradiated producing HD; the reaction is an ion chain process with an M/N yield of about 18,000. It was demonstrated that the radiation induced reaction was an ion chain by the fact that the addition of certain rare gases (Kr and Xe) essentially stopped the radiation induced reaction but had no effect on the photochemical or thermally induced exchange.

As with the alpha radiolysis of ortho-para hydrogen mixtures the initial ions are H_2^+ (or D_2^+), H^+ (or D^+) and because of the large cross section for the reaction, H_3^+ from the reaction

$$H_2^+ + H_2 \longrightarrow H_3^+ + H$$

In the presence of krypton and xenon, both of which have lower ionization potentials than hydrogen, the rate of the exchange is reduced enormously. However, in the presence of He, Ne or Ar, which have ionization potentials higher than that of H_2, a moderate inhibition of the reaction occurs when the concentration of these rare gases is high but an enhancement of the reaction when their concentrations are low. Originally it was thought that the reactions could be explained by simple charge exchange; however a more careful analysis of the energetics of the reacting system and photochemical and mass spectrographic studies provided a mechanism consistent with the energetics and observed experimental results.

It was found experimentally that the chain lengths were very long ($\sim 10,000$) and to account for this and the inhibition of the reaction by rare gas ions an ion-chain mechanism was postulated.

The ionic-chain mechanism and the effect of rare gases is explained as follows:

Chain initiation: $\quad H_2^+ + H_2 \longrightarrow H_3^+ + H \qquad$ (7-42)

Ion chain: $\quad H_3^+ + D_2 \longrightarrow H_2 + HD_2^+ \qquad$ (7-43)

Initiation inhibition: $\quad H_2^+ + R \longrightarrow RH^+ + H \qquad$ (7-44)
(R = any rare gas)

Chain inhibition: $\quad H_3^+ + Xe$ (or Kr) $\longrightarrow XeH^+ + H_2 \quad$ (7-45)

In the presence of
Ne, He or Ar: $\quad Ne^+ + H_2 \longrightarrow NeH^+ + H \qquad$ (7-46)
(enhancement)

$\quad NeH^+ + H_2 \longrightarrow Ne + H_3^+ \qquad$ (7-47)

Chain termination: $\quad H_3^+ + M$ (negative charge)

$\quad \longrightarrow H_2 + H + M \qquad$ (7-48)
or
$\quad H_3^+ M + e^- \longrightarrow H_2 + H + M \qquad$ (7-48a)

The ion-chain mechanism involves H_3^+ as the ion-chain carrier with a specific rate constant of 1.4×10^{-9} cm^3 per molecule-sec. Moderate inhibition occurs when the rare gas molecules react with H_2^+, as in Reaction (7-44), but for He, Ne, and Ar this only becomes important when the concentration of these rare gases is comparable to that of H_2. The fact that only traces of Xe or Kr practically stop the reaction indicates that they are interfering with the chain propagation step.

The energetics for Reactions (7-44), (7-45), and (7-46) may be estimated by standard thermodynamic techniques. The heat of Reaction (7-46) the reaction between a rare gas ion and hydrogen is given by

$$\Delta H = -E(RH^+) + I(H^+) + 2\Delta H_f (H) - I(R^+) \qquad (7\text{-}49)$$

where E is the bond energy of the rare gas hydride ion, $I(H^+)$ and $I(R^+)$ are the ionization potentials of the hydrogen atom and rare gas atom and $\Delta H_f (H)$ is the heat of formation of the hydrogen atom. For example, substituting the appropriate values for helium hydride ion formation gives:

$$\Delta H = -E(RH^+) + 313 + 103 - 563$$

$$\Delta H = -E(RH^+) - 147$$

This indicates a high probability that the heat of Reaction (7-46) is exothermic. (It has been established by mass spectrography that Reaction (7-46) is exothermic for all rare gas ions except Xe^+.)

The effect of addition of rare gases may also be explained by charge exchanges or energy exchange. For example, charge and energy exchanges have been invoked to explain the acceleration of the radiation induced decomposition of butane.[30, 31]

$$Ar^+ + C_4H_{10} \longrightarrow C_3H_7^+ + CH_3 + Ar \qquad (7\text{-}50)$$

$$Ar^* + C_4H_{10} \longrightarrow C_3H_7^+ + CH_3 + Ar + e^- \qquad (7\text{-}51)$$

where Ar^* is an excited argon atom which is at least 10.5 ev above the ground state.

7-9.3   Scavengers

The addition of I_2 or HI as radical scavengers is a technique commonly employed; however, the interpretation of the data is often complicated because of the high negative ion formation probability of the halogen. Other reactions such as the negative ion clustering described in Sec. 7-5.1 also may obscure the interpretation of data in these systems. The scavenger is added to remove free radicals by reactions such as

$$CH_3 + I_2 \longrightarrow CH_3I + I \qquad\qquad (7\text{-}52)$$

$$H + I_2 \longrightarrow HI + I \qquad\qquad (7\text{-}53)$$

The resulting alkyl iodides are detected by gas chromatography.

Tritium labeling usually involves the addition of tritium gas to the reaction mixture, using the tritium as a source of radiation. This technique may lead to the replacement of part of the hydrogen present in the compound by tritium. The mechanism for tritiation is complex and probably involves reactions of tritium ions with the compound or ions and excited species of the compound with T_2. Other "scavengers" may simply consist of trace amounts of deuterated molecules, or even normal molecules such as propane, or butane which may be added to detect hydride ion reactions with ions or other types of reactions.[32,33]

For example when 3 to 15 percent of deutero-cyclopropane is added to cyclohexane and the mixture irradiated, more than 90 percent of the propane formed consists of $C_3D_6H_2$ — indicating a transfer of a H_2 molecule.

Nitric oxide has been used extensively as a radical scavenger. In the radiolysis of ethane containing small amounts of NO, those products which are thought to arise from free radical reactions are reduced almost to zero.

Olefins have also been used as scavengers, for example to scavenge thermal H atoms via:

$$C_2H_4 + H \longrightarrow C_2H_5 \qquad\qquad (7\text{-}54)$$

Another common practice is to irradiate mixtures of deuterated and nondeuterated forms of the same molecule. This is usually referred to as *isotopic* labeling and has been one of the most useful techniques of elucidating complex reactions. For example, irradiation of an equimolar mixture of C_2H_6 - C_2D_6 and examination of the resulting products has indicated that hydrogen produced consisted mostly of H_2 and D_2. This evidence supports a "molecular detachment" process as:

$$C_2H_6 \overset{\wedge\!\wedge\!\wedge}{\longrightarrow} C_2H_4 + H_2 \qquad\qquad (7\text{-}55)$$

This is an example of isotopic labeling rather than scavenging.

Electron scavengers such as N_2O and SF_6 can be used to esti-mate the yield of free electrons[34,35] and can provide some insight into the neutralization process. Charge acceptors, which are sub-stances with relatively low ionization potentials, have been used to detect relatively unreactive intermediate ions.[36] These substances act, in a manner of speaking, as positive ion scavengers.

7-10 NEUTRAL REACTIVE SPECIES PRODUCED IN THE RADIOLYSIS OF GASES

Neutral reactive species will be produced in gas phase radioly-sis via ion-molecule reactions such as

$$CH_4^+ + CH_4 \longrightarrow CH_5^+ + CH_3 \tag{7-56}$$

and also as a result of direct excitation, for example

$$CH_4 \overset{\longrightarrow}{\sim\!\!\!\sim\!\!\!\sim} CH_4^* \longrightarrow CH_2 + H_2 \tag{7-57}$$

$$C_2H_6 \overset{\longrightarrow}{\sim\!\!\!\sim\!\!\!\sim} C_2H_6^* \longrightarrow CH_3 + CH_3 \tag{7-58}$$

Radicals and radical ions have been shown to occur as a result of charge exchange from the decomposition of ions from excitation energy exchange and by certain radical scavenging reactions. Re-actions of many of the simpler radicals are reasonably well charac-terized in terms of activation energies, order of magnitude of rate constants, and type of reactions (abstraction, disproportionation, etc.). The relative importance of the various reactions (ion-molecule reactions, direct excitation, etc.) in terms of their contri-bution in producing free radicals in gas phase radiolysis is not definitely known. It is well established that reactions of the type shown in (7-57) and (7-58) occur, but this reaction path for the pro-duction of radicals probably occurs to a much lesser extent than that initiated by ions.

7-11 IONIC MECHANISMS

The initial act in the radiolysis is to form ions, radicals and excited species which then undergo reaction resulting in the various products. It has been shown that an ionic mechanism can be used to explain the major product distribution in methane and propane radi-olysis, however it is now known that such a mechanism cannot fully explain what is actually occurring in the system. Experiment has shown that some products arise from reactions of excited neutral molecules, but it is not possible to describe this reaction path in quantitative terms. It has been estimated however that approxi-mately 10 to 20 percent of the overall products can be ascribed to neutral molecule decompositions in the case of methane, propane, and butane.[37]

Each system is relatively unique but it can be stated that probably processes initiated by ions predominate. In the absence of detailed kinetic information, ion reactions can often provide a reasonable qualitative picture of the radiolysis product distribution but it must be clearly understood that such a mechanism may have limited significance in terms of what is actually happening in the system.

As an example of this type of calculation the radiolysis of methane will be discussed.

EXAMPLE 7-7: Give a qualitative estimate of the products to be expected in the radiolysis of methane. The mass spectrum of methane shows the following relative ion abundances:

Ion	Relative abundance
CH_4^+	0.48
CH_3^+	0.40
CH_2^+	0.08
CH^+	0.04
C^+	0.01

It will be assumed that all the ions are present in the relative abundances shown, except C^+ which will not be considered.

SOLUTION: From Table 7-3 we observe that the following ion-molecule reactions of the primary ions will occur.

$$CH_4^+ + CH_4 \longrightarrow CH_5^+ + CH_3 \qquad (7\text{-}59)$$

$$CH_3^+ + CH_4 \longrightarrow C_2H_5^+ + H_2 \qquad (7\text{-}60)$$

$$CH_2^+ + CH_4 \longrightarrow C_2H_4^+ + H_2 \qquad (7\text{-}61)$$

$$CH_2^+ + CH_4 \longrightarrow C_2H_5^+ + H \qquad (7\text{-}61a)$$

$$CH_2^+ + CH_4 \longrightarrow C_2H_3^+ + H_2 + H \qquad (7\text{-}62)$$

$$CH^+ + CH_4 \longrightarrow C_2H_2^+ + H_2 + H \qquad (7\text{-}63)$$

In addition to these reactions there is the possibility of ion-molecule reactions between the product ions formed in Reactions (7-59) to (7-63) and methane and/or the products of the reaction. As a first approximation these possibilities will be ignored assuming no direct information concerning the probability of their occurrence, and that the principal reaction of the secondary ions is neutralization by electrons or hydride ion transfer or proton transfer. The probability of reaction of secondary ions may be considered as well as other reactions as a correction on the first approximation.

Neutralization Reactions

$$CH_5^+ + e^- \longrightarrow CH_3 + H_2 \tag{7-64}$$

$$CH_5^+ + e^- \longrightarrow CH_4 + H \tag{7-65}$$

Of the two possibilities, Reaction (7-64) is thermodynamically the more favorable*

$$\Delta H_{(7-64)} = \Delta H_f(CH_3) + \Delta H_f(H_2) - \Delta H_f(CH_5^+)$$

$$\cong -253 \text{ kcal/mol}$$

$$\Delta H_{(7-65)} = \Delta H_f(CH_4) + \Delta H_f(H) - \Delta H_f(CH_5^+)$$

$$\cong -186 \text{ kcal/mol}$$

For the ethyl ion there are two possibilities:

$$M + C_2H_5^+ + e^- \longrightarrow C_2H_5 \tag{7-66}$$

$$C_2H_5^+ + e^- \longrightarrow C_2H_4 + H \tag{7-67}$$

Reactions (7-66) and (7-67) are both possible; however (7-67) is equivalent to (7-66) because of (7-54). For the ions produced in Reactions (7-61) to (7-63), it will be assumed that neutralization of the ions produced in Reactions (7-61) and (7-62) lead to C_2H_4, that in (7-61a) to C_2H_5, and that in Reaction (7-63) to C_2H_2.

For the formation of the initial ions the following scheme will be used:

$$CH_4 \xrightarrow{\;\sim\sim\;} CH_3^+ + H \tag{7-68}$$

$$CH_4 \xrightarrow{\;\sim\sim\;} CH_2^+ + H + H \tag{7-69}$$

$$CH_4 \xrightarrow{\;\sim\sim\;} CH^+ + H_2 + H \tag{7-70}$$

---

*It must be kept in mind that this is not an absolute criteria for reaction and that other factors may affect the choice of reaction path. In the absence of other information, however, thermodynamics can provide some direction.

Hydride Ion Transfer

Hydride ion transfer will occur with a number of the ions. The reactions which may occur in this system are those with the ions produced by Reactions (7-60) and (7-62) and a product molecule (hydride ion transfer occurs with a low probability with methane).

$$C_2H_5^+ + RH \longrightarrow C_2H_6 + R^+ \qquad (7\text{-}71)$$

$$C_2H_3^+ + RH \longrightarrow C_2H_4 + R^+ \qquad (7\text{-}72)$$

where RH is any alkane other than CH_4.

Proton Transfer

Proton transfer reactions are also very possible with some of the ions

$$CH_5^+ + RH \longrightarrow CH_4 + RH_2^+ \qquad (7\text{-}73)$$

$$C_2H_5^+ + RH \longrightarrow C_2H_4 + RH_2^+ \qquad (7\text{-}74)$$

$$C_2H_3^+ + RH \longrightarrow C_2H_2 + RH_2^+ \qquad (7\text{-}75)$$

where RH is a molecule other than CH_4.

The question now arises as to what criteria can be applied to distinguish among all these possibilities. The available information is too sparse to make generalizations; however, it does appear that hydride ion reactions occur with great ease, particularly with $C_2H_5^+$. Hence for this ion, hydride ion transfer and neutralization will be considered as the principal reactions. For CH_5^+ it will be assumed that this ion undergoes proton transfer and neutralization — proton transfer presumably occurring to a product molecule such as ethane or propane. For the $C_2H_3^+$ ion we must assume hydride ion transfer, neutralization, and proton transfer.

Reactions of the Radicals

The CH_3 radical is formed primarily in (7-59) and (7-64); it can undergo reactions with methyl and ethyl radicals and H atoms.

$$2CH_3 \longrightarrow C_2H_6 \qquad (7\text{-}76)$$

$$CH_3 + H \longrightarrow CH_4 \qquad (7\text{-}77)$$

$$CH_3 + C_2H_5 \longrightarrow C_3H_8 \qquad (7\text{-}78)$$

The activation energy for Reaction (7-78) is about the same as that of Reaction (7-76) but the concentration of C_2H_5 will be smaller than CH_3 . Reaction (7-77) should occur with ease but since the concentration of CH_3 radicals is about twice that of H atoms, we will weigh the reaction in favor of (7-76). The CH_3 radical can also undergo an abstraction reaction but this has an appreciable activation energy and will be considered to be of secondary importance.

The C_2H_5 radical is formed by Reaction (7-66) and Reactions (7-61a) and (7-54). Possible C_2H_5 reactions other than (7-78) are

$$C_2H_5 + CH_4 \longrightarrow C_2H_6 + CH_3 \tag{7-79}$$

$$C_2H_5 + C_2H_5 \longrightarrow C_4H_{10} \tag{7-80}$$

$$C_2H_5 + H \longrightarrow C_2H_6 \tag{7-81}$$

The concentration of H atoms is roughly comparable to that of ethyl radicals but Reaction (7-54) is known to be very efficient hence it appears reasonable to assume that H atom concentration will be quite low and that Reactions (7-78) and (7-80) are the principal reaction of ethyl radicals since Reaction (7-79) has an activation energy of about 15 kcal per molecule.

The reaction of H atoms in addition to that cited above and (7-54) is

$$H + H + M \longrightarrow H_2 + M \tag{7-82}$$

Reaction (7-82) requires a third body (M). Reaction (7-54) is known to occur with thermalized H atoms, therefore even though the initial C_2H_4 concentration is low, Reaction (7-54) would appear to be favored over (7-82).

The possible products therefore from the radiolysis of methane based on the ions produced are ethane, ethylene, propane, butane, acetylene, and hydrogen.

Sources of Product

a. Ethane

The principal source is combination of methyl radicals and hydride ion transfer to $C_2H_5^+$. Reaction (7-59) would give an M/N yield of methyl radicals of 0.48 and Reaction (7-71) an M/N yield of ethane of 0.40. Maximum M/N = 0.24 + 0.40 = 0.64. Neutralization of $C_2H_5^+$ (7-66) would of course reduce this value.

b. Ethylene

Although ethylene may be produced by neutralization of the ions produced in Reactions (7-60) and (7-61) because of Reaction (7-54) it would be expected that most of the ethylene would be converted to ethyl radicals. Ethylene production should be very small. Maximum M/N yield for ethylene = 0.08.

c. Propane

Since the methyl radical yield is considerably larger than the ethyl radical yield, it would be expected that ethyl radicals are largely consumed by Reaction (7-78), but some ethyl radicals would react according to (7-80). Ethyl radicals are only formed by neutralization of $C_2H_5^+$ and by Reaction (7-54). Propane yield > 0.08.

d. Butane

The only source for butane according to the mechanism is combination of ethyl radicals (7-80). Considering what has been discussed, the yield of butane therefore should be less than the propane yield.

e. Acetylene

Neutralization of the $C_2H_2^+$ ion appears to be the sole source of acetylene hence the M/N yield for this product should not be greater than 0.04.

f. Hydrogen

The major sources of hydrogen are Reactions (7-60), (7-61), (7-61a), and/or (7-62), (7-63), (7-68), (7-69), (7-70), and the neutralization reaction (7-64). The maximum M/N yield of hydrogen would be:

From (7-60) = 0.40
From (7-64) = 0.48
From (7-61) = 0.08
or (7-62) or (7-61a)
From (7-63) = 0.04
From (7-68) = 0.20
From (7-69) = 0.04
From (7-70) = 0.03

M/N total = 1.27

g. Methane Disappearance

The M/N yield for CH_4 disappearance according to these calculations:

From Reaction (7-59) = 0.96
From Reaction (7-60) = 0.80
From Reaction (7-61) = 0.16
From Reaction (7-63) = 0.08

2.00

Summary

	$(-CH_4)$	(H_2)	(C_2H_6)	(C_2H_4)	(C_2H_2)	$(C_3H_8 + C_4H_{10})$
Calc. M/N	-2.00	1.27	0.64	0.08 (max)	0.04 (max)	0.08
Actual M/N	-2.5	1.90	0.70	0.01	0.01	0.06

The ion mechanism produces results in rough qualitative agreement with experiment, however under no circumstances should this mechanism be considered as being representative of the actual chemical events that occur in the system. It is definitely known that reactions such as (7-57) and (7-58) occur, followed by reactions of the methylene radical with methane and possibly product molecules. Also, some polymer is produced and there are indications that this is by an ion chain initiated by CH_5^+.

There is also good evidence that additional ion-molecule reactions (condensation) occur:

$$C_2H_5^+ + CH_4 \longrightarrow C_3H_7^+ + H_2$$

$$C_2H_3^+ + CH_4 \longrightarrow C_3H_5^+ + H_2$$

The ion reaction scheme is useful however as a first approximation to provide some rough idea as to the identity of the products to be expected and a rough estimate of their distribution.

As indicated earlier only reactions of the primary ions have been considered and contributions to the radical population by direct excitation have been ignored. For example at high pressures $C_2H_3^+$ disappears in the mass spectrum and is replaced by $C_3H_5^+$ and at higher pressures the $C_3H_7^+$ ion appears. Vacuum ultraviolet photochemistry indicates that CH_3, CH_2 and CH are the important primary reactive species.

PROBLEMS

1. Calculate the number of collisions an ion will make at pressures of 10^{-6} mm at 10^{-3} mm and at 10 atm.

2. At a dose rate of 1000 r per second estimate the mean life of an ion with respect to neutralization.

3. Calculate the rate constant and cross section for the reaction

$$C_2H_5^+ + CH_4 \longrightarrow C_3H_7^+ + H_2$$

given $E = 8.0 \ V/cm$

$$d = 2.5 \ mm$$

$$\alpha = 1.2 \times 10^{-24} \ cm^3$$

4. If the appearance potential of H_2O^+ is 12.61 ev and the heat of formation of H^+ is 365 kcal per molecule calculate the enthalpy of the reaction

$$H_2O^+ + H_2O \longrightarrow H_3O^+ + OH$$

Note: Enthalpy of formation of OH may be calculated from bond dissociation energy data.

5. Calculate the enthalpy of the reaction

$$C_2H_3^+ + C_2H_4 \longrightarrow C_2H_5^+ + C_2H_2$$

given the appearance potential of $C_2H_3^+ = 317$ kcal per molecule.

6. If the average excitation energy of CH_4^+ is 5.2 ev calculate the fraction of parent methane ions remaining after 10^{-10} sec. (Use the mass spectral data given in Prob. 7 and assume a pre-exponential factor of 10^{14} sec^{-1}.)

7. The mass spectra of propane is

Ion	Relative intensity
$C_3H_8^+$	29.2
$C_3H_7^+$	23.1
$C_3H_5^+$	12.9
$C_3H_3^+$	17.5
$C_2H_5^+$	100.0
$C_2H_4^+$	59.5
$C_2H_5^+$	40.3
$C_2H_2^+$	8.3

244 The Chemistry and Physics of High Energy Reactions

(a) Determine the relative abundances of the ions.

(b) Using the relative abundances and Table 7-3, give a qualitative estimate of the products to be expected in the radiolysis of propane.

8. The thermal conductivity of ethane is given approximately as
0.00027 cal/(sec) (cm^2) ($^{\circ}$C/cm). Estimate the mean temperature when an aluminum cylinder (1" by 5") containing ethane at
10 atm pressure is irradiated by a 2 Mev electron beam at a
current of 1×10^{-6} amp for 10 min. Is this temperature high
enough to change the primary ion yield?

BIBLIOGRAPHY FOR METHANE RADIOLYSIS

Abrahmson, F. P., and J. H. Futrell, *J. Chem. Phys.*, **46**:3264 (1967).

Ausloos, P. J., R. Gorden and S. G. Lias, *J. Chem. Phys.*, **40**:1854
(1964).

_____ and S. G. Lias, *H. Chem. Phys.*, **38**:2207 (1963).

_____, _____ and R. Gorden, *J. Chem. Phys.*, **39**:3341 (1963).

_____, R. E. Rebbert and S. G. Lias, *J. Chem. Phys.*, **42**:540 (1965).

Braun, W., K. H. Welge and J. R. McNesby, *J. Chem. Phys.*, **45**:2560
(1966).

Derwish, G. A., A. Galli, A. Giardini-Guiidoni, and G. G. Volpi,
J. Chem. Phys., **40**:5 (1964).

Field, F. H., J. L. Franklin, and M. S. P. Munson, *J.A.C.S.*, **85**:3575
(1963).

Gorden, R., and P. J. Ausloos, *J. Chem. Phys.*, **46**:188 (1967).

Gupta, S. K., E. G. Jones, A. G. Harrison, and J. J. Myher, *Can. J.
Chem.*, **45**:111 (1967).

Haynes, R. H., and P. Kebarle, *J. Chem. Phys.*, **45**:3899 (1966).

Lampe, F. W., *J.A.C.S.*, **79**:1055 (1957).

Meisels, G. G., W. H. Hamill, and R. R. Williams, *J. Phys. Chem.*,
61:1456 (1957).

Wexler, S., and N. Jesse, *J.A.C.S.*, **84**:3425 (1963).

REFERENCES

1. C. Rosenblum, *J. Phys. Chem.*, **41**:469 (1948).

2. J. H. Futrell and L. W. Siek, *J. Phys. Chem.*, **69**:892 (1965).

3. P. Kebarle and A. M. Hogg, *J. Chem. Phys.*, **43**:449 (1965).

4. J. Magee and K. Funabashi, *Rad. Res.*, **10**:622 (1959).

5. M. Burton and J. Magee, *J. Phys. Chem.*, **56**:842 (1952).

6. N. Boelrijk and W. H. Hamill, *J.A.C.S.*, **84**:730 (1962).

7. H. Eyring, J. Hirshfelder, and H. S. Taylor, *J. Chem. Phys.*, **4**:479 (1936).

8. D. P. Stevenson and D. O. Schissler, *J. Chem. Phys.*, **23**:1353 (1955).

9. G. Gioumousis and D. P. Stevenson, *J. Chem. Phys.*, **29**:294 (1958).

10. M. J. Henchman, *Annual Reports of the Chemical Society*, vol. 63, 1966.

11. D. Stevenson, "Mass Spectrometry," C. A. McDowell (ed.), p. 607, McGraw-Hill Book Company, New York, 1963.

12. D. P. Stevenson, *Rad. Res.*, **10**:618 (1959).

13. H. S. W. Massey and E. H. S. Burhop, "Electronic and Ionic Impact Phenomena," pp. 618-641, Clarendon Press, Oxford, 1952.

14. R. I. Shoen, *J. Chem. Phys.*, **40**:1830 (1964).

15. D. P. Stevenson and D. O. Schissler, "The Chemical and Biological Action of Radiations," M. Haissinsky (ed.), Academic Press, London, 1961.

16. J. L. Magee and M. Burton, *J.A.C.S.*, **73**:523 (1952).

17. H. M. Rosenstock, M. B. Wallenstein, A. L. Wahrhaftig, and H. Eyring, *Proc. Nat. Acad. Sci.*, *U.S.*, **38**:667 (1952).

18. H. M. Rosenstock and M. Kraus, "Current Status of the Statistical Theory of Mass Spectra, Advances in Mass Spectrometry," vol. 2, Pergamon Press, New York, 1963.

19. M. L. Vestal, *J. Chem. Phys.*, **43**:1356 (1965).

20. D. P. Stevenson, *Rad. Res.*, **10**:610 (1959).

21. T. Mariner and W. Bleakney, *Phys. Sci.*, **72**:807 (1947).

22. L. Friedman, F. A. Long, and M. Wolfsberg, *J. Chem. Phys.*, 27:613 (1957).

23. P. Ausloos, R. Gorden, and S. G. Lias, *J. Chem. Phys.*, **40**:1854 (1964).

24. F. H. Field and J. L. Franklin, "Electron Impact Phenomenon," Academic Press, New York, 1957.

25. Von H. Erhardt and G. Osberghaus, *Z. Naturforschung*, **15**:575 (1960).

26. H. Essex, *J. Phys. Chem.*, **58**:42 (1954).

27. G. G. Meisels and T. J. Sworski, *J. Phys. Chem.*, **69**:2867 (1965).

28. S. O. Thompson and O. A. Schaeffer, *J.A.C.S.*, **80**:553 (1958).

29. O. A. Schaeffer and S. O. Thompson, *Rad. Res.*, **10**:671 (1959).

30. R. P. Borkowski and P. J. Ausloos, *J. Chem. Phys.*, **37**:877 (1962).

31. V. Cermak and Z. Herman, *Coll. Czeck. Chem. Commun.*, **30**:169 (1965).

32. P. Ausloos and G. Lias, *J. Chem. Phys.*, **43**:127 (1965).

33. K. Yang and P. L. Gant, *J. Phys. Chem.*, **65**:1861 (1961).

34. G. R. A. Johnson and J. M. Warman, *Trans. Far. Soc.*, **61**:512 (1962).

35. J. M. Warman, *Nature*, 213:381 (1967).

36. R. D. Doepker and P. Ausloos, *J. Chem. Phys.*, **43**:3841 (1965).

37. P. Ausloos, S. G. Lias, and I. B. Sandoval, *Disc. Far. Soc.*, **36**:66 (1963).

8

RADIATION CHEMISTRY OF WATER AND AQUEOUS SYSTEMS

The decomposition of water by ionizing radiation was first studied in detail in 1913 by Duane and Scheuer[1] who found that water decomposed to yield hydrogen, oxygen, and some hydrogen peroxide when irradiated with α-rays. It was however not until 1927 when H. Fricke* began his study of chemical reactions induced by ionizing radiation, that an understanding of the mechanism of the decomposition of water was achieved. The radiation chemistry of water and aqueous solutions is now one of the better understood kinetic systems.[2]

8-1 EFFECT OF HIGH ENERGY RADIATION ON WATER

Fricke and colleagues determined that X-rays, unlike alpha rays, caused very little or no decomposition of water, especially if care had been exercised in its purification. They found that in the presence of solutes, considerable decomposition of water occurred, and that the amount of decomposition was independent of the concentration of solute over a wide solute concentration range.

To account for the chemical reactions in dilute solutions, Fricke postulated that the water was converted to some active form, and that it was this "activated water" that induced chemical reactions. The nature of the activated water was in doubt; however certain parallels between the action of UV and ionizing radiation could be drawn. In particular, Fricke showed that irradiation of aqueous solutions by light at wavelengths below 1900 Å produced many reactions similar to those he had observed with X-rays, including excited states of water which are dissociative

$$\text{H}_2\text{O} \xrightarrow{h\nu} \text{H} + \text{OH} \qquad (8\text{-}1)$$

---

*See "Hugo Fricke on the Occasion of his Seventeenth Birthday," Rad. Res. **17**:253 (1962) for a reasonably complete bibliography of Fricke's early publications.

Subsequent research showed, however, that the decomposition of water and aqueous solutions was considerably more complicated than could be explained by a simple free radical formation. The elucidation of the complex behavior of water required a knowledge of the spatial distribution, modes of formation, yields, and reactions of the intermediates responsible for the observed chemical processes.

8-2 PRIMARY SPECIES

Table 8-1 summarizes possible species and their formation reactions in liquid water which occur as a result of the passage of an ionizing particle. The primary species listed in Table 8-1 are formed in about the time of a molecular vibration ($10^{-14} - 10^{-15}$ sec).

Table 8-1. POSSIBLE REACTIVE INTERMEDIATE IN RADIOLYSIS OF H_2O

Specie	Energy of formation, ev	Formation reaction
H_2O^*	7.4 or 9.2	$H_2O \xrightarrow{\text{\Large$\sim$}\!\!\!\!\!\text{\Large$\sim$}} H_2O^*$
$H_2O^+ + e^-$	12.56	$H_2O \xrightarrow{\text{\Large$\sim$}\!\!\!\!\!\text{\Large$\sim$}} H_2O^+ + e^-$
OH^+	18.1	$H_2O \xrightarrow{\text{\Large$\sim$}\!\!\!\!\!\text{\Large$\sim$}} OH^+ + H + e^- + ke$†
H^+	19.6	$H_2O \xrightarrow{\text{\Large$\sim$}\!\!\!\!\!\text{\Large$\sim$}} H^+ + OH + e^-$
O^+	18.8	$H_2O \xrightarrow{\text{\Large$\sim$}\!\!\!\!\!\text{\Large$\sim$}} O^+ + H_2 + e^-$
O^-	e^- (5.6 ev) + H_2O	$H_2O + e^- \xrightarrow{\text{\Large$\sim$}\!\!\!\!\!\text{\Large$\sim$}} O^- + 2H$
H^-	e^- (7.5 ev) + H_2O	$H_2O + e^- \xrightarrow{\text{\Large$\sim$}\!\!\!\!\!\text{\Large$\sim$}} H^- + OH$

†ke = kinetic energy.

Knowledge of the existence of ions comes from mass spectroscopy; the spectra of water is shown in Table 8-2.

Table 8-2.* MASS SPECTRA OF H_2O

Specie	Abundance
H_2O^+	100
OH^+	23
H^+	5
O^+	2
O^-	1.5
H^-	0.6

*[Data of M. M. Mann, A. Hustrulid, and J. T. Tate, Phys. Rev., **58**:340 (1940).]

Within 10^{-14} to 10^{-12} sec after their formation, the species listed in Table 8-1 disappear; Eqs. (8-2) to (8-11) represent some of the more likely reactions.

$$H_2O^* + H_2O^* \longrightarrow H_2O_2 + H_2 \tag{8-2}$$

$$H_2O^* \longrightarrow OH + H + 2 \text{ ev of ke} \tag{8-3}$$

$$H_2O^* \longrightarrow OH^* + H \tag{8-4}$$

$$H_2O^+ + H_2O \longrightarrow H_3O^+ + OH \tag{8-5}$$

$$OH^+ + 2H_2O \longrightarrow H_3O^+ + 2OH \tag{8-6}$$

$$H_3O^+ + e^- \longrightarrow H_3O^* \tag{8-6a}$$

$$H^+ + H_2O \longrightarrow H_3O^+ \tag{8-7}$$

$$O^+ + H_2O \longrightarrow H^+ + HO_2 \tag{8-8}$$

$$O^- + H_2O \longrightarrow OH + OH^- \tag{8-9}$$

$$H^- + H_2O \longrightarrow H_2 + OH^- \tag{8-10}$$

$$e^- \text{ (secondary)} \longrightarrow e^- \text{ (thermal) or } e^-_{aq} \text{ (aqueous)} \tag{8-11}$$

8-2.1   Evidence for the Existence of Primary Species

Direct evidence for the existence of the H atom comes from paramagnetic studies of irradiated ice at $4.2°K$ and from irradiated frozen solutions at $77°K$.[3] In the latter system some reactions of trapped H atoms have been characterized. The OH radicals have been detected by both absorption and emission at 3064 Å, in electric discharge of water vapor, by paramagnetic absorption in irradiated ice at $77°K$, and by mass spectrographic techniques. Evidence for the HO_2 radical is found in the mass spectra from the reaction of H atoms produced in a gas discharge with O_2 and a rare gas atom[4] and by direct observation of the absorption spectra in irradiated 0.1 N H_2SO_4 solutions.[5]

The existence of the hydrated electron was postulated by Platzman in 1953,[6] however kinetic evidence was not forthcoming until 1959.[7,8] Direct spectroscopic evidence was obtained in 1963[9] and conductometric evidence also in 1963.[10]

8-2.2   Steady State Concentrations

The net result of Reactions (8-2) through (8-10) is to produce H, OH, e^-_{aq} and small amounts of H_2 and H_2O_2. Reaction (8-5) is an ion-molecule reaction and will occur in about 10^{-14} sec. It is very competitive with the direct dissociative reaction, and it is probable, therefore, that the ions O^+, H^+, and OH^+ do not form, or if they do, in very small amounts. This is borne out by the high energy of formations for these species (Table 8-1).

The secondary electron produced in the ionization process becomes thermalized and solvated within 10^{-11} sec [Reaction (8-11)]. It then can react with water (only if the water is especially pure) in the absence of dissolved solute to form $H + OH^-$, with another solvated electron to give H_2, or with H^+ to give H. The steady state concentration of any of the reactive species is very low.

EXAMPLE 8-1: Calculate the approximate steady state radical concentration in pure deaerated water irradiated at a dose rate of 10^3 rads per second. Assume that the mean rate constant for a radical-radical reaction is 10^{13} cm^3/M/sec and that G (radical formation) = 10.

SOLUTION: At the steady state, the rate of radical formation equals the rate of disappearance. Assuming the disappearance takes place via a radical-radical interaction,

$$R + R \xrightarrow{k_r} M,$$

where R = radical, M = molecule, and k_r = the rate constant.

$$\text{rate of disappearance} = k_r [R]^2 = \frac{10^{13} \text{ cm}^3}{\text{mol-sec}} [R]^2$$

rate of formation =

10 radicals	10^3 rad	mol	6.24×10^{13} ev	$1 g$
100 ev	sec	6×10^{23} radicals	rad g	cm^3

$$= 1.04 \times 10^{-8} \frac{\text{mol}}{\text{cm}^3\text{-sec}}$$

rate of disappearance = rate of formation

$$10^{13} \frac{\text{cm}^3}{\text{mol-sec}} [R]^2 = 1.04 \times 10^{-8} \frac{\text{mol}}{\text{cm}^3\text{-sec}}$$

$$[R] = 3.17 \times 10^{-11} \frac{\text{mol}}{\text{cm}^3}$$

8-3 SPATIAL DISTRIBUTION OF PRIMARY SPECIES

A schematic diagram of the spatial geometry of the primary events was shown in Fig. 2-8. As indicated in Chap. 2, the mean distance between primary ionizations is dependent on particle velocity and charge. Table 8-3 shows the mean distance between primary ionizations for different energies of the incident particle.

Table 8-3. MEAN DISTANCE BETWEEN
PRIMARY IONIZATIONS

Ion (energy)	Distance
0.5 Mev electron	5000 Å
1 kev electron	50 Å
100 ev electron	5 Å
5 Mev a particle	8 Å
1 Mev a particle	2 Å

(From C. J. Hochanadel, "Comparative Effects of Radiation," p. 159, John Wiley & Sons, New York, 1960.)

As was indicated in Chap. 5, the secondary electron ejected in the primary ionization is estimated to have an *average* energy of about 75 ev. This energy is dissipated in the formation of primary species which are localized in a small volume element (spur) about 20 Å in diameter. The secondary electron will produce about five dissociated water molecules in a spur. Some of the secondaries have very high energies and will produce delta rays.

There are two theories concerning the fate of the secondary electrons. According to Samuel and Magee,[11] after the electron is thermalized it may return to its sibling positive hole producing a highly excited water molecule which can decompose to give a H and an OH radical [Reaction (8-3)]. The other theory, the Lea-Platzman theory,[12] states that the secondary electron migrates a distance of some 150 Å from the sibling positive hole where it forms the hydrated electron; the parent ion reacting, via an ion-molecule reaction, to give H_3^+O + OH. In essence this produces a radical pair separated by about 150 Å for the Lea-Platzman model, in contrast to the Samuel and Magee model which produces a radical pair in a volume element of about 10 Å radius. The diffusion-kinetic theory gives results which support the Samuel-Magee theory.

For a fast particle, the spurs will be randomly spaced at about 5000 Å, whereas for a slow particle the spurs will overlap, forming a cylindrical track of about 20 Å in diameter. H, OH, HO_2, and e_{aq}^- formed in the spurs diffuse out of the spur and react with dissolved solutes and with each other. A number of like radicals will combine within the spurs to form the molecular products H_2 and H_2O_2; a number will combine to form H_2O, while the remainder will diffuse out into the body of the solvent. The H_2 and H_2O_2 which are formed in this process are called the *molecular yield* and the e_{aq}^-, H, and OH the *radical yield*.

This process may also be viewed as an expansion of the spur, and diffusion theory (see Sec. 8-5) provides a measure of the radius of a spur as a function of time as well as the fraction of the radicals within the spur that remain unreacted at time t. Typical results are given in Fig. 8-1. This representation is for the case of tracks of isolated spherical spurs containing 12 radicals per spur and an initial spur radius of 10 Å. The curve was calculated from Eq. (8-12) for the reaction of one radical at constant solute concentration (10^{-3} M/l), taking $\bar{D}$ = 4.0×10^{-5} cm^2 per second and k = k_s = 10^{-11} cm^3 per sec-rad. As can be seen from Fig. 8-1 radical disappearance is very rapid. [13]

If the solute concentration is high, the H atoms and OH radicals which normally combine in the spurs to form the molecular products

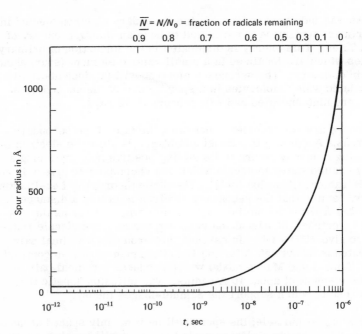

Fig. 8-1. Fraction of radicals remaining uncombined and spur size. (From A. Kupperman, Annual Report, June 1960, U.S.A.E.C. Contract No. At(11-1)-691.)

H_2 and H_2O_2 will be scavenged by the solutes, thus changing the molecular yield. As will be shown later this method may be used to detect if scavenging of the spurs has occurred. Radiation chemists employ a symbolism, which is used to distinguish between radical and molecular yields and observed yield, i.e., the actual yield observed under the conditions of the experiment.

The symbolism G_H, G_{H_2}, $G_{H_2O_2}$, etc., refers to radical and molecular yields whether scavenged or not, while $G(H_2)$, $G(H_2O_2)$, $G(H)$, etc., refer to the observed yield. Thus in air saturated water $G(H_2O_2)$ = 1.2 while $G_{H_2O_2}$ = 0.72.

8-4 LINEAR ENERGY TRANSFER, AND PRIMARY YIELDS

The rate at which energy is lost per unit of length traveled by an ionizing particle, $-dE/dx$, is the *linear energy transfer* (LET). Experimentally, LET has been characterized in aqueous systems by a determination of the G values of the radical and molecular yields in a particular system when exposed to radiation of different LET. Table 8-4 shows G_H, G_{OH}, G_{H_2} and $G_{H_2O_2}$ as measured in air-free $0.8N\ H_2SO_4$ irradiated with different sources. The G_{H_2} and $G_{H_2O_2}$ can be measured directly, but G_H and G_{OH} must be calculated from assumed kinetic mechanisms, as will be demonstrated.

Table 8-4. RADIATION YIELDS IN AIR-FREE $0.8N H_2SO_4$*

Type of radiation	G_H	G_{OH}	G_{H_2}	$G_{H_2O_2}$
^{60}Co	3.65	2.95	0.45	0.80
18 Mev D$^+$	2.39	1.75	0.71	1.03
8 Mev D$^+$	1.71	1.45	1.05	1.17
32 Mev He^{++}	1.28	1.06	1.14	1.25
^{10}B$(n,a)^7$Li	0.23	0.41	1.66	1.57

*Data from E. J. Hart, Proc. Int. Conf. U.S. Army Natick Laboratories, Jan. 14-16, 1963.

Since the energy required to form an ion pair is independent of the energy of the ionizing radiation,* the different G values observed for H_2 production, for example, with ^{60}Co and 8 Mev D$^+$ irradiation must be explained by factors other than the nature of the ionizing radiation. The accepted explanation is that for high LET (cylindrical track) the radical or active specie density is very much larger than that in low LET (spherical spurs) so that more combination occurs between the active species in the former than in the

*This is strictly true providing the particle velocity is at least that of a 2 Mev proton.

latter case. Thus, both the molecular yield and the radical yields will be different. For high LET, G (molecular yield) will be high and G (radical) will be low. Table 8-4 demonstrates why water irradiated with X-rays at modest dose rates shows much less decomposition than when irradiated with heavy particles. For heavy particles the molecular yield is greater than the radical yield, whereas for ^{60}Co irradiation, the reverse is true. Table 8-5 shows some initial LET values for various radiations calculated on the basis of relative rates of radical and molecular yields in ferrous and ceric sulfate solutions. The methods whereby LET values are obtained from rate data are detailed in a later section.

Table 8-5. INITIAL LET OF DIFFERENT RADIATIONS

Radiation	LET, ev per Å
^{60}Co	0.02
2 Mev electrons	0.02
^{35}Sβ^- (av. 46 kev)	0.07
250 kvp X-rays	0.10
10 kvp X-rays	0.20
8 kvp X-rays	0.28
Tritium β^- (av. 5.5 kev)	0.36
20 Mev D$^+$	0.45
8.4 Mev D$^+$	0.55
5.2 Mev D$^+$	1.30
2.0 Mev H$^+$	1.7
38 Mev He^{++}	2.2
2.7 Mev T$^+$	3.0
0.9 Mev H$^+$	3.0
12 Mev He^{++}	5.0
5.3 Mev He^{++} (^{210}Po)	8.8
^{6}Li (n, 205 Mev α) 2.73 Mev ^{3}H	~10.0
3.4 Mev He^{++}	12.0
65 Mev fission recoil (mass 138)	~700.0

8-5 DIFFUSION – KINETIC THEORY

This theory attempts to calculate radical and molecular yields from an assumed initial spatial distribution of the active species, i.e., a spur of some initial radius containing an average number density of active species, a certain spur separation, the diffusion coefficients, and rate constants. Calculations are then made of the fraction of radicals which escape combination as the original cluster or spur expands.

In its general form, the diffusion equation is

$$\frac{\partial C_i\,(r,\,t)}{\partial t} = \underline{D}_i \, \nabla^2 C_i \, - \, k_i \, C_i \, - \, \sum_j k_{ij} \, C_i \, C_j \, + \, \sum_e k_e \, C_e$$

$$+ \, \sum_{m,n} k_{m,n} \, C_m C_n \qquad\qquad (8\text{-}12)$$

where $\underline{D}_i$ = diffusion coefficient

∇^2 = Laplacian operator

k_i = first order rate constant for disappearance of the specie i

k_{ij} = second order rate constant for disappearance of the specie i by reaction with j

k_e = first order rate constant for the appearance of i from e

$k_{m,n}$ = second order rate constant for appearance of i from reaction of m with n

$C_i\,(r,\,t)$ = the average number density of particles of species i at position r and instant t

For H radicals in water assuming that H undergoes the reactions

$$H + H \xrightarrow{\ k_1\ } H_2 \qquad\qquad (8\text{-}13)$$

$$H + OH \xrightarrow{\ k_2\ } H_2O \qquad\qquad (8\text{-}14)$$

$$e_{aq}^- + H^+ \xrightarrow{\ k_3\ } H \qquad\qquad (8\text{-}15)$$

$$\frac{\partial [H]}{\partial t} = \underline{D}_H \, \nabla^2 \, [H] \, - \, k_1 \, [H]^2 \, - \, k_2 \, [H][OH] \, + \, k_3 \, [e_{aq}^-][H^+] \quad (8\text{-}16)$$

The initial concentration of hydrogen atoms is dependent on LET, the diffusion coefficient, the various reaction rate constants, concentrations, and the diffusion coefficients of the species with which it reacts. With a reasonably good knowledge of rate constants and diffusion constants, it has been possible to explain, at least qualitatively, the observed experimental data. The first reasonably successful attempt was made by Samuel and Magee.[11] These authors assumed that the initial distribution of radicals in a spur or track was Gaussian and that the Gaussian form is preserved as the spur expands. This is called the *prescribed diffusion hypothesis* and often referred to by the abbreviation pd. A further assumption is that the radius of the Gaussian distribution with time is the same as if diffusion only were occurring.

Samuel and Magee[11] calculated the ratio $(G_{H_2} + G_{H_2O_2})/G(-H_2O)$ for the case of one radical and no reaction with dissolved solutes, and obtained a value of 0.28, which was in very good agreement with the experimental value of 0.26. Kupperman[14,15] has presented excellent reviews of this subject along with his own calculations.

A particularly useful result of the diffusion theory are the calculations which show the number of radicals which combine to form molecular products $(H_2, H_2O_2$ and $H_2O)$ as a function of various parameters.

Consider the reaction scheme

$$M \xrightarrow{\hspace{1cm}} R + \text{ products} \qquad k_1 I \qquad\qquad (8\text{-}17)$$

$$R + S \longrightarrow \text{ products} \qquad k_s C_s C_r \qquad\qquad (8\text{-}18)$$

$$R + R \longrightarrow R_2 \qquad k(C_r)^2 \qquad\qquad (8\text{-}19)$$

where I = rate of energy absorption per unit volume

R = a radical

S = solute molecule

Reaction (8-18) is the reaction between the active specie R and a solute molecule S and Reaction (8-19) is the combination reaction of the radicals. If $\overline{N}$ be the fraction of radicals which undergo the first order reaction (the reaction is considered to be first order since the concentration of the solute remains essentially constant) then the value of $\overline{N}$ according to the treatment of Ganguly and Magee[16] can be obtained, after certain simplifying assumptions, by appropriate interpretation of Eq. (8-12). The final value of $\overline{N}$ is expressible as a function of three composite variables:

(1) Z, an energy deposition parameter $= \dfrac{1}{E} \displaystyle\int_{0}^{E_o} \dfrac{(-dE)}{dx} \, dE$,

(2) the second order rate constant k [Eq. (8-19)] and

(3) the parameter $q = k_s C_s t_o$ where t_o is the time of diffusion from a point source.

Figure 8-2 shows $(1 - \bar{N})$ the fraction of radicals which undergo the second order reaction [Eq. (8-19)] as a function of Z at constant k for various values of q. At high values of Z, $(1 - \bar{N})$ approaches unity, but at low values of Z, $(1 - \bar{N})$ is a sensitive function of the parameter q. The parameters held constant were $t_o = 1.25 \times 10^{-10}$ sec., $\bar{D} = 10^{-5}$ cm^2/sec and $\bar{\alpha} = 6$, the number of radicals per spur. Figure 8-3 shows clearly that the molecular yield increases as a function of LET. Also, since $q = k_s C_s t_o$, it can be seen that at low LET, for high values of q, the molecular yield should change by the addition of an appropriate solute.

8-6 MOLECULAR YIELDS AS A FUNCTION OF SOLUTE CONCENTRATION

The effect of solutes on the molecular yield of H_2O_2 is shown in Tables 8-6 and 8-7[17,18] for the irradiation of air saturated KBr and KCl solutions at two acid concentrations. In each of these solutions the OH radical is scavenged by the dissolved solute:

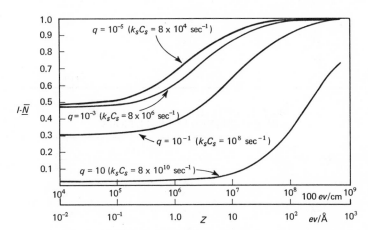

Fig. 8-2. $1 - \bar{N}$ vs Z at various values of $q = k_s C_s t_o$; $t_o = 1.25 \times 10^{-10}$ sec, $\bar{D} = 2 \times 10^{-5}$ cm^2/sec, $r_o = 10$ Å, $k = 10^{-11}$ cm^3/molecule sec, $\bar{a} = 6$. [From W. G. Burns and R. Barker, "Dose Rates and LET Effects in Radiation Chemistry," HERE Report R4240 (1963).]

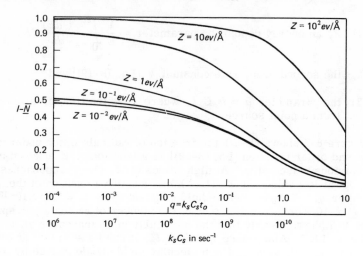

Fig. 8-3. $1-\bar{N}$ vs $q = k_s C_s t_o$ at various values of Z.
(From W. G. Burns and R. Barker, op. cit.)

Table 8-6. INITIAL YIELDS OF H_2O_2 IN
AIR SATURATED KBr SOLUTIONS

KBr M/l	$G(H_2O_2)$	
	$0.8N\ H_2SO_4$	pH = 2
10^{-2}		0.555
10^{-3}	0.675	0.66
10^{-4}	0.725	0.70
10^{-5}	0.76	0.73
0	0.78	0.75

Table 8-7. INITIAL YIELDS OF H_2O_2 IN
AIR SATURATED KCl SOLUTIONS

KCl M/l	$G(H_2O_2)$	
	$0.8N\ H_2SO_4$	pH = 2
1	0.18	0.36
10^{-1}	0.67	0.84
10^{-2}	0.95	0.97
10^{-3}	1.06	1.03
10^{-4}	1.12	—

$$Cl^- + OH + H^+ \longrightarrow Cl + H_2O \qquad\qquad (8\text{-}20)$$

$$Br^- + OH \longrightarrow OH^- + Br \qquad\qquad (8\text{-}20a)$$

Table 8-8 shows the change in the molecular yield as a function of solute concentration for various solutes, and Fig. 8-4 shows the effect of scavengers on the molecular yields observed experimentally and calculated by Eq. (8-12) under certain simplifying assumptions.[19] The experimental points have been adjusted to take into account the differences in yield of H_2O_2 and H_2 and the relative differences in reactivity of "scavenger solute" with the same radical. This permits plotting all experimental points on the same curve.

Table 8-8. $G(H_2)$ IN SOLUTIONS OF VARIOUS SOLUTES

$G(H_2)$	Solute	Concentration M/l
0.45	KNO_2	4×10^{-5}
0.41	KNO_2	1.2×10^{-3}
0.36	KNO_2	1.6×10^{-2}
0.28	KNO_2	0.165
0.38	$CuSO_4$	1.25×10^{-3}
0.32	$CuSO_4$	1.74×10^{-2}
0.21	$CuSO_4$	1.0
0.45	H_2SO_4	2.5×10^{-2}

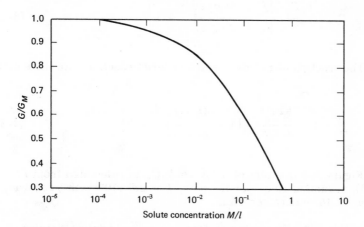

Fig. 8-4. Ratio of G (molecular yield) to G_M as a function of solute concentration. Note: G_M is the normal unscavenged molecular yield. [From H. A. Schwartz, J.A.C.S., 4960:77 (1955).]

8-7 DOSE RATE EFFECTS

At very high dose rates, one might expect the reactive species to be homogeneously distributed throughout the reaction medium instead of in isolated spurs or cylindrical tracks and thus the system could be treated in terms of homogeneous kinetics. In the true sense this would mean a homogeneous concentration of all the species found in a spur, i.e., the concentration of the active specie should exceed that in the initial spur concentration which is about $1\,M$. This concentration would have to be produced in a time comparable to the first few diffusion steps (about 10^{-11} sec) which would require a dose rate of about 10^{19} rads sec^{-1}; an impossibly high rate of energy deposition. Dose rate effects can be discussed in terms of homogeneous kinetics however, because they occur in a time scale of microseconds. This is a very long time as far as spur reactions are concerned, i.e., reactions in the spur are over with in about 10^{-8} to 10^{-9} seconds, and therefore one can speak only of those species that have survived initial spur reactions. Since spurs are distributed homogeneously (for X-rays and electrons) the kinetics are homogeneous. Hence there is a steady state with respect to the formation and disappearance of the reactive species in the sense referred to above. Using the reaction scheme in Eqs. (8-17)–(8-19), at the stationary state:

$$\frac{d[C]}{dt} = k_1 I - k_s C_s C_r - k C_r^2 = 0 \qquad (8-21)$$

$$C_r = \frac{k_s C_s}{2k} \left\{ \left(1 + \frac{4k\,k_1\,I}{k_s^2\,C_s^2} \right)^{1/2} - 1 \right\} \qquad (8-22)$$

The fraction of radicals which undergo reaction with the solute is:

$$\overline{N} = 1 - \frac{k_s^2\,C_s^2}{2Ikk_1} \left\{ \left(1 + \frac{4k\,k_1\,I}{k_s^2\,C_s^2} \right)^{1/2} - 1 \right\} \qquad (8-23)$$

Figure 8-5 is a plot of $1 - \overline{N}$ vs $k_s C_s$ as calculated from Eq. (8-23), assuming 10 ev per ion pair, $k = 2.8 \times 10^{-11}$ cm^3/sec-rad, and $k_s = 10^{-11}$ cm^3/sec-rad.

EXAMPLE 8-3: Estimate the dose rate when incipient overlap of the spurs or tracks occur, assuming that only 10 percent of the radicals formed initially survive, and that the mean distance between spurs at any time is given by $n^{-1/3}$. The number of

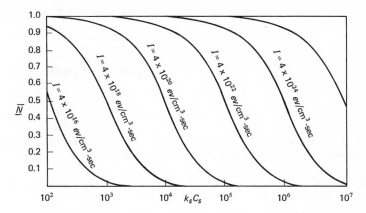

Fig. 8-5. $\bar{N}$ vs $k_s C_s$ at various values of I, $k = 10^{-11}$ cm^3/molecule-sec., $k_1 = 0.05$ radical/ev. (From W. G. Burns and R. Barker, op. cit.)

radicals per spur $\bar{\alpha}$ is 12, and the conditions for Fig. 8-1 prevail.

SOLUTION: The number of spurs each containing $\bar{\alpha}$ number of radicals, produced per unit volume in time t is

$$n = \frac{D\bar{\bar{N}}t}{\bar{\bar{\alpha}}} \qquad (8-24)$$

where $\bar{N}$ = number of radicals produced per ev

D = dose rate in ev/cm^3-sec

$\bar{\alpha}$ = number of radicals produced per spur = 1.2

From Fig. 8-1 the time at which 10 percent of the radicals have survived is 2.8×10^{-7} sec and the spur radius is 550 Å. The value of D at which the spurs just begin to overlap is when the mean distance between spurs, $n^{-1/3}$, is equal to the spur radius, r.

$$r = n^{-1/3} = \left(\frac{\bar{\bar{\alpha}}}{D\bar{\bar{N}}t} \right)^{1/3}$$

$$D = \frac{\bar{\bar{\alpha}}}{\bar{\bar{N}}tr^3}$$

$\bar{\underline{\alpha}}$ = number of radicals remaining per spur = 1.2

$$D = \frac{1.2 \text{ radicals}}{\left(10 \ \frac{\text{radicals}}{100 \text{ ev}}\right) (2.8 \times 10^{-7} \text{ sec}) (550 \times 10^{-8} \text{ cm})^3}$$

$D = 2.7 \times 10^{24}$ ev cm^{-3}-sec^{-1}

It is seen that at only extremely high intensities will the irradiation produce a homogeneous distribution of radicals.

8-8 REACTIONS OF THE REACTIVE INTERMEDIATES

The intermediates undergo reactions which depend upon the nature of the solute. In general, however, the reactions are oxidation by the OH radical; reduction by H atoms and solvated electrons; and charge neutralization by solvated electrons.

The products existing at the end of the spur reactions, which last to about 10^{-8} sec after energy deposition, are the radicals and solvated ions produced in Reactions (8-2) to (8-11), and molecular products formed in further reactions. Many of the reactions of these species with each other and with H_2O have been characterized, and rate constants obtained. The reactions are summarized in Table 8-9.

From the reaction rate constants shown in Table 8-9 we observe that in the absence of solutes (except molecular H_2 and H_2O_2) the effective species are essentially e_{aq}^-, H, OH, H_2 and H_2O_2 at modest dose rates and neutral pH. At high and low pH the effective species are different; at pH 11-14 the OH radical is in equilibrium with OH^- to produce O^-, viz

$$OH + OH^- \rightleftarrows O^- + H_2O \qquad (8\text{-}27)$$

8-8.1 Reactions of the Reducing Species

There are two reducing species in aqueous systems, the hydrated electron, e_{aq}^-, and the hydrogen atom, H.[*] These species

---

[*]Just prior to the discovery of the hydrated electron, radiation chemists realized that there were two reducing species, a hydrogen atom, which was designated as H^1, and another species thought to be a hydrated electron and designated as H. It is now established that the specie designated as H is in reality the hydrated electron and the H^1, hydrogen atoms. This notation is found in the literature between 1957 and 1962.

Table 8-9. REACTIONS AND RATE CONSTANTS
OF INTERMEDIATES IN IRRADIATED H_2O

Reaction	k
$e_{aq}^- + H_3O^+ \longrightarrow H + H_2O$	$2.2 \times 10^{10} M^{-1} \sec^{-1}$
$e_{aq}^- + e_{aq}^- \longrightarrow H_2 + 2OH^-$	$1.1 \times 10^{10} M^{-1} \sec^{-1}$*
$e_{aq}^- + H_2O_2 \longrightarrow OH + OH_{aq}^-$	$1.2 \times 10^{10} M^{-1} \sec^{-1}$
$e_{aq}^- + H_2O \longrightarrow H + OH_{aq}^-$	$16 \pm 1 M^{-1} \sec^{-1}$
$H + H \longrightarrow H_2$	$2 \times 10^{10} M^{-1} \sec^{-1}$*
$H + OH \longrightarrow H_2O$	$1.2 \times 10^{10} M^{-1} \sec^{-1}$
$OH + OH \longrightarrow H_2O_2$	$1.1 \times 10^{10} M^{-1} \sec^{-1}$*
$H_3O + OH_{aq}^- \longrightarrow 2H_2O$	$1.4 \times 10^{11} M^{-1} \sec^{-1}$
$e_{aq}^- + H \xrightarrow{H_2O} H_2 + OH_{aq}^-$	$2.5 \times 10^{10} M^{-1} \sec^{-1}$
$OH + H_2 \longrightarrow H_2O + H$	$4.5 \times 10^7 M^{-1} \sec^{-1}$
$H + H_2O_2 \longrightarrow H_2O + OH$	$9 \times 10^7 M^{-1} \sec^{-1}$
$OH + H_2O_2 \longrightarrow HO_2 + H_2O$	$4.5 \times 10^7 M^{-1} \sec^{-1}$
$HO_2 + HO_2 \longrightarrow H_2O_2 + O_2$	(pH = 0.4) $4.7 \times 10^6 M^{-1} \sec^{-1}$
	(pH = 2.7) $2.5 \times 10^6 M^{-1} \sec^{-1}$
	(pH = 5.5) $2.9 \times 10^7 M^{-1} \sec^{-1}$

*For the reaction written as $2k$

can react to give identical products in many systems, hence the discovery of the e_{aq}^- was delayed until kinetic evidence was obtained which indicated the presence of more than one reducing species.

Hydrated electrons are converted to H atoms by the reactions:

$$e_{aq}^- + H_2O \longrightarrow H + OH^- \qquad (8\text{-}28)$$
and
$$e_{aq}^- + H^+ \longrightarrow H \qquad (8\text{-}29)$$

Reaction (8-28) is slow whereas (8-29) is very fast (Table 8-9). In acid solutions e_{aq}^- is converted very rapidly to H atoms leaving as the only reactive species H and OH. In $0.1 M$ acid solutions, for example, the hydrated electron is converted in 10^{-9} to 10^{-10} sec to H atoms. In neutral or alkaline solutions, this is not the case and the reactants are distinguishable.

The similarity between reactions of the hydrated electron and the H atom is demonstrated by the following reactions:

$$Cu^{++} + H \longrightarrow Cu^{+} + H^{+} \qquad (8\text{-}30)$$

$$Cu^{++} + e_{aq}^{-} \longrightarrow Cu^{+} \qquad (8\text{-}30a)$$

$$H + O_2 \longrightarrow HO_2 \qquad (8\text{-}31)$$

$$e_{aq}^{-} + O_2 \longrightarrow O_2^{-} \qquad (8\text{-}31a)$$

$$H^{+} + O_2^{-} \longrightarrow HO_2 \qquad (8\text{-}31b)$$

$$\underset{\overset{\|}{O}}{CH_3C}-CH_3 + H \longrightarrow \underset{\overset{|}{OH}}{CH_3C}-CH_3 \qquad (8\text{-}32)$$

$$\underset{\overset{\|}{O}}{CH_3C}-CH_3 + e_{aq}^{-} \longrightarrow \underset{\overset{|}{O^{-}}}{CH_3C}-CH_3 \qquad (8\text{-}32a)$$

$$\underset{\overset{|}{O^{-}}}{CH_3CCH_3} + H^{+} \longrightarrow \underset{\overset{|}{OH}}{CH_3CCH_3} \qquad (8\text{-}32b)$$

Reactions in which the hydrogen atom and solvated electron are distinguishable take place in H_2O_2 and chloroacetic acid solutions. In the former:

$$H + H_2O_2 \longrightarrow H_2O + OH \qquad (8\text{-}33)$$

$$e_{aq}^{-} + H_2O_2 \longrightarrow OH^{-} + OH \qquad (8\text{-}34)$$

The ratio of reaction rate constants k_{34}/k_{33} is about 500.

In dilute solutions of chloroacetic acid, $G(H_2)$ increases because of Reaction (8-29) and

$$H + ClCH_2COOH \longrightarrow H_2 + ClCHCOOH \qquad (8\text{-}35)$$

As the concentration of chloroacetic acid increases, reactions of the *undissociated* fraction of the acid (which is relatively weak) become competitive with Reaction (8-29) and

$$e_{aq}^{-} + ClCH_2COOH \longrightarrow Cl^{-} + CH_2COOH \qquad (8\text{-}36)$$

occurs, producing HCl thus making this reaction distinguishable from Reaction (8-35).

Since the hydrated electron has a known spectrum[10] it is possible, by pulsed radiolysis technique, to measure directly the rate constants for many of its reactions. It is relatively simple to distinguish reactions of the hydrated electron from those of the H atom using the pulsed radiolysis technique, since spectrum measurements can be made at these high dose rates. A summary of some properties of the hydrated electron are given in Table 8-10.

Table 8-10. PROPERTIES OF THE HYDRATED ELECTRON

Wavelength at maximum absorption	7200 $\overset{\circ}{A}$
Extinction coefficient at 7200 $\overset{\circ}{A}$	15,800 M^{-1} cm^{-1}
Extinction coefficient at 5780 $\overset{\circ}{A}$	10,600 M^{-1} cm^{-1}
Half life ($e_{aq}^- + H_2O$)	780 microseconds
Radius of charge distribution	2.5 to 3.0 $\overset{\circ}{A}$
Hydration energy (calculated)	1.82 ev
Diffusion constant	4.7×10^{-5} cm^2 sec^{-1}
$E^{\circ}(e_{aq}^- + H_3O^+ \longrightarrow 1/2\ H_2 + H_2O)$	-2.56 V

The hydrated electron is a much more powerful reducing agent than the H atom. The redox potential E° for H atoms is -2.1 V for the couple (H, H/H_2) (written as H atom oxidizing) whereas for the hydrated electron it is -2.56 volts. This value was calculated by Baxendale[20] and the method used is an example of how redox potentials may be obtained.

EXAMPLE 8-4: Calculate E° for the reaction

$$e_{aq}^- + H^+ = \frac{1}{2} H_2$$

$$K = \frac{[H_2]^{1/2}}{[e_{aq}^-][H^+]}$$

SOLUTION: What is needed is ΔG° for this reaction, since $\Delta G^{\circ} = -nfE^{\circ}$, where f = faraday, n = charge, E° = potential. From the measured rates of the following reactions:

$$e_{aq}^- + H_2O \xrightarrow{k_f} H + OH_{aq}^- \qquad k_f \cong 16\ M^{-1} sec^{-1}$$

$$H + OH_{aq}^- \xrightarrow{k_r} e_{aq}^- + H_2O \qquad k_r = 1.8 \times 10^7\ M^{-1} sec^{-1}$$

the equilibrium constant K_1 is

$$K_1 = \frac{k_f}{k_r} = \frac{[\text{H}][\text{OH}^-]}{[e_{aq}^-][\text{H}_2\text{O}]} = \frac{16}{1.8 \times 10^7} = 8.9 \times 10^{-7}$$

$$\Delta G^\circ = -RT \ln K \cong 9120 \text{ cal}/g \text{ mole}$$

The desired equilibrium constant is obtained by multiplying K_1 by the reciprocal of the equilibrium constant, K_w, for the reaction

$$\text{H}_2\text{O} \rightleftharpoons \text{H}^+ + \text{OH}^-$$

$$K_w = \frac{[\text{OH}^-][\text{H}^+]}{[\text{H}_2\text{O}]} = 10^{-14} \quad (\Delta G^\circ = 19{,}300 \text{ cal}/g \text{ mole})$$

and by the reciprocal of the equilibrium constant, for

$$\frac{1}{2}\text{H}_2 \rightleftharpoons \text{H}$$

$$K_{H_2} = \frac{[\text{H}]}{[\text{H}_2]^{1/2}} \quad (\Delta G^\circ = 48{,}500 \text{ cal}/g \text{ mole})$$

thus

$$K = \frac{[\text{H}_2]^{1/2}}{[e_{aq}^-][\text{H}]} = \left(K \times \frac{1}{K_w}\right)\left(\frac{1}{K_{H_2}}\right) = \frac{[\text{H}_2]^{1/2}}{[e_{aq}^-][\text{H}]}$$

and

$$\Delta G^\circ = 9120 - 19{,}300 - 48{,}500 = -58{,}680 \text{ cal}/g \text{ mole}$$

$$-58{,}680 = nfE^\circ; \quad E^\circ = -2.56 \text{ volts}$$

This shows that the hydrated electron is a stronger reducing agent than H atoms by 0.46 volts.*

Table 8-11 summarizes the redox potentials, E°, of some important oxidizing and reducing species in aqueous systems.

---

*This value is slightly higher than that calculated by Baxendale due to the use of different values for the rate constants.

Table 8-11. OXIDATION-REDUCTION POTENTIALS

Couple	$E°$ volts ($H^+ = 1.0\ M$)
OH/OH^-	-2.8
$H, H^+/H_2$	-2.1 (H atom oxidizing)
$H_2O_2, 2H/H_2O$	1.8
$HO_2, H^+/H_2O_2$	1.7
$H^+, HO_2/H_2O, OH$	-1.35
$O_2, 2H^+/H_2O_2$	-0.68 (H_2O_2 reducing)
$H^+/1/2H_2$	0.00 (H_2 reducing)
$H^+, O_2/HO_2$	+0.30 (HO_2 reducing)
H^+/H	+2.1 (H atom reducing)

8-8.2 Reactions of the Oxidizing Species

The principal oxidizing species in H_2O is OH, however, the secondary radicals HO_2 and H_2O_3 (hydrogen sesquioxide), O_2^- and O_3^-, must be considered under certain circumstances. All of these species have been observed in irradiated oxygenated water. Some optical properties are summarized in Table 8-12. The HO_2 radical is produced by reactions:

$$H + O_2 \longrightarrow HO_2 \qquad\qquad (8\text{-}31)$$

$$OH + H_2O_2 \longrightarrow H_2O + HO_2 \qquad\qquad (8\text{-}37)$$

$$e_{aq}^- + O_2 \longrightarrow O_2^- \qquad\qquad (8\text{-}31a)$$

followed by $O_2^- + H^+ \longrightarrow HO_2$

Table 8-12. OPTICAL PROPERTIES OF TRANSIENT SPECIES
IN IRRADIATED OXYGENATED WATER

Radical	Molar Extinction Coefficient ($M^{-1}cm^{-1}$)	Wavelength (Å)
HO_2	1150	2300
O_3^-	1900	4300
O_2^-	1060	2400
OH	370	2600

The species H_2O_3 is only found under conditions of high intensity and is postulated to form via the reaction

$$OH + HO_2 \longrightarrow H_2O_3 \tag{8-38}$$

The yield of H_2O_3 above pH = 2 is $G(H_2O_3) \cong 1.6$.

At the intensities usually employed in radiation chemistry the steady state concentrations of OH and HO_2 are not sufficiently high to form H_2O_3, other species competing actively for the OH and HO_2 radical.

The hydroxyl radical behaves like a very weak acid and at sufficiently high pH dissociates:

$$OH + OH \rightleftharpoons O^- + H_2O \tag{8-38a}$$

The two forms of the OH radical, OH and O^-, exhibit different rates of reactivity with certain solutes.[21] The pK for Reaction (8-38a) has been determined to be 11.9 ± 0.2.

8-9 RADICAL AND MOLECULAR YIELDS-EFFECT OF pH

In aqueous systems, the actual reactive radical species will be different at the different pH's because of dissociation reactions such as $HO_2 \rightleftharpoons H^+ + O_2^-$ (pK = 4.5) and Reaction (8-38a) above. In addition, certain fast reactions such as $e_{aq}^- + H^+$ may occur to such an extent that other reactions of the hydrated electron may not be observed. G values for the reactive species appear to be a function of pH. Table 8-13 shows the yields of the reactive species as a function of pH.

Table 8-13. G VALUES FOR THE REACTIVE SPECIES AS A FUNCTION OF pH

	H_2O	$0.8N\ H_2SO_4$	pH = 10.5
$G_{e_{aq}^-}$	2.58	—	2.6
G_H	0.55	3.65	0.52
G_{OH}	2.59	2.95	2.6
G_{H_2}	0.45	0.45	0.45
$G_{H_2O_2}$	0.72	0.80	0.65

It may be observed from Table 8-13 that $G\ (-H_2O)$, which equals $G_{OH} + 2G_{H_2O_2}$ is greater in acid than in neutral or alkaline solutions. One explanation that has been proposed is that in the acid solutions the hydronium ion scavenges the electrons in the spurs (essentially increasing the spur dimensions), the resulting H atom because of its much higher diffusion rate escapes into the body of the solvent which increases the radical yields.

8-9.1 Determination of Molecular Yield

Irradiation of many dilute aqueous deaerated solutions of inorganic salts (Ce^{4+}, Fe^{2+}, Br^-, I^-, H_2O_2, As^{3+}, $Fe(CN)_6^{4+}$, and others) produces H_2 in identical yields, these yields being independent of pH. This fact is, to a large degree, responsible for the current theories of aqueous radiation chemistry. The H_2 along with the H_2O_2 constitute the molecular yield, the accepted value for G_{H_2} being 0.45, as is shown in Table 8-13.

Direct determination of the molecular yield of H_2O_2 was not as simple as that for H_2, however, it was found that the reaction

$$H_2O_2 + 2Fe^{++} \rightleftharpoons 2Fe^{3+} + 2OH^-$$

is fairly slow, the rate constant being 61.9 $M^{-1}sec^{-1}$, hence the H_2O_2 produced during irradiation of dilute (10^{-6} M) solutions of Fe^{2+} could be conveniently followed by observing the post irradiation oxidation of the Fe^{2+}. Such studies produced good values of the molecular yield of H_2O_2. Subsequent research on complex systems such as ceric sulfate and oxygen saturated acid solutions produced the values shown in Table 8-13.

The molecular yield of H_2O_2 does not appear to be independent of pH. The value for $G_{H_2O_2}$ at very high pH (14) decreases to 0.45. This is attributed in part to Reaction (8-38a) and the relative rates of reactivity of O^- and OH to form H_2O_2.

8-9.2 Determination of Radical Yields

The radical yields have been determined by careful study of the reaction mechanism in the presence of solutes such as ferrous sulfate, ceric sulfate, oxygen, hydrogen, CO, dilute bromide (with and without added peroxide), and formic acid solutions.

The ability of the experiment to produce values for the radical yields depends on the correctness of the assumed kinetic mechanism. If the mechanism is correct, and the experiments are done carefully, it is possible to obtain G values for the active species.

As an example of the methods employed to determine radical yields, as well as the kinetic notation commonly used in radiation chemistry, the system, Br, H_2O_2, O_2 will be discussed.*

---

*The chemistry presented in Example 8-6 has very recently been shown to be an oversimplification. The reaction of the OH radical with Br^- is pH-dependent and the Br atom formed from this reaction reacts immediately to form Br_2^-. It is this latter species which subsequently reacts with H_2O_2.

EXAMPLE 8-6: Allen and Czapski have studied the reaction of bromide solutions with and without added O_2 and H_2O_2 in neutral
and acid solution.[22] Using the reaction scheme given below,
establish the yields of $G(H)$ and $G(e_{aq}^-)$.

SOLUTION: In dilute, neutral, or acid environment, KBr solutions
saturated with oxygen, with or without added hydrogen peroxide,
the following reactions take place.

$$H_2O \xrightarrow{\text{\tiny $\sim\!\!\sim$}} H, OH, e_{aq}^-, H_2, H_2O_2$$

(1) $Br^- + OH \longrightarrow OH^- + Br$ (8-39)

(2) $Br + H_2O_2 \longrightarrow HO_2 + H^+ + Br^-$ (8-40)

(3) $e_{aq}^- + H_2O_2 \longrightarrow OH + OH^-$ (8-34)

(4) $e_{aq}^- + O_2 \longrightarrow HO_2 + OH^-$ (8-31a,b)

(5) $H + O_2 \longrightarrow HO_2$ (8-31)

(6) $2HO_2 \longrightarrow H_2O_2 + O_2$ (8-41)

(7) $e_{aq}^- + H^+ \longrightarrow H_2O + H$ (8-29)

(8) $H + H_2O_2 \longrightarrow H_2O + OH$ (8-33)

The bromide ion scavenges the OH radicals and prevents the
reaction $OH + H_2 \longrightarrow H_2O + H$ from occurring. Reaction (8-39) is
very fast as are Reactions (8-40), (8-34), (8-31a), and (8-29). (See
Table 8-9.) Reactions (8-31) and (8-33) are relatively slow, as is
Reaction (8-41).

Four variations of this system will be considered:

  I. Acid bromide solutions saturated with O_2

 II. Acid bromide solutions saturated with O_2, containing added
    H_2O_2, with $[H^+] \gg [H_2O_2]$

III. Neutral bromide solutions saturated with O_2

IV. Acid bromide solutions saturated with O_2 and containing
    H_2O_2, with $[H^+] \cong [H_2O_2]$.

For simplicity in dealing with the kinetics of this system, the
numbering system to the left of each equation will be used.

Case I — In acid solution $[H^+] \gg [O_2]$, or H_2O_2 hence (7) will be the only reaction of e_{aq}^- to be considered. Thus, for the initial H_2O_2 yield we may write

$$\text{Initial } [H_2O_2] = G_o = G_{H_2O_2} - (2) + (6) \tag{a}$$

The active radicals that are involved in these reactions are: Br, HO_2, OH and H.

Br is formed by Reaction (1) and disappears by Reaction (2), therefore,

$$(1) = (2) \tag{b}$$

HO_2 is formed in Reactions (2) and (5) and disappears by (6). The disappearance of a radical by reaction with a like radical is, by convention, written as $2k_6 (HO_2)^2$, whereas the rate of appearance of H_2O_2 in this reaction is written $k_6 (HO_2)^2$. Therefore

$$(2) + (5) = 2(6) \tag{c}$$

OH formation = G_{OH} and disappearance is by Reaction (1). Therefore,

$$G_{OH} = (1) \tag{d}$$

H — Since Reaction (7) occurs with such rapidity, the formation of H atoms is just G_H where in this case $[H] = [e_{aq}^-] + [H]$. The H atoms disappear by (5); hence

$$G_H = (5) \tag{e}$$

Substituting (b), (c), (d), and (e) into (a), we obtain

$$\text{Initial } H_2O_2 = G_o = G_{H_2O_2} + 1/2 (G_H - G_{OH}) \tag{8-42}$$

By measuring the initial H_2O_2 in these solutions, and knowing $G_{H_2O_2}$, the value $1/2 (G_H - G_{OH})$ may be obtained.

Case II — With added H_2O_2, O_2 saturated acid bromide solutions, and assuming $[H^+] \gg [H_2O_2]$, Reaction (7) is again the only reaction of e_{aq}^-.

Since there is added H_2O_2, Reaction (8) must be considered, and the yield of H_2O_2 is now $G(H_2O_2)$ with

$$G(H_2O_2) = G_{H_2O_2} - (2) - (8) + (6) \tag{a}$$

The active radicals are Br, OH, H, and HO_2.

$\underline{H}$ — As in Case I, the formation of H is G_H, disappearance is by Reaction (5) and since H_2O_2 has been added, competition for H atoms by Reaction (8) must be considered

$$G_H = (5) + (8) \tag{b}$$

$\underline{Br}$ is formed by Reaction (1) and disappears by Reaction (2). Therefore, as in Case I

$$(1) = (2) \tag{c}$$

$\underline{HO_2}$ — Identical to Case I.

$$(2) + (5) = 2(6) \tag{d}$$

$\underline{OH}$ — This radical is formed by G_{OH} and (8) and disappears by Reaction (2), which is large compared with (1).

$$G_{OH} + (8) = (2) \tag{e}$$

Substituting for (2) in (a) from (e)

$$G(H_2O_2) = G_{H_2O_2} - G_{OH} - 2(8) + (6) \tag{f}$$

Reactions (8) and (6) involve the HO_2 and H radicals, which may be eliminated from the final expression. We note first that since both Reactions (5) and (8) contain H atom concentration terms

$$\frac{(8)}{(5)} = \frac{k_8[H_2O_2][H]}{k_5[O_2][H]} \tag{g}$$

or

$$(5) = (8) \frac{k_5[O_2]}{k_8[H_2O_2]}$$

Substituting into the stoichiometric Eq. (b) for H atoms:

$$G_H = (5) + (8) = (8) + (8) \frac{k_5[O_2]}{k_8[H_2O_2]}$$

or

$$\frac{G_H}{1 + \frac{k_5[O_2]}{k_8[H_2O_2]}} = (8) \tag{h}$$

Reaction (8) is now expressed in terms of the measurable quantities (O_2) and (H_2O_2).

By adding the stoichiometric equations for H, OH, and HO_2, (b), (e) and (d), Eq. (6) can be expressed in terms of measurable quantities.

$$G_H + (5) + (2) + G_{OH} + (8) = (5) + (8) + 2(6) + (2)$$

$$\frac{G_H + G_{OH}}{2} = (6) \qquad\qquad (i)$$

Substituting (h) and (i) into (f)

$$G(H_2O_2) = G_{H_2O_2} - G_{OH} - \frac{2G_H}{1 + \dfrac{k_5[O_2]}{k_8[H_2O_2]}} + \frac{G_H}{2} + \frac{G_{OH}}{2}$$

or

$$G(H_2O_2) = G_{H_2O_2} - \frac{2G_H}{1 + \dfrac{k_5[O_2]}{k_8[H_2O_2]}} + \frac{(G_H - G_{OH})}{2}$$

Substituting for the initial peroxide yield G_o, as determined in Case I [Eq. (8-42)]:

$$1 + \frac{k_5[O_2]}{k_8[H_2O_2]} = -\frac{G_H}{G(H_2O_2) - G_o} \qquad\qquad (8\text{-}43)$$

the slope of a plot of

$$\frac{1}{G(H_2O_2) - G_o} \quad \text{vs} \quad \frac{[O_2]}{[H_2O_2]}$$

divided by the intercept will yield a value of G_H (or rather G_{red}).

Case III — Initial peroxide yield in oxygen saturated, neutral bromide solutions: In neutral bromides solutions the principal reactions are (4), (5), (1), (2) and (6). Since the H^+ concentration is low, Reaction (4) will predominate over Reactions (3) and (8).

The stoichiometric equations for the reactions of the radicals are:

$$H: \quad G_H = (5) \tag{a}$$

$$OH: \quad G_{OH} = (1) \tag{b}$$

$$HO_2: \quad (4) + (5) + (2) = 2(6) \tag{c}$$

$$e_{aq}^-: \quad G_{e_{aq}^-} = (4) \tag{d}$$

$$Br: \quad (1) = (2) \tag{e}$$

$$G_o = G_{H_2O_2} - (2) + (6) \tag{f}$$

$$(6) = G_H + G_{OH} + G_{e_{aq}^-}$$

$$G_o = G_{H_2O_2} + 1/2 \left(G_H + G_{e_{aq}^-} - G_{OH} \right) \tag{8-44}$$

Measurement of initial peroxide yields and knowledge of $G_{H_2O_2}$ gives $G_H + G_{e_{aq}^-} - G_{OH}$

__Case IV — Acid (dilute) bromide solutions saturated with O_2 containing added H_2O_2:__ In the presence of added H_2O_2, there is considerable competition between the various reactive intermediates and dissolved solutes, however, since Reaction (8) is slow compared to (5), and if $(O_2) > (H_2O_2)$ then competition between these reactions is essentially eliminated.

$$G(H_2O_2) = G_{H_2O_2} - (2) - (3) + (6) \tag{a}$$

Stoichiometric equations for the reactive intermediates are:

$$H: \quad G_H + (7) = (5) \tag{b}$$

$$e_{aq}^-: \quad G_{e_{aq}^-} = (3) + (4) + (7) \tag{c}$$

$$OH: \quad G_{OH} + (3) = (1) \tag{d}$$

$$HO_2: \quad (2) + (4) + (5) = 2(6) \tag{e}$$

$$Br: \quad (1) = (2) \tag{f}$$

A value for (6) in terms of measurable quantities is obtained by adding all the stoichiometric equations to give

$$\frac{G_H + G_{e_{aq}^-} + G_{OH}}{2} = (6) \tag{g}$$

Values for (2) and (3) are obtained as follows:

$$\frac{(7)}{(3)} = \frac{k_7[H^+]}{k_3[H_2O_2]} \quad ; \quad \frac{(4)}{(3)} = \frac{k_4[O_2]}{k_3[H_2O_2]}$$

substituting for (7) and (4) in (c)

$$\frac{G_{e_{aq}^-}}{1 + \dfrac{k_4[O_2]}{k_3[H_2O_2]} + \dfrac{k_7[H^+]}{k_3[H_2O_2]}} = (3) \qquad \text{(h)}$$

From the stoichiometric equations

$$(2) = (3) + G_{OH}$$

$$G(H_2O_2) = G_{H_2O_2} + 1/2 \left(G_H + G_{e_{aq}^-} - G_{OH} \right)$$

$$- \frac{2G_{e_{aq}^-}}{1 + \dfrac{k_4[O_2]}{k_3[H_2O_2]} + \dfrac{k_7[H^+]}{k_3[H_2O_2]}}$$

substituting for G_o [Eq. (8-44)]

$$G(H_2O_2) = G_o - \frac{2G_{e_{aq}^-}}{1 + \dfrac{k_4[O_2]}{k_3[H_2O_2]} + \dfrac{k_7[H^+]}{k_3[H_2O_2]}}$$

or

$$\frac{2G_{e_{aq}^-}}{G_o - G(H_2O_2)} = 1 + \frac{k_4[O_2]}{k_3[H_2O_2]} + \frac{k_7[H^+]}{k_3[H_2O_2]} \qquad (8\text{-}45)$$

From a knowledge of G_o and a measurement of $G(H_2O_2)$ at various solute concentrations a value for $G(e_{aq}^-)$ can be obtained.

EXAMPLE 8-7: A recent determination of radical yields makes use of the reaction of CO with OH to scavenge the OH radicals and O_2 to scavenge the H atoms and hydrated electrons. The reaction of CO with OH radicals has been well characterized by photochemical experiments as well as radiation chemistry.

In the gas phase OH reacts with CO to give $CO_2 + H$ whereas in solution it reacts to give the COOH radical. The reactions of e_{aq}^- and H with O_2 are known.

Develop a mechanism for the system and show how radical yields may be obtained.

SOLUTION: The system of equations is:

$$H_2O \xrightarrow{} e_{aq}^-, \ H, \ OH, \ H_2, \ H_2O_2$$

(1) $e_{aq}^- + O_2 \longrightarrow O_2^-(+H^+ \longrightarrow HO_2)$ (8-31a,b)

(2) $H + O_2 \longrightarrow HO_2$ (8-31)

(3) $OH + CO \longrightarrow HCOO$ (8-46)

(4) $HCOO + O_2 \longrightarrow CO_2 + HO_2$ (8-47)

(5) $2HO_2 \longrightarrow H_2O_2 + O_2$ (8-41)

Thus we have

$$G(H_2O_2) = G_{H_2O_2} + (5) \qquad\qquad \text{(a)}$$

$$e_{aq}^-: \quad G_{e_{aq}^-} = (1) \qquad\qquad \text{(b)}$$

$$H: \quad G_H = (2) \qquad\qquad \text{(c)}$$

$$OH: \quad G_{OH} = (3) \qquad\qquad \text{(d)}$$

$$HO_2: \quad (1) + (2) + (4) = 2(5) \qquad\qquad \text{(e)}$$

$$HCOO: \quad (3) = (4) \qquad\qquad \text{(f)}$$

Substituting within (a) to (f) yields

$$G(H_2O_2) = G_{H_2O_2} + 1/2 \left[G_{e_{aq}^-} + G_H + G_{OH} \right] \qquad \text{(8-48)}$$

or

$$G(H_2O_2) = G_{H_2O_2} + 1/2 \left[G_{red} + G_{ox} \right] \qquad \text{(8-49)}$$

The measured yield for $G(H_2O_2)$ was found to be 3.58,[23,24]

$$3.58 = G_{H_2O_2} + 1/2 \left(G_{red} + G_{ox} \right)$$

Individual values for G_{red} and G_{ox} can be obtained by combining this result with those of Example 8-6, and the experimentally determined G_o for initial H_2O_2 production in O_2-saturated dilute KBr solutions, which is 0.99. Substituting this value of G_o into Eq. (8-44)

$$G_o = 0.99 = G_{H_2O_2} + 1/2 \left[G_{red} - G_{OH} \right] \qquad (8\text{-}50)$$

Subtracting Eq. (8-50) from (8-49)

$$3.58 - 0.99 = 2.59 = G_{OH} \text{ (or } G_{ox}) \qquad (8\text{-}50a)$$

The material balance equation in all aqueous systems which is generally accepted is:

$$2G_{H_2} + G_{red} = 2G_{H_2O_2} + G_{ox} \qquad (8\text{-}51)$$

Substituting (8-49)

$$G_{H_2} + G_{red} = 3.58$$

From the known value of $G_{H_2} = 0.45$,

$$G_{red} = 3.13$$

As indicated previously, if the solute concentration is high, scavenging of the radicals in the spurs will occur and the G values obtained will not be the normal values for water. There are several methods of determining if scavenging of the radicals from the spurs is occurring; these usually depend on a determination of the molecular yield of either H_2 or H_2O_2 as a function of concentration. From a knowledge of the change in the molecular yield, corrections are made of the percentage of the radicals scavenged and for $G_{(radical)}$. For example, in the $CO + O_2$ system, a 1 percent correction to $G(H_2O_2)$ must be made to compensate for spur scavenging. This method is not accepted by all radiation chemists; however, it is the one most frequently used.

As demonstrated in the foregoing examples, in an aqueous system it is necessary to maintain a material balance for the production of the oxidizing and reducing species:

$$G_{e^-} + G_H + 2G_{H_2} = G_{OH} + 2G_{H_2O_2} \qquad (8\text{-}52)$$

In all cases, for each equivalent of oxidizing species formed, an equivalent amount of reducing species is formed. Before any kinetic mechanism can be developed, stoichiometry must be established.*

8-10 FRICKE DOSIMETER

The radiation chemistry of the Fricke dosimeter has been intensely studied, both because of its value as a dosimeter, and because of general chemical interest.

A chemical reaction which was known to be occurring in the ferrous sulfate system is

$$Fe^{2+} + H_2O_2 \longrightarrow Fe^{3+} + OH + OH^- \qquad (8\text{-}53)$$

This reaction had been studied and well characterized by several different groups. The OH radical produced in this reaction was identified by its reaction with added substances, hence some knowledge of the rate the reaction of OH radicals with Fe^{2+} was available prior to radiolysis studies. The Fenton Reaction (8-53) is, therefore, a reaction which can be considered a starting point for mechanism studies.

A mechanism for the oxidation of air saturated $FeSO_4$ in $0.8\,N$ H_2SO_4 that is now widely accepted is:

$$\text{Primary act:} \quad H_2O \xrightarrow{\;\sim\!\!\sim\!\!\sim\!\!\sim\;} H_2 + H_2O_2 + H + OH + e_{aq}^-$$

$$e_{aq}^- + H^+ \longrightarrow H + H_2O \qquad (8\text{-}29)$$

$$Fe^{2+} + H_2O_2 \longrightarrow Fe^{3+} + OH + OH^- \qquad (8\text{-}53)$$
$$\text{(Fenton Reaction)}$$

$$Fe^{2+} + OH \longrightarrow Fe^{3+} + OH^- \qquad (8\text{-}54)$$

$$H + O_2 \text{ (Dissolved air)} \longrightarrow HO_2 \qquad (8\text{-}31)$$

$$Fe^{2+} + HO_2 \longrightarrow Fe^{3+} + HO_2^- \qquad (8\text{-}55)$$

$$HO_2^- + H^+ \rightleftharpoons H_2O_2$$

According to Table 8-13, the G values for the active intermediates in $0.8\,N\,H_2SO_4$ are:

$$G_{H_2} = 0.45 \qquad G_{OH} = 2.95$$
$$G_{H_2O_2} = 0.80 \qquad G_H = 3.65$$

---

*Allen [A. O. Allen, Rad. Res., Suppl. 4:69 (1964)] has suggested the possibility of O atoms contributing to the yield of oxidizing species.

Summing (8-29), (8-53), (8-54), (8-31) and (8-55), we obtain

$$G(\mathrm{Fe}^{3+}) = 2G_{H_2O_2} + G_{OH} + 3G_H = 1.6 + 2.95 + 10.95$$

$$G(\mathrm{Fe}^{3+}) = 15.5$$

This is the generally accepted G value for the Fricke dosimeter with $^{60}\mathrm{Co}$ radiation or high energy electrons (0.5 - 2 Mev).

The oxidation of air saturated Fe^{3+} occurs by Reactions (8-53), (8-54), and (8-55), the reactions having been characterized by pulse-radiolysis studies.[25]

(1) $\mathrm{Fe^{2+} + OH \longrightarrow Fe^{3+} + OH^-}$ $\qquad k > 10^8 \ M^{-1}\mathrm{sec}^{-1}$

(2) $\mathrm{Fe^{2+} + HO_2 \longrightarrow Fe^{3+} + HO_2^-}$ $\qquad k = 7.3 \times 10^5 \ M^{-1}\mathrm{sec}^{-1}$

(3) $\mathrm{2Fe^{2+} + H_2O_2 \longrightarrow 2Fe^{3+} + 2OH^-}$ $\qquad k = 61.9 \ M^{-1}\mathrm{sec}^{-1}$

The fastest reaction of $\mathrm{Fe^{2+}}$ is with OH radicals and the slowest is with $\mathrm{H_2O_2}$. In air saturated solutions, the reaction $\mathrm{H + O_2}$ occurs with such rapidity that it is often excluded from the reaction mechanism and the product $\mathrm{HO_2}$ is included.

The oxidized product is $\mathrm{Fe^{3+}}$ and this is accompanied by an equivalent reduction of $\mathrm{O_2}$ to $\mathrm{H_2O}$, plus a small amount of $\mathrm{H_2}$ from $\mathrm{H_2O}$ reduction. In the absence of oxygen the products of the reaction are $\mathrm{Fe^{3+}}$ and $\mathrm{H_2}$ in the molecular ratio of 2:1; the oxidized product again is $\mathrm{Fe^{3+}}$, but the reduced product is $\mathrm{H_2O}$. The reaction mechanism postulated is

$$\mathrm{H_2O} \longrightarrow\!\!\!\!\wedge\!\!\!\wedge\!\!\!\to \ e_{aq}^-, \ \mathrm{H, \ OH, \ H_2, \ H_2O_2}$$

$$e_{aq}^- + \mathrm{H^+ \longrightarrow H + H_2O} \tag{8-29}$$

$$\mathrm{Fe^{2+} + H_2O_2 \longrightarrow Fe^{3+} + OH + OH^-} \tag{8-53}$$

$$\mathrm{Fe^{2+} + OH \longrightarrow Fe^{3+} + OH^-} \tag{8-54}$$

$$\mathrm{(H + H^+) \longrightarrow H_2^+} \tag{8-56}$$

$$\mathrm{Fe^{2+} + (H + H^+) \longrightarrow Fe^{3+} + H_2} \tag{8-56a}$$

or

$$\mathrm{Fe^{2+}(H_2O) + H \longrightarrow Fe\,(OH)^{2+} + H_2} \tag{8-57}$$

$$\mathrm{Fe\,(OH)^{2+} \longrightarrow Fe^{3+} + OH^-} \tag{8-57a}$$

Summing the above:

$$G(\text{Fe}^{3+}) = 2G_{H_2O_2} + G_{OH} + G_H = 1.6 + 2.95 + 3.65 = 8.2$$

$$G(H_2) = 0.45 + 3.65 = 4.10$$

Reaction (8-57) is the reaction generally thought to be responsible for H_2 production. Reactions (8-56) and (8-56a) were proposed by Rigg, Stein, and Weiss[26] and Reaction (8-57) by Davis, Gordon, and Hart.[27] The mechanism is supported by the fact that when H atoms formed in a gas discharge are bubbled through ferrous sulfate solutions, ferric ion is formed.[23]

It is apparent that in sealed air-saturated solutions when the oxygen is depleted $G(\text{Fe}^{3+})$ will change abruptly from 15.5 to 8.2. There may be an overall depletion of oxygen or, at high dose rates, local depletion of oxygen may take place, giving spurious results.

8-10.1 Pulse Radiolysis Yields for the Fricke Dosimeter

At dose rates below 10^{25} ev/l/sec, $G(\text{Fe}^{3+})$ remains constant at 15.5, however, at higher dose rates $\sim 10^{28}$ ev/l/sec, $G(\text{Fe}^{3+})$ falls to about 8.[28] The effect of dose rate is shown in Fig. 8-6. This is a total dose effect, not a dose rate effect, i.e., the pulses are short compared to radical lifetimes which shows up when solutions are irradiated at about 10^6 to 10^7 rads per second for longer times. There is no true dose rate effect in ferrous solutions because the reactions are so rapid that ferrous ion is depleted before a steady state is reached.

8-10.2 Effect of LET on the Fricke Dosimeter

The yield of Fe^{2+} oxidation as a function of LET has been studied under virtually all conditions. The results were summarized in Fig. 4-5 and are given again in Table 8-14.

The oxidation mechanism for the different LETs is the same as shown in Reactions (8-27), (8-31), (8-53) to (8-55), however, $G(H_2)$, $G(H_2O_2)$ and consequently $G(H)$ and $G(OH)$ have values which depend on the LET. At high LET the radical HO_2 is often included in the primary radical yield. This is formed by reaction in the spurs of OH with H_2O_2.

Using the G values for the radicals and molecular products shown in Table 8-4, $G(\text{Fe}^{3+})$ and, therefore, the LET may be determined by dividing $G(\text{Fe}^{3+})$ by the range-energy relation of the particle.

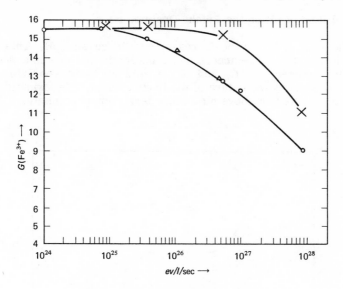

Fig. 8-6. The effect of intensity on $G(Fe^{3+})$.
O, Δ = aerated solution; X = 1.2 × 10^{-3} M [O$_2$]
and 10^{-2}M[Fe^{2+}]. [From J. K. Thomas and
E. J. Hart, Rad. Res. 17:408 (1962).]

Table 8-14. $G(Fe^{3+})$ AS A FUNCTION OF LET

Type of radiation	LET (ev per Å)	$G(Fe^{3+})$
10 Mev electrons	0.02	15.7 ± 0.3
2 Mev electrons	0.02	15.45 ± 0.3
^{60}Co γ-rays	~0.10	15.68 ± 0.07
100 kvp X-rays	~0.15	14.7 ± 0.5
60 kvp X-rays	~0.28	13.1 ± 0.5
8 kvp X-rays	0.36	13.4 ± 0.6
Tritium β^-	0.45	12.9 ± 0.2
21.16 Mev D$^+$	~1.2	11.3 ± 0.5
6.2 Mev D$^+$	1.7	8.5 ± 0.4
1.99 Mev H$^+$	~2.1	8.0 ± 0.4
40 Mev a's	—	8.7 ± 0.4
20 Mev a's	—	7.05 ± 0.4
Po-210 a's	8.8	5.1 ± 0.1
^{10}B $(n, a)^7$ Li	—	4.38 ± 0.08

8-10.3 Effect of pH on the Fricke Dosimeter

The yield of ferric ion decreases with increasing pH. This is shown in Fig. 8-7. The accepted explanation is that this is associated with the change in G_H and G_{OH} in acid solutions (see Table 8-13) and possibly the nature of the iron complex. The oxidation cannot be carried on above pH 3 since ferric ion precipitates.

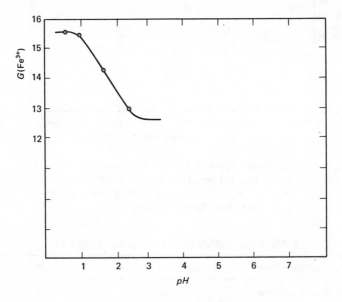

Fig. 8-7. The effect of pH on $G(\text{Fe}^{3+})$.

8-10.4 The Role of Cl⁻ in the Fricke Dosimeter

The prescribed recipe for the Fricke dosimeter as stated in Sec. 4-4.1 is $10^{-3}\,M$ in NaCl. The reason for the addition of chloride ion is that organic impurities affect the true yield of Fe^{3+} in the aerated and deaerated solutions. Before this fact was realized several different values for the ratio $G(\text{Fe}^{3+})$,(air saturated)$/G(\text{Fe}^{3+})$, (deaerated) were reported. These values ranged from about 2 to 2.8. In air saturated solutions, OH radicals attack the organic material to give a radical

$$\text{OH} + \text{RH} \longrightarrow \text{H}_2\text{O} + \text{R}' \tag{8-60}$$

The radical thus formed reacts with the dissolved oxygen to form a peroxide (RO_2) which acts like the HO_2 radical and oxidizes three ferrous ions. In deaerated solutions the radical formed in Eq. (8-60) can reduce ferric to ferrous. Hence, the change in ratios of $G(Fe^{3+})$ in air saturated and deaerated solutions.

The chloride ion in acid solution presumably reacts with the OH radical to form a Cl atom which oxidizes the ferrous ion more rapidly than it reacts with organic impurities. In more concentrated NaCl solutions, however, the Cl_2^- ion is formed. The chemistry here is not so simple since the Cl atom or Cl_2^-, whichever is the active specie, would be expected to react readily with the H_2O, however, $G(Fe^{3+})$ in $1 M$ HCl is no different than in $0.8 N H_2SO_4$ solutions (15.5).

8-10.5 Reduction of Ferric Ion

In deaerated solutions the oxidation of ferrous ion is linear to quite high doses, but then some reduction of ferric ion by H atoms occurs, and the linearity falls off. The mechanism for the reduction and oxidation processes undoubtedly depends on the relative concentrations of the various ferrous and ferric complexes in sulfate solution. Those which have been identified include $FeSO_4^+$, $Fe(OH)^{2+}$, $Fe(H_2O)^{2+}$, $Fe(OH_2)$ Fe^{4+}.

8-10.6 Competition Kinetics in Ferric Solutions

In most aqueous radiation chemistry systems, competition by molecules and radicals for the active species occurs. To prevent this, substances are added that preferentially scavenge one of the radicals, or the concentrations of the added substances are adjusted to reduce the probability of certain reactions from occurring. An excellent example of a system involving competition kinetics is given by Sweet and Thomas.[29]

EXAMPLE 8-8: A dilute deaerated ferric sulfate solution, saturated with H_2 and maintained under H_2 pressure, was irradiated with 1 microsecond pulses of 13 Mev electrons. The solutions were analyzed immediately following the pulse. Develop the proper rate expression, and an equation which expresses the fraction of H atoms reacting with ferric ion.

SOLUTION:

$$H_2O \xrightarrow{\hspace{0.8cm}\rule[0.5ex]{0.8cm}{0.4pt}\hspace{-0.8cm}\wedge\hspace{-0.2cm}\wedge\hspace{-0.2cm}\wedge\hspace{0.8cm}} H, \ OH, \ H_2, \ H_2O_2$$

$$H + H \xrightarrow{k_1} H_2 \tag{1}$$

$$Fe^{3+} + H \xrightarrow{k_2} [Fe^{3+}H] \longrightarrow Fe^{2+} + H^+ \tag{2}$$

$$OH + H_2 \xrightarrow{k_3} H_2O + H \tag{3}$$

In this system the reactions

$$H_2O_2 + Fe^{2+} \longrightarrow Fe^{3+} + OH + OH^- \tag{4}$$

and

$$OH + Fe^{2+} \longrightarrow Fe^{3+} + OH^- \tag{5}$$

can be neglected because the system is analyzed immediately following the pulse, hence Reaction (4), which is slow, could not occur. The concentration of Fe^{2+} at any time was very much less than that of H_2 hence Reaction (5) has a very low probability compared to Reaction (3). The competition was therefore between Reactions (1) and (2)

$$\frac{d[H]}{dt} = -2k_1[H]^2 - k_2[H][Fe^{3+}] \tag{6}$$

Integrating Eq. (6) by parts,

$$[H] = \frac{k_2[Fe^{3+}]}{\left[C \exp k_2[Fe^{3+}] t\right] - 2k_1} \tag{7}$$

where C, the constant of integration, is evaluated from the boundary condition that at $t = 0$ (the end of the pulse), the concentration of H atoms has a finite value I. Thus

$$C = \frac{k_2[Fe^{3+}] + 2k_1 I}{I} \tag{8}$$

Substituting into Eq. (7)

$$[H] = \frac{k_2[Fe^{3+}] (I)}{\left(k_2[Fe^{3+}] + 2k_1 I\right)\left(\exp k_2[Fe^{3+}] t\right) - 2k_1 I} \tag{9}$$

If the total concentration of H atoms at the end of the pulse is I; the fraction of H atoms, f, reacting with Fe^{3+} from $t = 0$ to some time long compared to the half time (which, for practical purpose is infinity) is:

$$f = \int_0^\infty \frac{k_2[Fe^{3+}][H]}{I} dt$$

Substituting for $[H]$, from Eq. (9),

$$f = \int_0^{\infty} \frac{(k_2[Fe^{3+}]^2 I}{(k_2[Fe^{3+}] + 2k_1 I) e^{k_2[Fe^{3+}]t} - 2k_1 I}$$

Let

$$(k_2[Fe^{3+}] + 2k_1 I) e^{k_2[Fe^{3+}]t} - 2k_1 I = S$$

$$\frac{dS}{dt} = k_2[Fe^{3+}] (S + 2k_1 I)$$

$$f = \int_{k_2[Fe^{3+}]}^{\infty} \frac{(k_2[Fe^{3+}])^2 \, dS}{S k_2[Fe^{3+}] (S + 2k_1)}$$

$$t = 0, \qquad S = k_2[Fe^{3+}]$$

$$t = \infty, \qquad S = \infty$$

Integrating by parts

$$f = \frac{k_2[Fe^{3+}]}{2k_1 I} \left[\log \frac{S}{S + 2k_1 I} \right]_{k_2[Fe^{3+}]}^{\infty}$$

$$f = \frac{k_2[Fe^{3+}]}{2k_1 I} \log \left(1 + \frac{2k_1 I}{k_2[Fe^{3+}]} \right)$$

8-10.7 Ferric Sulfate-Cupric Sulfate Dosimeter

The addition of cupric salt to the Fricke dosimeter has the effect of making the reaction independent of O_2. The H, and HO_2 radicals reduce cupric ion to the cuprous state, and this in turn reduces ferric to ferrous:

$$Cu^{2+} + H \longrightarrow H^+ + Cu^+$$

$$H + O_2 \longrightarrow HO_2$$

$$HO_2 + Cu^{2+} \longrightarrow Cu^+ + H^+ + O_2$$

$$Cu^+ + Fe^{3+} \longrightarrow Cu^{2+} + Fe^{2+}$$

The addition of cupric ion is especially useful for high dose rates.

8-11 CERIC SULFATE SYSTEM

When acid solutions of ceric sulfate are irradiated, the products are cerous ion and oxygen. The yield of cerous ion is independent of the presence of oxygen; therefore the yield is the same in deaerated and aerated solutions.

An accepted mechanism is:

$$H_2O \xrightarrow{} e_{aq}^-, \ H, \ OH, \ H_2, \ H_2O_2$$

$$e_{aq}^- + H^+ \longrightarrow H \tag{8-29}$$

$$2Ce^{4+} + H_2O_2 \longrightarrow 2Ce^{3+} + O_2 + 2H^+ \tag{8-61}$$

$$H + O_2 \longrightarrow HO_2 \tag{8-31}$$

$$Ce^{4+} + HO_2 \longrightarrow Ce^{3+} + H^+ + O_2 \tag{8-62}$$

$$Ce^{3+} + OH \longrightarrow Ce^{4+} + OH^- \tag{8-63}$$

In ceric sulfate solution H_2 is produced with $G = 0.45$, which is G_{H_2}, and hence there is no reaction of OH radicals with H_2. Reaction (8-63) is supported by studies of the $Ce^{4+} \rightleftharpoons Ce^{3+}$ exchange reactions [30, 31] and Reaction (8-61) is well known from ordinary solution kinetics. From the mechanism, therefore:

$$G(Ce^{3+}) = 2G_{H_2O_2} + G_H - G_{OH}$$

From Table 8-13

$$G(Ce^{3+}) = 2(0.80) + 3.65 - 2.95 = 2.30$$

As was demonstrated for the ceric sulfate system, the reactions of inorganic ions in aqueous solution are characterized by reactions with the intermediates produced during the irradiation. These reactions, in general, are as follows:

(1) The solutes will react with the intermediates providing the redox potentials are in the correct direction.

(2) If the reaction can be characterized by reactions of H and OH radicals, the yield will show a pH dependence.

(3) The ionic species undergoing reaction are subject to equilibria between the various aquo or other complexes.

(4) All mechanisms must show a material balance

Equivalents oxidized = Equivalents reduced

$$2G_{H_2} + 2G_{red} = 2G_{H_2O_2} + G_{ox}$$

(5) Reactions in dilute solutions should be dose rate independent but may depend on total dose.

(6) At high solute concentrations scavenging of the reactive species in the spurs will occur.

(7) Product yields will depend on LET.

8-12 REACTIONS OF AQUEOUS SOLUTIONS OF ORGANIC COMPOUNDS — FORMIC ACID

The formic acid system has been the subject of considerable study.[32] The mechanism for the radiation induced reaction of dilute $(10^{-3}\ M)$ deaerated solutions at pH below 3 is postulated to be:

$$H_2O \xrightarrow{\text{---\hspace{-0.5em}\scriptsize W\hspace{-0.5em}---}} e_{aq}^-,\ H,\ OH,\ H_2O_2,\ H_2$$

$$HCOOH \rightleftharpoons H^+ + HCOO^-$$

$$e_{aq}^- + H^+ \longrightarrow H \tag{8-29}$$

$$H + HCOOH \longrightarrow H_2 + COOH \tag{8-64}$$

$$H + HCOO^- \longrightarrow H_2 + COO^- \tag{8-65}$$

$$OH + HCOOH \longrightarrow H_2O + HCOO\ (or\ COOH) \tag{8-66}$$

$$OH + HCOO^- \longrightarrow OH^- + HCOO\ (or\ COO^- + H_2O) \tag{8-67}$$

$$HCOO + COOH \longrightarrow HCOOH + CO_2 \tag{8-68}$$

$$COO^- + H_2O_2 \longrightarrow CO_2 + OH + OH^- \tag{8-69}$$

$$COOH + H_2O_2 \longrightarrow H_2O + CO_2 + OH \tag{8-70}$$

$$2COO^- \longrightarrow (COO^-)_2 \tag{8-71}$$

The overall reaction,

$$HCOOH \longrightarrow CO_2 + H_2$$

is a chain oxidation of formic acid.

$$G(-HCOOH) = G(CO_2) = G(H_2) = G_{H_2O_2} + 1/2 \left[G_{red} + G_{OH} \right]$$

$$= 0.80 + 1/2 (3.65 + 2.95)$$

$$G(-HCOOH) = 4.10$$

In agreement with experiment, $G(CO_2)$ increases with increasing formic acid concentration. This is explained by the chain reactions:

$$HCOO + HCOOH \longrightarrow CO_2 + HCO + H_2O \qquad (8\text{-}72)$$

$$HCO + HCOOH \longrightarrow HCHO + HCOO \qquad (8\text{-}73)$$

The reaction is sensitive to pH; it has been shown that the formate ion reacts much more rapidly with H atoms and OH radicals than does the undissociated acid.

In the scheme shown, Reaction (8-71), (the production of oxalic acid), was not taken into account. This reaction becomes important only above pH 6-7. As the pH is increased $G(CO_2)$ falls off until at pH = 7 the major products are H_2 and oxalic acid.

Carbon monoxide is also formed but with a relatively low G value. The CO presumably arises from the reaction of a small fraction of the COOH radicals with H_2O_2.

$$COOH + H_2O_2 \longrightarrow CO + H_2O + HO_2 \qquad (8\text{-}74)$$

As the pH increases, reactions of the hydrated electron with the formic acid molecule occur; however, the products of the reaction have not been characterized.

8-12.1 Nitrogen Compounds

Radiolysis of deaerated solutions of glycine at pH 6.5 produces H_2, NH_3, CH_3COOH, $CHOCOOH$, CH_2O, and CO_2 as principal products. The mechanism given [33-35] is

$$H_2O \xrightarrow{} e_{aq}^-, \ H, \ H_2, \ OH, \ H_2O_2$$

$$NH_2CH_2COOH \longrightarrow NH_3^+CH_2COO^- \qquad (8\text{-}75)$$

$$e_{aq}^- + NH_3^+CH_2COO^- \longrightarrow NH_3 + CH_2COO^- \qquad (8\text{-}76)$$

$$H + NH_3^+CH_2COO^- \longrightarrow NH_3^+CHCOO^- + H_2 \qquad (8\text{-}77)$$

$$OH + NH_3^+CH_2COO^- \longrightarrow NH_3^+CHCOO^- + H_2O \qquad (8\text{-}78)$$

These are the principal reactions which occur. The OH radicals preferentially react with the alpha carbon in these systems, abstracting H; the hydrated electron reacting with the Zwitter ion according to (8-76). Small amounts of diamosuccinic acid, succinic acid and aspartic acid are found, giving good support for the presence of the radicals CH_2COOH and $NH_2CHCOOH$ formed by hydrogen abstraction.

The reactions of the radicals are speculative, however, those which appear to be quantitatively consistent with the observed products are:

$$CH_2COOH + NH_3^+CH_2COO^- \longrightarrow CH_3COO^- + NH_3^+CHCOO^- + H^+$$
$$(8\text{-}79)$$

$$2NH_3^+CHCOO^- \longrightarrow NH_2^+=CHCOO^- + NH_3^+CH_2COO^- \qquad (8\text{-}80)$$

$$H_2O + NH_2^+=CHCOO^- \longrightarrow NH_3 + HCOCOOH \qquad (8\text{-}81)$$

$$\longrightarrow NH_3 + CH_2O + CO_2 \qquad (8\text{-}82)$$

$$H_2O_2 + NH_3^+CHCOO^- \longrightarrow NH_2^+=CHCOO^- + H_2O + OH \qquad (8\text{-}83)$$

These reactions may be summarized and generalized as follows:

(1) Hydrogen abstraction by H or OH occurs at labile hydrogens (α hydrogen). This is supported by evidence obtained from studies of H radicals in a rigid matrix of various alcohols.[36]

(2) Dissociative reaction of the hydrated electron takes place when stable ions or molecules can be produced.[37] Reactions of the type

$$e_{aq}^- + RX \longrightarrow R + X^-$$

are known to occur very rapidly when X = Cl, Br or I. The rate is dependent on the other substituents in the molecule. Rate constants for this reaction are found to be of the order of 10^8 to 10^{10} $M^{-1}sec^{-1}$.

(3) Reaction of H_2O_2 with the radicals produced or with the parent substance are common.

(4) Reactions of the radicals resulting from solute-H or OH interactions lead to molecular products.

(5) Hydrogen abstraction from NH_3 or NH_4^+ or NH_3^+ does not occur, i.e.

$$NH_3 + H \longrightarrow NH_2 + H_2 \qquad (8\text{-}84)$$

$$NH_4^+ + H \longrightarrow NH_3^+ + H_2 \qquad (8\text{-}85)$$

$$NH_3^+ + H \longrightarrow NH_2^+ + H_2 \qquad (8\text{-}86)$$

appear to be endothermic. Reaction (8-85) has been found to be endothermic by about 27 kcal.[38] However, the reaction

$$NH_4^+ + e_{aq}^- \longrightarrow NH_3 + H$$

occurs. The rate of this reaction is estimated to be about $10^6 \ M^{-1} \sec^{-1}$.

EXAMPLE 8-9: From the foregoing generalization, predict the products of the radiolysis of aqueous solutions of primary amines.

SOLUTION:

$$H_2O \xrightarrow{\hspace{0.3cm}\rotatebox{0}{\scriptsize\/\/\/}\hspace{0.3cm}} H, \ OH, \ e_{aq}^-, \ H_2, \ H_2O_2$$

$$NH_3^+CH_2R + e_{aq}^- \longrightarrow NH_3 + CH_2R \qquad \text{(Generalization 2)}$$

$$H + NH_3^+CH_2R \longrightarrow NH_3^+CHR + H_2 \qquad \text{(Generalization 1)}$$

$$OH + NH_3^+CH_2R \longrightarrow NH_3^+CHR + H_2O \qquad \text{(Generalization 1)}$$

$$2(CH_2R) \longrightarrow RCH_2CH_2R \qquad \text{(Generalization 4)}$$

$$H_2O_2 + NH_3^+CHR \longrightarrow NH_4^+ + RCHO + OH \qquad \text{(Generalization 3)}$$

The principal initial products should be NH_3, RCH_2CH_2R, and RCHO for small amounts of decomposition of the amine.

8-12.2 Aqueous Solutions of Alcohols

The products of the radiolysis of deaerated methanol solutions are ethylene glycol, hydrogen, and formaldehyde. A plausible mechanism to account for these products is:

$$H_2O \xrightarrow{\hspace{0.3cm}\rotatebox{0}{\scriptsize\/\/\/}\hspace{0.3cm}} e_{aq}^-, \ H, \ H_2, \ OH, \ H_2O_2$$

$$CH_3OH + H \longrightarrow CH_2OH + H_2 \qquad (8\text{-}87)$$

$$CH_3OH + OH \longrightarrow CH_2OH + H_2O \qquad (8\text{-}88)$$

$$2(CH_2OH) \longrightarrow CH_2OHCH_2OH \qquad (8\text{-}89)$$

$$CH_2OH + H_2O_2 \longrightarrow HCHO + H_2O + OH \qquad (8\text{-}90)$$

$$e_{aq}^- + H^+ \longrightarrow H \qquad (8\text{-}29)$$

The hydrated electron has a very low reactivity with methanol, hence its principal reaction will be to form H atoms. Initial product yields should be

$$G(H_2) = G_{H_2} + G_{red}$$

$$G(CH_2O) = G_{H_2O_2}$$

$$G(\text{ethylene glycol}) = 1/2 \ (G_{red} + G_{OH}) - 1/2 \ G_{H_2O_2}$$

The reaction however is more complicated than shown because even small amounts of product will appreciably affect the results. For example such reactions as

$$e_{aq}^- + HCHO \longrightarrow [HCHO^-] \qquad (8\text{-}91)$$

will affect the H atom yield, however the mechanism is approximately valid.

8-12.3 Benzene Solutions

The radiolysis of aqueous solutions of benzene have attracted attention because of interest in this system as a dosimeter and because of the possibility of commercially producing phenol this way. Recent pulsed radiolysis studies have shown that previous mechanisms were in error in the assignment of the reactions of the OH and H atoms. In air saturated solutions

$$H_2O \overset{\text{\textasciitilde}\!\!\text{\textasciitilde}\!\!\text{\textasciitilde}}{\longrightarrow} e_{aq}^-, \ H, \ OH, \ H_2, \ H_2O_2$$

$$e_{aq}^- + H^+ \longrightarrow H \qquad (8\text{-}29)$$

$$OH + C_6H_6 \longrightarrow C_6H_6OH \qquad (8\text{-}92)$$

$$e_{aq}^- + O_2 \longrightarrow O_2^- (O_2^- + H^+ \longrightarrow HO_2) \qquad (8\text{-}31a,b)$$

$$H + O_2 \longrightarrow HO_2 \qquad (8\text{-}93)$$

$$OHC_6H_6 + O_2 \longrightarrow OHC_6H_6O_2 \qquad (8\text{-}94)$$

$$OHC_6H_6O_2 \longrightarrow C_6H_5OH + HO_2 \qquad (8\text{-}95)$$

$$2HO_2 \longrightarrow H_2O_2 + O_2 \qquad (8\text{-}96)$$

$$HO_2 + OHC_6H_6O_2 \longrightarrow \text{organic hydroperoxides} \qquad (8\text{-}97)$$

The material balance for H_2O_2 is:

$$G(H_2O_2) = G_{H_2O_2} + 1/2\ G_{red} + 1/2\ G(C_6H_5OH)$$

$$- 1/2\ G \text{ (hydroperoxide)}$$

$$= 0.72 + 1/2(3.13) + 1/2(0.19) - 1/2\ G(\text{H.P.})$$

$$G(H_2O_2) = 2.38 - 1/2\ G \text{ (hydroperoxide)}$$

$G(H_2O_2)$ found was 2.2 ± 0.4. This is quite good agreement considering that the hydroperoxide yield is not known.

An interesting factor is that the OH radical does not abstract hydrogen from the aromatic ring but rather adds to it. In deaerated as well as aerated solutions the OH radical is scavenged by the benzene. The available evidence indicates that H atoms also add to the benzene forming the cyclohexadienyl radical C_6H_7. The net result of the irradiation of deaerated benzene solutions is to form hydrogen, phenol, and diphenyl plus various other organic products formed by the reactions of the C_6H_6OH and C_6H_7 radicals. It is found that there is a post-irradiation effect, i.e., the diphenyl is formed in a post-irradiation process as are some other dimer products. The phenol is presumed to be formed by the disproportionation reaction.

$$2(C_6H_6OH) \longrightarrow C_6H_5OH + C_6H_7OH \tag{8-98}$$

8-12.4 Oxidation of Organic Compounds

Organic molecules dissolved in water and undergoing exposure to radiation for a sufficiently long time become oxidized to CO_2 and H_2O. At moderate dose rates a general mechanism which appears representative of the radiation induced reaction in air saturated solutions of many organic compounds is

$$H_2O \xrightarrow{} e_{aq}^-,\ H,\ OH,\ H_2,\ H_2O_2$$

$$RH + OH \longrightarrow R + H_2O \tag{8-99}$$

$$H_2R + O_2 \longrightarrow RH + HO_2 \tag{8-100}$$

$$\text{(neutral)}\ e_{aq}^- + O_2 \longrightarrow O_2^- \tag{8-31a}$$

$$\text{(acid)}\ e_{aq}^- + H^+ \longrightarrow H \tag{8-29}$$

$$O_2^- + H^+ \longrightarrow HO_2 \tag{8-31b}$$

$$H + O_2 \longrightarrow HO_2 \tag{8-93}$$

$$2HO_2 \longrightarrow H_2O_2 + O_2 \qquad\qquad (8\text{-}96)$$

$$G(\text{-RH}) = G(R) = G_{OH}$$

from the foregoing

$$G(H_2O_2) = G_{H_2O_2} + 1/2\, G_H + 1/2\, G_{OH}$$

For example, irradiation of dilute, air saturated ethanol gives

$$H_2O \xrightarrow{\hspace{0.5cm}} e_{aq}^-,\ H,\ OH,\ H_2,\ H_2O_2$$

$$e_{aq}^- + O_2 \longrightarrow O_2^-(O_2^- + H^+ \rightleftharpoons HO_2) \qquad (8\text{-}31a)$$

$$H + O_2 \rightleftharpoons HO_2 \qquad\qquad (8\text{-}93)$$

$$OH + C_2H_5OH \longrightarrow C_2H_4OH + H_2O \qquad (8\text{-}99)$$

$$C_2H_4OH + O_2 \longrightarrow CH_3CHO + HO_2 \qquad (8\text{-}100)$$

$$2HO_2 \longrightarrow H_2O_2 + O_2 \qquad\qquad (8\text{-}96)$$

from which

$$G(H_2O_2) = G_{H_2O_2} + 1/2\, G_{red} + 1/2\, G_{OH} = 3.58$$

$$G(H_2O_2) \text{ experimental} = 4.0$$

Organic peroxides form in many of these solutions, and can initiate a chain via

$$R + O_2 \longrightarrow RO_2$$

$$RO_2 + RH \longrightarrow RO_2H + R \qquad\qquad (8\text{-}103)$$

thus increasing the amount of reaction.

PROBLEMS

1. Calculate the rate of e_{aq}^- disappearance in a $0.1\,M$ HCl solution when the solution is irradiated at a dose rate of 300 rads per second.

2. Give ten examples of reactions in which H atoms and e_{aq}^- give identical products.

3. Calculate $E°$ for the reaction

$$Fe^{2+} + H^+ \longrightarrow Fe^{3+} + 1/2\ H_2$$

4. Calculate the heat of the reaction

$$e^- + H_2O \rightleftharpoons e_{aq}^-$$

5. Using the data in Table 8-4 calculate the LET for the different radiations.

6. The principal products found in the radiolysis of aqueous solutions of ethanol are hydrogen, 2,3-butanediol and acetaldehyde. Assuming the acetaldehyde arises from the disproportionation of the α-ethanol radical, develop a mechanism consistent with these products.

7. Calculate the OH concentration in 4 cm^3 of H_2O that has absorbed a 10 milliamp pulse of 3 Mev electrons in 0.4 microseconds assuming no reaction of the radicals during the pulse.

8. Devise a mechanism for the radiation induced reaction of dilute air saturated propanol solutions. What are the principal products?

9. What would be the temperature of an aqueous solution irradiated at a dose rate of 10^{20} ev/cm^3/sec and at 10^{24} ev/cm^3/sec under adiabatic conditions for 5 sec, 20 sec, 1 min.

10. Are the reactions shown below equivalent? Explain.

$$e_{aq}^- + O_2 \longrightarrow O_2^-$$

$$H + O_2 \longrightarrow HO_2$$

REFERENCES

1. W. Duane and O. Scheuer, *Le Radium*, 10:33 (1913).

2. A. O. Allen, "Radiation Chemistry of Water and Aqueous Systems," D. Van Nostrand Company, New York, 1961.

3. L. Kevan, P. W. Moorthy, and J. Weiss, *J.A.C.S.*, 86:771 (1964).

4. S. N. Foner and R. L. Hudson, *J. Chem. Phys.*, 21:1608 (1953).

5. S. Gordon, E. J. Hart, and J. K. Thomas, *J. Phys. Chem.*, 68:1262 (1964).

6. R. L. Platzman, "Basic Mechanisms in Radiobiology II, Physical and Chemical Aspects," pp. 34-35, Nat. Acad. Sci., Publ. No. 305 (1953).

7. A. O. Allen and N. Barr, *J. Phys. Chem.*, **63**:920 (1959).

8. G. Czapski and H. A. Schwartz, *J. Phys. Chem.*, **66**:471 (1962).

9. J. W. Boag and G. Hart, *Nature*, **197**:45 (1963).

10. J. W. Boag, *Amer. J. Roent., Radium Therapy, Nucl. Med.*, **40**:896 (1963).

11. A. H. Samuel and J. L. Magee, *J. Phys. Chem.*, **21**:1080 (1953).

12. R. L. Platzman, *U. S. Nat. Res. Council*, Publ. No. 305 (1953).

13. A. Kupperman and G. G. Belford, *J. Chem. Phys.*, **36**:1412 (1962).

14. A. Kupperman, Diffusion Kinetics in Radiation Chemistry, in V. M. Haissinski (ed.), "The Chemical and Biological Action of Radiations," vol. V, p. 85, Academic Press, London, 1961.

15. A. Kupperman, Diffusion Model of Radiation Chemistry in G. Silini (ed.), "Radiation Research," pp. 212-233, North Holland Publishing Co., Amsterdam, 1967.

16. A. K. Ganguly and J. L. Magee, *J. Chem. Phys.*, **25**:129 (1956).

17. T. J. Sworski, *J.A.C.S.*, **76**:4687 (1954).

18. T. J. Sworski, *Rad. Res.*, **2**:26 (1955).

19. H. A. Schwartz, *J.A.C.S.*, **4960**:77 (1955).

20. J. H. Baxendale, *Rad. Res.*, Suppl. **A**:139 (1964).

21. J. Rabani and M. S. Matheson, *J. Phys. Chem.*, **70**:761 (1966).

22. G. Czapski and A. O. Allen, *J. Phys. Chem.*, **66**:262 (1962).

23. C. J. Hochanadel, *ORNL Report* no. 3815, May 6, 1965, p. 32.

24. C. J. Hochanadel, personal communication.

25. J. P. Keene, *Rad. Res.*, **22**:14-20 (1964).

26. T. Rigg, G. Stein, and J. Weiss, *J. Proc. Roy. Soc.*, **A211**:375 (1952).

27. T. W. Davis, S. Gordon, and E. J. Hart, *J.A.C.S.*, **80**:4487 (1958).

28. J. K. Thomas and E. J. Hart, *Rad. Res.*, **17**:408 (1962).

29. J. P. Sweet and J. K. Thomas, *J. Phys. Chem.*, **68**:1363 (1964).

30. G. E. Challenger and B. J. Masters, *J.A.C.S.*, **77**:1063 (1955).

31. G. E. Challenger and B. J. Masters, *J. Phys. Chem.*, **59**:1093 (1955).

32. E. J. Hart, J. K. Thomas, and S. Gordon, *Rad. Res.*, Suppl. **4**:79 (1964).

33. W. M. Garrison, *Rad. Res.*, Suppl. 4 (1964).

34. B. M. Weeks, S. A. Cole, and W. M. Garrison, *J. Phys. Chem.*, **69**:4131 (1965).

35. R. Braams, *Rad. Res.*, **30** (1967).

36. M. Fumimoto and D. J. E. Ingram, *Trans. Far. Soc.*, **54**:1304 (1958).

37. M. Anbar and E. J. Hart, *J. Phys. Chem.*, **71**:3700 (1967).

38. V. L. Talroze and M. Frankevich, All Union Conference on Radiation Chemistry, Moscow, 1957.

EFFECT OF RADIATION ON LIQUID HYDROCARBONS

9-1 INTRODUCTION

The literature on the effects of high energy radiation on hydrocarbons is at least as extensive as that for aqueous systems. Early studies[1,2] were largely concerned with qualitative results. Clark and Pickett, for example, using X-rays, irradiated a number of solutions including those of anthracene, maleic acid, and iodine plus benzene. They also studied the condensation reactions of aldehydes and ketones which they found to be "markedly catalyzed by X-irradiation." In the system benzene and iodine they reported that 6.5 percent of the iodine was absorbed. Subsequent research in this area was sparse until the late 1940s and early 1950s.

The radiolysis of hydrocarbons and related molecules may be examined from much the same point of view as aqueous systems; however, hydrocarbon systems exhibit a number of unique properties which make them a separate area of research.

9-2 PRIMARY SPECIES

An ionizing particle in traversing a hydrocarbon medium produces ionizations, excitations, and decompositions in much the same manner as discussed in Chapter 8, i.e., in spurs separated at some mean distance, which for the alkanes would be of the order of about 5000 Å for gamma radiation. The subsequent reactions of the species formed in the spurs will be considerably more complex than in water. There will be essentially four types of species formed:

(1) Ions both positive and negative (excited and in the ground state)

(2) Excited molecules

(3) Radicals (excited and in the ground state)

(4) Electrons (free, trapped, or solvated)

The ions, excited species, and radicals formed undergo reaction and those species which escape the spur become part of the radical yield (or strictly speaking an active specie yield) whereas those species that react in the spur to produce identifiable products are part of the molecular yield. Thus, in hydrocarbons (or any organic liquid system), there is a molecular yield and a radical yield, but the nature of these yields is considerably more complex than it is in water.

9-3 TIME SCALE FOR PRIMARY EVENTS

The time scale for primary events shown in Table 9-1 is similar to that shown previously; however, there are some important differences in emphasis. Ions, for example, will undergo neutralization, decomposition, or ion molecule reactions to produce a much larger variety of reactive species (radicals) than in water, and it is this feature which makes hydrocarbon systems unique. The electron ejected in the ionization process may become thermalized, form a negative ion, become solvated, or react with a positive ion in a neutralization reaction. Experiment has shown[3-5] that in liquid hexane practically all of the "thermalized" electrons are captured by the ions in the spur and only a small fraction of the ions escape into the body of the solution, the G value for separated ion pairs being about 0.1.* This is in contrast to water where conductivity experiments and direct spectroscopic observation confirms the presence of the hydrated (solvated) electron with a half life of about 0.6 microsecond.

The secondary electrons become thermalized. In hydrocarbon systems, however, the electron affinity for the alkanes or alkenes is apparently such that no long lifetime "solvated electron" is normally seen in these systems, the neutralization process occurring in about 10^{-10} to 10^{-9} sec. Solvation of the electron through self-polarization would be expected only for polar liquids. Whether or not a solvated electron would be observable by fast spectrographic techniques depends upon its rate of removal by chemical reaction in competition with the neutralization process. The solvated electron has been observed in several organic liquids such as the aliphatic alcohols[6] (methanol, ethanol, n-propanol, and iso-propanol) and ethylenediamine.[7] In solutions of diphenyl in ethanol the diphenylide ion is formed $(C_{12}H_{10})^-$. Other cases of observed electron attachment are solutions of anthracene and terphenyl in ethanol.[8]

There is ample evidence therefore to show that solvation of the electron will occur in polar organic media. In some cases, such as

---

*The addition of C_2H_2OD as a proton scavenger in the radiolysis of cyclohexane indicates however that the scavengeable positive ion yield may be as high as 2.6 ions/100 ev. [See J. W. Buchanan and F. Williams, J. Chem. Phys. 44:4577 (1966).]

Table 9-1. TIME SCALE FOR PRIMARY EVENTS
IN HYDROCARBON RADIOLYSIS

Event	Time (sec)
Ionization and excitation	10^{-15}
Molecular vibration, possible dissociation	10^{-14}
Electron thermalization	10^{-12} to 10^{-14}
Collision time in liquid (ion-molecule reactions)	10^{-13}
Neutralization of ions (in spherical spur, Samuel and Magee model)	10^{-12} to 10^{-13}
Radical jump time, in diffusion ($\overline{D} = 2$ to 8×10^{-5} cm^2 sec^{-1})	10^{-12}
Radical combination in cylindrical track	10^{-9}
Radical combination in spherical track	10^{-8}
Radiative lifetime of excited triplet	$> 10^{-4}$

in solutions containing iodine, and in the substances referred to above, separated ion pairs will form. However, in the alkanes or alkenes, no such species has been observed and it appears that separated ion pairs have a very short lifetime. Theoretical arguments have been advanced to show that in nonpolar liquids solvation may occur, but the bonding would be extremely weak and a spectrum, if detected, would be in the infrared region. However, the lifetimes of these solvated electrons may be such that they cannot be observed with present techniques.

According to Table 9-1 it is seen that within 10^{-12} sec the primary species will react in some manner to form the reactive radical intermediates and possibly some stable products. These primary species (ions, excited species) are the precursors of the observable reactive intermediates, however, the role of these individual species in the formation of the active intermediates is still open to debate. The major product distribution formed in the radiolysis of hydrocarbons is usually explained on the basis of the free radicals produced during irradiation. These free radicals have their origin in the various species formed in the initial act (ions, excited molecules, etc.).

9-4 EXCITED SPECIES

Voedvodsky and Molin[9] have proposed that excited states in saturated hydrocarbons are rapidly changed by internal conversion to the lowest optically allowed excited state. This is about 7 ev above the ground state, and more than sufficient for carbon-carbon or carbon-hydrogen bond cleavage. This, then, could be one of the primary modes of formation of the alkyl radicals observed in these systems. Some support for the importance of excited states as precursors for the observed free radicals comes from photochemistry,[10] from kinetic studies,[11] and studies on LET effects.[12] In aromatic systems triplet states have been reported in pulsed radiolyses studies of anthracene, phenanthrene, and naphthalene. The radiolysis of pure cyclohexanone and pure cyclopentanone produces the isomerization products 5-hexenal and 4-pentenal in addition to others. About three fourths of the yield of these open chain olefinic aldehydes occurs via the lowest triplet state of the ketone, the other one fourth occurring via a different excited state, possibly the lowest singlet state. In benzene solution these molecules also undergo the same isomerization reaction, but in this case via energy transfer from excited benzene molecules.[13]

The production of excited molecules as a result of ion recombination has been postulated as a source of free radicals.[14] The decomposition of n-hexane has been explained by this mechanism. For example:

$$C_6H_{14}^+ + e^- \longrightarrow C_6H_{14}^*$$

$$C_6H_{14}^* \longrightarrow C_6H_{13} + H$$

$$\longrightarrow C_5H_{11} + CH_3$$

$$\longrightarrow C_4H_9 + C_2H_5$$

$$\longrightarrow C_3H_7 + C_3H_7$$

9-5 IONS — UNIMOLECULAR DECOMPOSITION

Ions are formed during the passage of the charged particles through the medium. In hydrocarbons they can, in addition to other reactions, undergo unimolecular decompositions, as in isobutane:

$$iso\text{-}C_4H_{10}^+ \longrightarrow CH_3 + C_3H_7^+ \tag{9-1}$$

The radical produced in this process is called a *fragment* radical, and the ion a fragment ion. For this process to occur, the molecular ions must have excess energy since these reactions are appreciably endothermic and a one-electron, carbon-carbon bond must be broken. An estimate of the bond strengths for the one-electron bonds $(C-C^+)$ may be calculated from the thermodynamic cycle:

$$D(RC \cdot C^+ R') = D(RC:CR) + I(RC \cdot) - I(RC:CR') \tag{9-2}$$

where $D(RC \cdot C^+R')$ = the dissociation energy of the one-electron bond

$I(RC)$ = the ionization potential of the radical RC

$I(RC:CR')$ = the ionization potential of the parent molecule (two-electron bond)

$D(RC:CR)$ = dissociative energy of the (RC:CR) bond

EXAMPLE 9-1: Show the validity of Eq. (9-2) and calculate the bond-dissociation energy of the carbon-carbon bond in the ethane ion $C_2H_6^+$.

SOLUTION: The value desired is that for the bond dissociation energy for the reaction

$$(C_2H_6^+) \longrightarrow CH_3^+ + CH_3 \tag{1}$$

$$D(H_3C \cdot CH_3^+) = \Delta H_f(CH_3) + \Delta H_f(CH_3^+) - \Delta H_f(C_2H_6^+) \tag{2}$$

$\Delta H_f(C_2H_6^+)$ is obtained as shown in Example 7-2

$$C_2H_6 \longrightarrow C_2H_6^+ + e^- \quad \Delta H = \text{I.P.} = 11.65 \text{ ev}$$

$$I(C_2H_6) = \Delta H_f(C_2H_6^+) - \Delta H_f(C_2H_6) \tag{3}$$

substituting (3) into (2)

$$D(H_3C \cdot CH_3^+) = \Delta H_f(CH_3) + \Delta H_f(CH_3^+) - I(C_2H_6) - \Delta H_f(C_2H_6) \tag{4}$$

$\Delta H_f(CH_3^+)$ may be obtained similarly

$$CH_3 \longrightarrow CH_3^+ + e \quad \Delta H = \text{I.P.} = 9.84 \text{ ev}$$

$$\Delta H_f(CH_3^+) = I(CH_3) + \Delta H_f(CH_3) \tag{5}$$

substituting (5) into (4)

$$D(H_3C \cdot CH_3^+) = 2\Delta H_f(CH_3) + I(CH_3) - I(C_2H_6) - \Delta H_f(C_2H_6) \tag{6}$$

but

$$D(CH_3CH_3) = 2\Delta H_f(CH_3) - \Delta H_f(C_2H_6) \tag{7}$$

therefore, introducing (7) into (6)

$$D(H_3C \cdot CH_3^+) = D(CH_3CH_3) + I(CH_3) - I(C_2H_6)$$

$$D(CH_3CH_3) = 3.67 \text{ ev}$$

$$D(H_3C \cdot CH_3^+) = 3.67 + 9.84 - 11.65 = 1.86 \text{ ev}$$

Support for unimolecular decomposition of ions as a source of alkyl radicals comes from the fact that branching increases fragment radical yields and that nonequivalent yields of fragment alkyl radicals are observed. For example, 33 percent of the total primary radicals in n-pentane radiolysis are fragment radicals, whereas the fragment alkyl radical yield is 48 percent of the total in 2,4-dimethylpentane, 64 percent in 2,2,4-tri-methyl-pentane, and 79 percent in neopentane. For the fragment radical yield to be high requires that the molecule-ion decompose to form an alkyl radical and a fragment ion [as in Eq. (9-1)] and that the fragment ion decomposes further, for example:

$$iso\text{-}C_4H_{10}^+ \longrightarrow CH_3 + C_3H_7^+ \tag{9-1}$$

$$C_3H_7^+ + e^- \longrightarrow H + C_3H_6 \tag{9-3}$$

The probability for these reactions is related to the bond strengths. Table 9-2 summarizes a number of one-electron bond strengths as calculated from Eq. (9-2). Comparison of the $C - CH_3$ bond strengths for neopentane (8 kcal per mole) and n-pentane (39 kcal per mole) accounts qualitatively for the differences in fragment alkyl radical yields observed (79 percent vs 33 percent).

9-5.1 Ion-Molecule Reactions

Since the ions are formed in a condensed phase, ion-molecule reactions such as (9-4) appear to be favored

$$RH^+ + RH \longrightarrow RH_2^+ + R \cdot \tag{9-4}$$

The resulting molecule-ion may undergo neutralization with or without subsequent decomposition, as was discussed in Chap. 7. Ion-molecule reactions generally have large cross sections, however, the rates of these reactions must be considered relative to the rates of the neutralization process, and the unimolecular decomposition of the molecular ion. The specific rate constant for these ion-molecule reactions may in some instances not be high enough to compete with the other two processes particularly in condensed phases.

Undoubtedly ion-molecule reactions occur, however their role in the formation of the observed radicals is difficult to assess. Ion-molecule reactions have been used to explain the observed distribution of dodecanes from the radiolysis of solid n-hexane[15] and radiolysis of cyclopropane-hexane solutions.[16]

Table 9-2. STRENGTHS OF ONE ELECTRON BONDS*

Carbon-carbon bonds	Energy, kcal/mole	Carbon-hydrogen bonds	Energy, kcal/mole
C—C	44	C—H	34
CC—C	30	CC—H	27
CCC—C	35	CCC—H	40
CC—CC	39	$C\underset{C}{C}-H$	17
$\underset{C}{C}C-C$	14	CCCC—H	48
CCCC—C	39	$C\underset{C}{C}C-H$	44
CCC—CC	41	$CC\underset{C}{C}-H$	27
$C\underset{C}{C}C-C$	34	$C\overset{C}{\underset{C}{C}}-H$	15
$\underset{C}{C}C-CC$	19		
$CC\underset{C}{C}-C$	20		
$C\overset{C}{\underset{C}{C}}-C$	8		
CCCC—CC	47		
CCC—CCC	41		
$C\underset{C}{C}C-CC$	38		
$C\underset{C}{C}-CCC$	21		
$CC\underset{C}{C}-CC$	24		

(Table continues)

Table 9-2. STRENGTHS OF ONE ELECTRON BONDS* (Continued)

Carbon-carbon bonds	Energy, kcal/mole	Carbon-hydrogen bonds	Energy, kcal/mole
C$\overset{\text{C}}{\underset{\text{C}}{\text{C}}}$—CC	14		
C$\underset{\text{C}}{\text{C}}$—C$\underset{\text{C}}{\text{C}}$	17		
CCCC—CCC	42		
C$\underset{\text{C}}{\text{C}}$C—CCC	34		
C$\underset{\text{C}}{\text{C}}$—CCCC	19		
CC$\underset{\text{C}}{\text{C}}$—CCC	22		
C$\overset{\text{C}}{\underset{\text{C}}{\text{C}}}$—CCC	17		
C$\underset{\text{C}}{\text{C}}$C—C$\underset{\text{C}}{\text{C}}$	23		
CC$\underset{\text{C}}{\text{C}}$—C$\underset{\text{C}}{\text{C}}$	21		
C$\overset{\text{C}}{\underset{\text{C}}{\text{C}}}$—C$\underset{\text{C}}{\text{C}}$	13		
CCCC—CCCC	38		
C$\underset{\text{C}}{\text{C}}$C—CCCC	38		
CC$\underset{\text{C}}{\text{C}}$—CCCC	21		
C$\overset{\text{C}}{\underset{\text{C}}{\text{C}}}$—CCCC	15		

(Table continues)

Table 9-2. STRENGTHS OF ONE ELECTRON BONDS* (Continued)

Carbon-carbon bonds	Energy, kcal/mole	Carbon-hydrogen bonds	Energy, kcal/mole
CC̲C–CC̲C (C below)	36		
CCC̲–CC̲C (C below)	31		
CCC̲–C̲CC (C below)	20		
CC̲C–CC̲C (C above and below)	13		
CC̲C̲–C̲CC	12		
CC̲C̲–C̲CC	14		

*Data from J. L. Franklin and F. W. Lampe, *Trans. Far. Soc.*, **57**:1449 (1961).

A neutralization reaction following an ion-molecule reaction that is believed to occur[17,18] is:

$$RH_2^+ + e^- \longrightarrow R + H_2 \tag{9-5}$$

This reaction would lead to the formation of radicals — e.g.,

$$cyclo\text{-}C_6H_{13}^+ + e^- \longrightarrow cyclo\text{-}C_6H_{11} + H_2 \tag{9-6}$$

and H_2, without involving H atoms.

9-5.2 Dissociative Electron Capture

There is good evidence[19-21] that this process occurs in the halogen substituted alkanes, viz., $CHCl_3$, CH_3I, $C_2F_2Cl_2$, etc. The process is

$$CCl_4 + e^- \longrightarrow Cl^- + CCl_3 \tag{9-7}$$

$$CH_3I + e^- \longrightarrow I^- + CH_3 \tag{9-8}$$

These reactions would be favored by the high electron affinity of the halogen and the low bond energy, thus this process should definitely be considered as a source of radicals in irradiation of systems containing halogen-substituted hydrocarbons.

In Table 9-3 are summarized the appearance potentials for the negative ions of some of the halogen-substituted alkanes.

Table 9-3. APPEARANCE POTENTIALS (AP)
FOR SOME NEGATIVE IONS

Substance	Negative ion	AP, ev
CF_3SF_5	SF_5^-	0.20
ClO_3F	ClO_3^-	0.20
CCl_4	Cl^-	0.20
CF_2ClCF_2Cl	Cl^-	0.20
CCl_3F	Cl^-	0.10
SF_6	SF_5^-	0.05
CCl_2F_2	Cl^-	0.50
C_2F_3Cl	Cl^-	0.90
$CHCl_2F$	Cl^-	0.90

A particularly striking example of a dissociative electron capture reaction is in the irradiation of cyclohexane containing only 1 mole percent of CH_3I.[19,22] It was found that radiolysis of this system produced a considerable amount of decomposition of the CH_3I, a fact which could only be explained by reactions such as (9-8). The high CH_3 radical yield in cyclohexene radiolysis containing millimolar quantities of CH_3I is also explained by dissociative electron capture.

9-5.3 Other Ion Reactions

There are many other reactions which may occur during radiolysis; for example:

$$CH_4 \xrightarrow{\hspace{0.5cm}\rule[0.3ex]{0.8cm}{0.4pt}\hspace{-0.9cm}\sim\hspace{-0.15cm}\sim\hspace{0.5cm}} CH_2^+ + H_2 + e^-$$

$$C_4H_{10} \xrightarrow{\hspace{0.5cm}\rule[0.3ex]{0.8cm}{0.4pt}\hspace{-0.9cm}\sim\hspace{-0.15cm}\sim\hspace{0.5cm}} CH_4 + C_3H_6^+ + e^-$$

$$cyclo\text{-}C_6H_{12} \xrightarrow{\hspace{0.5cm}\rule[0.3ex]{0.8cm}{0.4pt}\hspace{-0.9cm}\sim\hspace{-0.15cm}\sim\hspace{0.5cm}} C_6H_{10} + H_2$$

may give rise to product molecules. It is also possible for secondary reactions of ions to occur; however, considering the low yield of separated ion pairs in liquid hydrocarbons, ion neutralization may occur in a time scale sufficient to compete with ion-molecule reactions of the secondary ions with the substrate.

9-6 RADICAL YIELDS

The only active species that have been quantitatively determined in hydrocarbon radiolysis are radicals. Excited species and ions are known to be directly involved in some of the observed reactions; however, no quantitative measure of their role in hydrocarbon radiolysis is known.

The radical yields in hydrocarbon radiolysis have been determined by a variety of methods. In most instances good qualitative agreement concerning the relative yields of the different radicals has been obtained by different methods and, in many cases, good quantitative agreement also. Most of the techniques for determining radical yields involve the use of scavengers. The usual scavenger technique gives information concerning the radical yield and under certain circumstances it can give information concerning the total radical yield. The radical yields are the "scavengeable" radicals and do not include those radicals which react in the spur to form products; they only include those which escape the spur.

9-6.1 Detection of Radicals by Electron Spin Resonance

Using this technique, the radicals and their relative yields in a variety of hydrocarbons have been determined.[23] These are summarized in Table 9-4. It must be recalled that this technique has a time resolution of about 0.2 millisecond and therefore one can only detect those radicals which have survived to that time.

In systems where good resolution is possible, accurate quantitative measurements can be made. When such a condition prevails it is often possible to measure absolute rate constants for the disappearance of the radical in a manner analogous to the pulsed radiolysis technique, since the ESR method permits a direct observation of the reacting species. The method of determining absolute rate constants by this technique is demonstrated in Example 9-2.

EXAMPLE 9-2: The number of spins in an ethane sample relative to 1 cm^3 of the reference sample (galvinoxyl) was 2.35×10^{-4}. The reference sample (1 cm^3) contained 3.31×10^{17} spins. The cavity was 0.524 cm^3 and the absorbed energy rate is equal to 2.62×10^{17} ev per second. Assuming a G value of 4.4 for ethyl radicals calculate the rate constant for the bimolecular disappearance of ethyl radicals.

Table 9-4. RADICALS OBSERVED IN HYDROCARBON
RADIOLYSIS BY ESR*

Substance	Radicals observed	Relative intensity
CH_4	CH_3, H	
C_2H_6	C_2H_5, CH_3, C_2H_3	$C_2H_5 > CH_3 > C_2H_3$
C_2H_4	C_2H_5, C_2H_3, $CH_2CHCH_2CH_2$	$C_2H_3 > C_4H_7 > C_2H_5$
C_3H_8	iso-C_3H_7, C_3H_7	
n-C_4H_{10}	CH_3, C_2H_5, sec-C_4H_9, C_3H_7 C_4H_9	$CH_3 > C_2H_5 > C_3H_7$ $> C_4H_9 > sec$-C_4H_9
iso-C_4H_{10}	tert-C_4H_9, CH_3, iso- C_4H_9, iso-C_3H_7	tert-$C_4H_9 >$ iso- $C_4H_9 > CH_3 >$ iso-C_3H_7
C_5H_{12}	CH_3, C_2H_5, C_5H_9, 1-methylbutyl, 1-ethyl propyl	1-methylbutyl> > 1-ethylpropyl $C_5H_9 > CH_3$, C_2H_5
neo-C_5H_{12}	tert-C_4H_9, neopentyl	
iso-C_5H_{12}	tert-C_5H_{11}, CH_3, C_2H_5 iso-C_3H_7	tert-$C_5H_{11} >$ all others
neo-C_6H_{14}	CH_3, C_2H_5, tert-C_4H_9 tert-C_5H_{11}	
2,2,4-tri- methylpentane	tert-C_4H_9, iso-C_4H_9 (or C_8 radical) iso-C_3H_7, neo-C_5H_{11}, (CH_3 perhaps)	tert-$C_4H_9 >$ all others
3,3-diethyl- pentane	1,1-diethylpropyl, 1-methyl 2,2-diethylbutyl, C_2H_5	$C_2H_5 >$ weakest
Cyclobutane	C_2H_5, 3-butenyl, cyclobutyl	$C_2H_5 >$ all others
Cyclopentane	Cyclopentyl (only radical observed)	
Cyclohexane	Cyclohexyl (only radical observed)	
Cycloheptane	Cycloheptyl (only radical observed)	
Cyclopropane	Cyclopropyl, allyl (only radical observed)	
1,4- cyclo hexadiene	Cyclohexadienyl (only radical observed)	

*Data from Ref. 23.

SOLUTION: $3.31 \times 10^{17} \times 2.35 \times 10^{-4} = 7.78 \times 10^{13}$ spins in the sample cavity (0.524 cm^3) or

$$\frac{7.78 \times 10^{13} \text{ radicals}}{0.524 \text{ cm}^3} \left| \frac{\text{mol}}{6.02 \times 10^{23} \text{ radicals}} \right| \frac{1000 \text{ cm}^3}{\text{liter}}$$

$$= 2.47 \times 10^{-7} \frac{\text{moles}}{\text{liter}}$$

The rate constant k_r in terms of dose rate is given in Chap. 6, Eq. (6-26).

$$k_r = \frac{D \ G}{[R]^2}$$

The dose rate $D = 2.62 \times 10^{17}$ ev per sec and the G value = 4.4 radicals per 100 ev

$$DG = \frac{2.62 \times 10^{17} \text{ ev}}{0.524 \text{ cm}^3 \text{ sec}} \left| \frac{4.4 \text{ radicals}}{100 \text{ ev}} \right| \frac{\text{mol}}{6.02 \times 10^{23} \text{ radicals}} \left| \frac{1000 \text{ cm}^3}{\text{liter}} \right.$$

$$DG = 3.61 \times 10^{-5} \frac{\text{mol}}{\text{liter-sec}}$$

$$k_r = 3.61 \times 10^{-5} \frac{\text{mol}}{\text{liter-sec}} \left| \frac{1}{\left(2.47 \times 10^{-7} \frac{\text{mol}}{\text{liter}} \right)^2} \right.$$

$$k_r = 5.85 \times 10^8 \frac{\text{liters}}{\text{mol-sec}}$$

9-6.2 Detection of Radicals by Chemical Means

Many substances have been used to scavenge the radicals and determine yield. Among these are HI, ^{3}HI, I_2 (normal and radioactive), $FeCl_3$, anthracene, NO, "galvinoxyl," $^{14}C_2H_4$, $^{14}CH_3I$, etc. These substances have varying effectiveness as radical scavengers, iodine being considered one of the most effective. It is extremely important, of course, that the addition of a scavenger does not affect the nature of the primary chemical processes. There is reasonable assurance that no such effect will occur if the scavenger concentration is kept very low.

As indicated in Chap. 5, Sec. 4, there are several possible reactions for a radical, R.

Reaction with a scavenger

$$R + S \longrightarrow RS \tag{9-9}$$

Reaction with a neutral molecule

$$R + R'H \longrightarrow RH + R' \tag{9-10}$$

Reaction with another radical

$$R + R \text{ (or } R') \longrightarrow RR \text{ (or } RR') \tag{9-11}$$

Reaction (9-9) must occur readily if a solute is to act as a scavenger. Because of Reaction (9-9), the steady state concentration of radicals will be too low (except in the spurs) for Reaction (9-11) to be of any consequence.[24] Reaction (9-10), the radical exchange reaction, can occur and must be considered in scavenger kinetics, since it leads to a change in identity of the primary radicals. If Reaction (9-10), for example, is a hydrogen abstraction reaction it will have, according to Table 5-2, an activating energy of 10.4 kcal per mole for a CH_3 radical, and 6.4 kcal per mole for a hydrogen atom. It is apparent, therefore, that there must be a balance between scavenger concentration and the difference in the activation energies of Reactions (9-9) and (9-10).

EXAMPLE 9-3: What must be the difference in activation energies if Reaction (9-9) is to predominate over Reaction (9-10) with I_2 concentrations of 10^{-4} M in pentane at room temperature?

SOLUTION: In order for (9-9) to be favored over (9-10)

$$\frac{k_9 [R][S]}{k_{10}[R][R'H]} \gg 1$$

since $k_r = A\,e^{-\Delta E/RT}$

$$\frac{A_9\,e^{-\Delta E_9/RT}[R][S]}{A_{10}\,e^{-\Delta E_{10}/RT}[R][R'H]} \gg 1$$

Assuming $A_9 \cong A_{10}$

$$\frac{[S]\,e^{(\Delta E_T/RT)}}{[R'H]} \gg 1$$

where $\Delta E_T = \Delta E_{10} - \Delta E_9$.

The concentration of pentane $[R'H]$ is

$$\frac{620}{72} = 8.6 \ M$$

hence

$$\frac{[S]}{[R'H]} = \frac{10^{-4}}{8.6} \cong 1.2 \times 10^{-6}$$

for $e^{\Delta E_T/RT} \times 1.2 \times 10^{-6}$ to be greater than unity

$$\Delta E_T \cong 7 \ \text{kcal/mole}$$

Thus Reaction (9-9) must have an activation energy which is 7 kcal/mole less than Reaction (9-10).

9-6.2a Iodine

Iodine (normal or radioactive iodine-131) has been used extensively. The reaction

$$R + I_2 \longrightarrow RI + I \tag{9-12}$$

has a rate constant of the order of $10^9 \ M^{-1} \ \text{sec}^{-1}$. The reaction is very fast and the scavengeable radical yield may be determined by measuring the amount of iodine consumed and by quantitatively determining the relative yields of the alkyl iodides formed; the latter is accomplished by gas chromatography techniques. A variation of this method for determining alkyl iodides is an electron capture detector used in conjunction with gas chromatography.[25] This method depends on the relatively high electron capture rate of alkyl iodides, and is very sensitive.

The use of iodine as a scavenger is not straightforward, since iodine can undergo dissociative electron capture

$$I_2 + e^- \longrightarrow I^- + I \tag{9-13}$$

The iodide ion formed would then be directly involved in a neutralization reaction or electron exchange reaction. Such reactions could affect the nature of the radiolysis product. For example, the neutralization reaction

$$RH^+ + I^- \longrightarrow RH + I \tag{9-14}$$

would lead to the production of more iodine atoms.

Iodine may also enter in competition with the hydrocarbon for H atoms:

$$H + I_2 \longrightarrow HI + I \tag{9-15}$$

competing with

$$H + RH \longrightarrow R + H_2 \tag{9-16}$$

This has the net effect of reducing the radical yield by preventing H atom reactions with neutral molecules to produce alkyl radicals and also by preventing H addition to olefins (for example, C_2H_4 + H $\rightarrow$ C_2H_5), which results in the production of radicals. If the H atom concentration is reduced it becomes very difficult to obtain a reasonably true picture of the radical yields. If the product contains olefins then the addition of HI, I_2, and I atoms to the olefins will occur readily. In addition to these effects, if the alkyl iodide concentration is high as a result of high I_2 concentrations, then dissociative electron capture of the alkyl iodides

$$CH_3I + e^- \longrightarrow CH_3 + I^- \tag{9-8}$$

may also occur.

It is apparent that considerable care must be employed in using I_2 as a scavenger. The concentration must be kept at a sufficiently low level to prevent the buildup of alkyl radicals and HI. It is recommended that I_2 concentrations be kept below 10^{-3} M. At these concentrations the resulting alkyl iodide concentrations will be about 10^{-6} M. Also, at low I_2 concentrations, addition of HI to olefins will be minimal.

9-6.2b Hydrogen Iodide

The reaction of HI with hydrocarbon radicals has been characterized as

$$R + HI \longrightarrow RH + I \tag{9-17}$$

the resulting iodine atoms combining to form I_2. The iodine formed is then a measure of the radical yield. A common technique is to employ tritium iodide. This results in the formation of labeled hydrocarbons which can be determined by counting techniques. This technique has the advantage of providing a double check on the number of radicals formed, in addition to permitting the identification of the radicals.

As with I_2, dissociative electron capture may occur.

$$HI + e^- \longrightarrow H + I^- \tag{9-18}$$

This may affect the determination of radical yields. Competition with H atoms may also take place.

$$H + HI \longrightarrow H_2 + I \tag{9-19}$$

As in the case of I_2, this affects the determination of the radical yield by replacing H atoms with I atoms which cannot abstract hydrogen to form a radical.

Just as with I_2, the concentration of HI or ^3HI must be less than 10^{-3} M. Studies[26] on the effect of ^3HI concentration on the radiolysis of n-hexane have shown that a concentration of 0.3×10^{-3} M is sufficient to scavenge all the alkyl radicals in this system.

The application of homogeneous kinetics to radiolytically produced radicals have provided a value for the ratio of the rate constants for Reactions (9-12) and (9-17). It has been found that over the temperature range $-78°C$ to $25°C$, this ratio, k_{R+I_2}/k_{R+HI} may be expressed[27] by $(1/0.13) \exp - 800/RT$. This is in reasonable agreement with the value of 1.4 found for this ratio at room temperature using fewer simplifying assumptions in the kinetic analysis.[28]

9-6.2c Galvinoxyl

Galvinoxyl is a stable radical whose concentration is very easily determined. It has not been used often as a scavenger in radiolysis experiments since it does not appear to be too efficient. It is reported that iodine is 16 times more reactive than galvinoxyl toward methyl radicals.[29]

9-6.2d Ferric Chloride

This has been used in a variety of organic systems. The concentration is readily determined by spectrophotometric absorption at 350 mμ. It has been observed[30] that in several systems where $FeCl_3$, DPPH, and I_2 were employed as radical scavengers that

$$G(-FeCl_3) = G(-DPPH) = G(-I_2)$$

However, ferric chloride has not been studied as thoroughly as I_2, HI, or DPPH. $FeCl_3$ is soluble to about 10^{-3} M in nearly all organic liquids with an available electron pair.

9-6.2e α,α'-diphenyl-picryl-hydrazyl (DPPH)

DPPH was at one time used extensively as a radical detector in the radiolysis of organic compounds. The compound is light sensitive, susceptible to energy transfer from the solvent, and the product of the reaction of DPPH with the radical is difficult to separate by the usual chromatographic techniques. In addition there also appear to be some kinetic complications; however, in several studies DPPH appeared to give the same radical yield as I_2.

9-6.2f Radical Sampling

This is the name applied to the technique of adding labeled ethylene ($^{14}C_2H_4$) or methyl iodide ($^{14}CH_3I$) to the system in low concentrations.[31-34] A labeled radical is produced in the solution via the reactions

$$H + {}^{14}C_2H_4 \longrightarrow {}^{14}C_2H_5 \tag{9-20}$$

$$H + {}^{14}CH_3I \longrightarrow {}^{14}CH_3 + HI \tag{9-21}$$

or $\quad {}^{14}CH_3I + e^- \longrightarrow {}^{14}CH_3 + e^- + I \tag{9-22}$

The technique implies that C_2H_4 as well as CH_3I are very efficient scavengers of H atoms; this has been established.

The resulting labeled radicals can then react with a radical generated during the radiolysis to produce a labeled product. The product may be separated and quantitatively determined. This technique is a little more difficult to use than the other radical scavenger methods; irradiation conditions must be such as to favor radical-radical reactions, e.g., high dose rates ($>10^{22}$ ev per liter per second) and a correction must be made for disproportionation reactions. Only a small fraction of the radicals are sampled by this technique; this is sufficient to characterize the radicals present and to obtain knowledge of their relative yields.

9-6.2g Other Radical Scavengers

Other radical scavengers used in hydrocarbon radiolysis are oxygen, triphenylmethane, nitric oxide, nitrous oxide, olefins, and monomers such as styrene. Olefins, in general, appear to be less reactive toward radicals (other than H atoms) than many other scavengers (DPPH, $FeCl_3$, HI, I_2); oxygen has been found to be as effective as iodine in some cases; nitric oxide is a well known scavenger and a good deal of information concerning some of its reactions in the gas phase is known; triphenyl methane has a reactive hydrogen and has been used effectively, and nitrous oxide is an efficient electron scavenger. By and large, however, the use of these scavengers has been limited in hydrocarbon systems.

9-6.3 Radical Yields

Radical yields as determined by the techniques discussed are shown in Tables 9-5 and 9-6 for some normal and branched alkanes and *cyclo*-alkanes.

Methyl radical yields for normal cyclic and branched chain alkanes may be expressed as a simple function of the numbers of carbon atoms and the position of the methyl group in the molecule.[35] Three types of methyl groups are distinguishable: (1) type A in which only one methyl group is attached to the same carbon atom (the normal paraffins are in this category), (2) type B which contains two methyl groups attached to the same carbon atom, and (3) Type C which contains three methyl groups attached to the same carbon (isobutane, for example). The empirical formula expressing the relation between methyl radical yields and structure of the parent molecule is:

$$G(CH_3) = \frac{1}{(n-1)^2} [1.02\ a + 2.79\ b + 7.89\ c] \qquad (9-23)$$

where n = number of carbon atoms

   a, b, c = number of A, B, C type methyl groups

The equation predicts the yields, with few exceptions, to better than 15 percent. The major exception is 3,3-dimethyl-pentane where the discrepancy is 62 percent. One important feature of this equation is that it predicts decreased yields with increasing molecular weight and highest yields from low molecular weight, highly branched hydrocarbon.

EXAMPLE 9-4: Calculate the methyl radical yield from 2,2-dimethylbutane.

SOLUTION:

$$n = 6$$

$$G(CH_3) = \frac{1}{(6-1)^2} [1.02 + (7.89)\ (3)]$$

$$G(CH_3) = 0.987$$

Table 9-5. RADICAL YIELDS FROM NORMAL AND BRANCHED CHAIN HYDROCARBONS*

Radical	n-butane	n-pentane	n-hexane	n-heptane	i-pentane	neo-pentane	2,4-di-methyl-pentane	2,2,4-tri-methyl-pentane	2,2-di-methyl-butane	n-tri-decene
CH_3	0.4	0.10	0.08	0.04	0.71	2.3	0.28	0.69	0.99	0.012
C_2H_5	0.94	0.34	0.27	0.21	0.91	0	0	0	0.6	0.046
n-C_3H_7	0.09	0.34	0.25	—	0.12	0	0	0	<0.1	⎱ 0.05
i-C_3H_7	0.04	0.20	0.04	0.24	0.66	0	0.53	0.12		⎰
n-C_4H_9	1.04	0.05	0.23	—	0.07	0	0	—		⎱ 0.05
i-C_4H_9	—	—	—	—	0	0.16	0.54	0.74	—	⎰
sec-C_4H_9	2.14	0.05	0.05	0.23	0.18	0	0	0	—	⎱ 0.06
t-C_4H_9	—	—	—	—	0	0.55	0	0.51	⎱ 0.2	⎰
n-C_5H_{11}	—	0.78	0.03	⎱ 0.22	—	—	—	—	⎰	⎱ 0.07
sec-C_5H_{11}	—	2.84	—	⎰	—	—	—	—		⎰
n-C_6H_{13}	—	—	0.5	⎱ 0.02	—	—	—	—		
sec-C_6H_{13}	—	—	2.3	⎰	—	—	—	—		
Parent										
Primary	—	—	—	⎱ 4.04	⎱ 1.44	0.78	0.64	0.60	⎱ 1.2	⎱ 4.4
Secondary	—	—	—	⎟	⎰	0	0.46	0.50	⎰	⎰
Tertiary	—	—	—	⎰		0	0.30	0.05		

*Data from Ref. 16.

Table 9-6. RADICAL YIELDS FROM
SOME CYCLIC HYDROCARBONS*

Substance	Cyclopentane	Cyclohexane
CH_3	0.21	0.22
C_2H_5	0.06	0.06
C_3H_7	0.09	0.08
C_4H_9	0.04	0.07
n-C_5H_{11}	0.22	0.03
sec -C_5H_{11}	0.10	0.02
Cyclopentyl	2.86	—
n-C_6H_{13}	—	0.92
sec -C_6H_{13}	—	0.05
Cyclohexyl	—	2.93

*Data from Ref. 16.

9-7 MOLECULAR YIELD

The molecular yield due to radical combination is difficult to
determine. It is obtained usually by calculating total radical yields
from the observed product yields and subtracting the radical yields
determined by scavenging techniques. For example, in the radiolysis of cyclohexane the only radical observed is the cyclohexyl and
the principal products observed are dicyclohexyl, cyclohexene, and
hydrogen. This product distribution is readily explained if it is assumed that cyclohexyl radicals may react to form dicyclohexyl and
may also disproportionate:

$$2\,(cyclo\text{-}C_6H_{11}) \longrightarrow \text{dicyclohexyl}$$

$$\longrightarrow cyclo\text{-}C_6H_{10} + cyclo\text{-}C_6H_{12}$$

If some knowledge is available concerning the relative rates of these
reactions, one may estimate the total cyclohexyl radical yield. Such
an estimate indicates that the actual cyclohexyl radical yield is
twice the yield determined by scavenger techniques.

As stated in Sec. 9-2, the molecular yield arises from radicals
that react in the spur to form products. The "molecular yield" of
methyl radicals from the radiolysis of neopentane, for example, is
obtained in this manner. The known radicals in neopentane radiolysis are methyl, isobutyl, neopentyl, and t-butyl. Methyl radicals
may react in the spur with these radicals to produce ethane, iso-
pentane, 2,2-dimethylbutane, and neopentane. If these products are

formed by reactions with methyl radicals in the spurs, then scavengers in low concentrations should not affect their yields. If this is the case then a measurement of these products plus a measure of the scavengeable yield would give a measure of the molecular yield of methyl radicals (the yield of neopentane of course must be determined from knowledge of the t-butyl radical concentration). Studies such as these indicate that in hydrocarbon radiolysis less than 70 percent of the radicals formed escape the spur[20] to diffuse into the body of the liquid. The molecular yield therefore is estimated to be greater than 30 percent of the total radical yield.

9-8 ENERGY TRANSFER

The subject of energy transfer during radiolysis is one which has received considerable attention, and has been invoked to explain a variety of results. Energy transfer between a solvent M and a solute S may take the form of electron exchange (as observed in gases), exchange of excitation energy ($M^* + S \rightarrow S^* + M$), formation of an ion pair and subsequent neutralization ($M^+ + S^- \rightarrow M + S^*$) or internal conversion process.

An example of energy transfer is the effect of benzene on the radiolysis of cyclohexane. This has been termed a *protective effect* since the result of the addition of benzene to cyclohexane is to reduce the net amount of decomposition. The products of the decomposition of cyclohexane are primarily cyclohexene, bicyclohexyl and hydrogen. When mixtures of benzene and cyclohexane are irradiated, the hydrogen yields observed are not those expected from a consideration of the contribution of each species as determined by their electron fraction.[36] This is shown in Fig. 9-1. At about 0.05 electron fraction of benzene the yield of hydrogen is reduced by a factor of 2. Various mechanisms have been offered to explain this, the most important being electron transfer and transfer of excitation energy.[37,38] Since benzene has a lower ionization and excitation potential than cyclohexane either or both of these processes could be involved. Increased benzene decomposition occurs in these systems, but the increase in the decomposition of the benzene is by no means equivalent to the decrease in cyclohexane decomposition. Low concentrations of solutes which have high electron affinities, namely I_2, CH_3I, and SO_2, also decrease the decomposition of cyclohexane.[37]

It has been established that when certain two-component, dilute (10^{-3} M), organic solutions are irradiated with gamma rays, luminescence is observed which is characteristic of the fluorescence of the solute.[39] The efficiency of this process is low, but it is proportional to the concentration of the solute. Studies of the transfer of energy (luminescence) in solutions of benzene and p-terphenyl in cyclohexane have shown that the rate constants for the transfer of energy from cyclohexane to benzene and to p-terphenyl are very high.

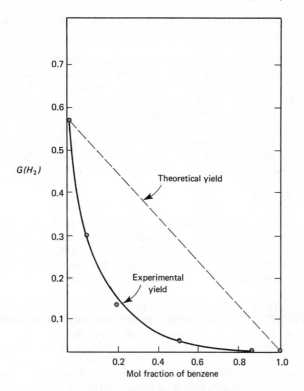

Fig. 9-1. $G(H_2)$ for mixtures of cyclohexane and benzene as a function of the
electron fraction of benzene (Ref. 36).

The first singlet excited state of cyclohexane is repulsive and
the transfer of this excitation energy to benzene solute molecules
cannot be readily explained in terms of collision with isolated molecules. An explanation offered to account for energy transfer in this
system is the existence of ordered domains over which energy migration can take place, and that this migration in a domain can compete with dissociation. Theoretical arguments support a peak in the
energy loss spectrum in condensed systems which corresponds to a
collective excitation involving the electrons in a volume element
about 100 Å in diameter.[41] Substantial experimental evidence is
found in support of this migration concept[42-44] not only in terms of
solute effects but also in terms of LET.[45] Hydrogen yields in cyclohexane radiolysis are independent of LET, which can be explained if
it is assumed that the initial region over which the hydrogen atoms
are generated is large. The important observation is that the decrease in $G(H_2)$ for example is not compensated for by increase in

other products either from the cyclohexane or the benzene, hence the benzene is conferring a "protective" effect.

The effect of anthracene, oxygen, and naphthalene on the radiation induced isomerization of 2-butane has been explained by an energy transfer mechanism.[46] The effect of argon on the radiolysis of n-butane has also been explained in part by an energy transfer mechanism.[47] Studies on the radiation induced isomerization of solutions of cis- and trans-stilbenes in benzene show that the reaction proceeds via excited triplet states of the stilbenes formed by energy transfer from triplet state benzene molecules. Estimates of G (triplet benzene) as high as 10 have been reported.[48-50]

9-9 LET EFFECTS

Each organic system has to be examined to determine if an effect of LET exists, since it is not possible to generalize. One of the major difficulties in determining if LET effects exist is the overlapping effect of dose rate, since so many of the reactions involve reactions with substrate, or with other radicals.

Hydrogen yields in the radiolysis of cyclohexane appear to be independent of LET, and the changes in product ratios that have been observed in LET studies on n-hexane, cyclohexane, or n-pentane have been attributed to dose rate effects rather than LET effects; Falconer and Burton,[51] however, have observed a LET effect in cyclohexane. If the spur size is large, and radical combinations occur within the spur, these reactions will continue even as the spurs overlap, and there are no significant changes in product yields which can be distinguished from dose rate effects. If the radicals are hydrogen atoms and alkyl radicals, combination of H atoms, and reactions of H atoms with radicals may occur which would tend to give the same product distribution as would be expected at high dose rates. There does not appear to be any appreciable dependence on LET for aliphatic hydrocarbons, however, LET effects have been observed in benzene,[52] biphenyl, orthoterphenyl[53] and several other organic systems. The great effect of LET in aqueous systems in contrast to hydrocarbons is due to the active competition in the particle tracks between pseudo first- and second-order reactions.

9-10 DOSE RATE EFFECTS

High dose rates generally favor radical-radical reactions rather than abstraction or addition reactions. In hydrocarbons it is expected that the following reactions will occur:

$$RH \xrightarrow{\quad\quad} H, R, R_1, R_2 \qquad\qquad (9\text{-}24)$$

$$H + RH \xrightarrow{k_s} H_2 + R \qquad\qquad (9\text{-}25)$$

$$H + H \xrightarrow{k} H_2 \qquad\qquad (9\text{-}26)$$

$$R_1 + RH \xrightarrow{k_1} R_1H + R \qquad\qquad (9\text{-}27)$$

$$R_1 + R_2 \xrightarrow{k_2} R_1R_2 \qquad\qquad (9\text{-}28)$$

If only the reactions of H atoms are considered it is seen that a dose rate effect will be observed when the rate of reaction of (9-25) is equal to that of (9-26). If the concentration of H atoms is C, and of RH molecules, C_s, and the rate of reaction of (9-25), $k_s C_s C$ and of (9-26), kC^2, then a dose rate effect should be observed when $kC^2 \cong k_s C_s C$. There will be no dose rate effect on H_2 yields if one of these terms predominates over the entire dose rate range.

The spurs are homogeneously distributed throughout the liquid (for gamma and fast electron irradiation); hence it is possible to think of the active species as being homogeneously distributed especially as the spurs expand. Under these conditions it is then possible to examine a particular radical reaction and determine when the situation will prevail that favors radical-radical combination reactions such as (9-26) and (9-28).

Equation (8-23) gives the fraction of radicals which combine as in Reaction (9-25) to form H_2, assuming a homogeneous initial distribution. If it is assumed that an effect of dose rate will be observed when $\overline{N} = 0.5$ then a value of the dose rate, I, may be calculated which achieves this condition. This assumes, of course, that Eq. (8-23) applies.

EXAMPLE 9-5: Calculate the onset of a dose rate effect in a hydrocarbon as determined by the H atom reactions [(9-25) and (9-26)], given $G(H) = 6$, $k_s = 10^{-14}$ cm^3 molecule^{-1} sec^{-1}, $k = 10^{-11}$ cm^3 molecule^{-1} sec^{-1} and $C_s = 6 \times 10^{21}$ molecules cc^{-1}.

SOLUTION: Using Eq. (8-23) and assuming a dose rate effect is observed when $\overline{N} = 0.5$, the value of the fraction $k\ kI/k_s^2 C_s^2$ is set equal to A.

$$\frac{k_1 kI}{k_s^2 C_s^2} = A$$

$$-0.5 = -\frac{1}{2A} \left[(1 + 4A)^{1/2} - 1\right]$$

solving, $A \cong 2$.

$$I = \frac{2 \times 10^{-28} \times 36 \times 10^{42} \text{ ev}}{0.06 \times 10^{-11} \text{ cm}^3\text{-sec}} = 1.2 \times 10^{28} \text{ ev/cm}^3\text{-sec}$$

Similar calculations can be done for any of the radicals formed, providing the appropriate rate constants are available. The calculation is at best an approximation since it is assumed that the radicals are (1) homogeneously distributed and (2) the reactions are limited to abstraction and intercombination. Radicals will, in general, combine randomly (i.e., methyl will combine with methyl, ethyl, or any other radical which is present). The calculation in Example 9-5 shows that in hydrocarbons, if hydrogen is formed only by Reactions (9-25) and (9-26), very high dose rates are needed to demonstrate a dose rate effect. It is possible that a better picture could be established for LET effects in hydrocarbon radiolysis if one consider radical competition, i.e., competition as expressed in Reactions (9-27) and (9-28). There is some uncertainty as to the role of thermal H atoms in hydrocarbon radiolysis and furthermore H atoms will readily undergo the reaction $H + R \rightarrow$ products.

If the calculation in Example 9-5 is done in reverse, it is possible to estimate the fraction of radicals which combine at the different dose rates. The principal reactions of the radicals (especially the lower molecular weight radicals) will be combination and abstraction, and consideration of the differences in activation energy for these two processes would lead to differences for low dose rates and high dose rates yields.

In general the effect of dose rate may be summarized as follows:

(1) At low dose rates hydrogen atoms and alkyl radicals will primarily abstract hydrogen from parent molecules.

(2) At high dose rates the principal reaction of hydrogen atoms will be to abstract; for alkyl radicals, the principal reactions will be to combine.

(3) At very high dose rates, for both hydrogen atoms and alkyl radicals, the principal reaction will be combination.

The foregoing does not necessarily apply to high molecular weight radicals, since the probability for abstraction generally decreases with the number of carbon atoms in the radical.

9-11 KINETICS AND MECHANISM OF HYDROCARBON RADIOLYSIS

It is generally accepted that the kinetics of hydrocarbon decomposition may be treated in terms of radical reactions, however, in some systems there is very definite evidence that some of the hydrogen (and therefore products) may be formed directly by molecular detachment. Aside from this, the bulk of the reactions are those of the free radicals, and the products of a decomposition may be qualitatively determined by considering a random statistical interaction of the radicals formed.[54] This assumes that collision efficiencies are independent of radical structure and since activation energies for radical-radical reaction are very close to zero, this amounts to assuming that steric factors are independent of structure. Several arguments support this supposition.

The yield of radicals (including H atoms) and directly formed products does not exceed about 10 species per 100 ev, indicating the absence of a chain reaction. This is in contrast to the gas phase thermal decompositions of hydrocarbons which often do involve chain decomposition. Since the same radicals are often present in both systems, it must be presumed that the principal reaction of the radicals in liquid hydrocarbon radiolysis is combination.

It has been shown by direct measurement of the rate constants for some radical-radical reactions in hydrocarbon systems that these reactions are diffusion controlled;[20,23,55] this implies that the rate constants are of the same order of magnitude.

The rate constants for the combination and the intercombinations of these radicals therefore may be obtained from a knowledge of diffusion coefficients, and encounter parameters, using the Smoluchowsky equation:

$$k = 4\pi N \rho \bar{D}/1000 \ M^{-1} \ sec^{-1} \tag{9-29}$$

where N = Avogadro's number, ρ = encounter parameter, and $\bar{D}$ = diffusion coefficient.

As an example, the rate constant for ethyl-ethyl radical combination may be determined by Eq. (9-29) and the results compared with that found in Example 9-2.

EXAMPLE 9-6: Calculate the rate constant for the combination of ethyl radicals using the Smoluchowsky equation assuming $\bar{D} = 0.75 \times 10^{-5} \ cm^2 \ sec^{-1}$ and $\rho = 2.0 \ \text{Å}$.

SOLUTION:

$$k = 4\pi N \rho \delta/1000$$

$$k = 4 \times 3.14 \times 2 \times 10^{-8} \text{ cm} \times 0.75 \times 10^{-5} \frac{\text{cm}^2}{\text{sec}}$$

$$\times 6.03 \times 10^{23} \frac{\text{molecules}}{\text{mol}} \Big/ 1000$$

$$k = 1.1 \times 10^9 \text{ liters mol}^{-1} \text{ sec}^{-1}$$

The rate constant is not appreciably different from that found in Example 9-2 (0.6×10^9 liters mol^{-1} sec^{-1}).

To obtain a qualitative knowledge of the products to be expected from the radiolysis of hydrocarbon it is necessary to have some knowledge of the identity and relative yields of the radicals that are formed. In the absence of such knowledge a broad generalization (for straight chain hydrocarbons) is that the principal radicals will be those formed by (1) removal of an H atom from a methylene carbon of the parent molecule, (2) removal of an H atom from a methyl carbon, and (3) carbon-carbon bond cleavage to form smaller radicals. The validity of this generalization may be seen by examining Tables 9-2, 9-5, and 9-6. Radicals are also formed by secondary reactions such as abstraction and addition of H atoms to olefins.

For moderate dose rates, radiolysis of a liquid hydrocarbon will yield

$$\text{RH} \xrightarrow{\quad\text{\textasciitilde}\!\text{\textasciitilde}\!\text{\textasciitilde}\quad} H_1, R_1, R_2, R_3 \ldots \tag{9-30}$$

The products are then determined by a random (statistical) addition of the radicals to each other. For $R_1 \ldots R_4$:

(1) $R_1 + R_1 \longrightarrow 2R_1R_1$

(2) $R_1 + R_2 \longrightarrow R_1R_2$

(3) $R_1 + R_3 \longrightarrow R_1R_3$

(4) $R_1 + R_4 \longrightarrow R_1R_4$

(5) $R_2 + R_2 \longrightarrow 2R_2R_2$

(6) $R_2 + R_3 \longrightarrow R_2R_3$

(7) $R_2 + R_4 \longrightarrow R_2R_4$

(8) $R_3 + R_3 \longrightarrow 2R_3R_3$

(9) $R_3 + R_4 \longrightarrow R_3R_4$

(10) $R_4 + R_4 \longrightarrow 2R_4R_4$

If R_1 is methyl, R_2 ethyl, R_3 propyl, and so forth, then the products will be ethane, propane, butane, etc. Ethane is only formed by Reaction (1), butane would be formed by Reactions (3) and (5), and hexane by Reactions (7) and (8). If the total radical concentration is $[A]$ and the radical yields $[R_1]$, $[R_2]$, etc., then the butane concentration for example would be given by

$$\frac{[R_1][R_3]}{[A]} + \frac{[R_2]^2}{2[A]}$$

Using this method it is possible to obtain a product distribution which is in good qualitative agreement with experiment. This method assumes that little or no disproportionation occurs as a result of radical combination.

This approach is taken in Example 9-7, using the data of de Vries and Allen.[56]

EXAMPLE 9-7: Given that the radicals and their yields for the radiolysis of n-pentane are

(1) $G(CH_3) = 0.1$ (2) $G(C_2H_5) = 1.1$

(3) $G(C_3H_7) = 1.0$ (4) $G(C_4H_9) = 0.3$

(5) $G(sec\text{-}C_5H_{11}) = 5.0$ (6) $G(n\text{-}C_5H_{11}) = 2.2$

predict the G values of the products at moderate dose levels.*

SOLUTION: At moderate dose rate levels hydrogen abstraction will be at a minimum and the only reactions to be considered are the radical reactions. Let $(CH_3) = a$, $(C_2H_5) = b$, $(C_3H_7) = c$, $(C_4H_9) = d$, $(sec\text{-}C_5H_{11}) = e$, $(n\text{-}C_5H_{11}) = f$ and the total radical yield = R. The $G_{(calc)}$ and $G_{(obs)}$ are:

---

*In Example 9-7 the yields actually observed are included to provide a comparison. The radical yields used are not in agreement with those in Table 9-5 but are those estimated by the authors on the basis of product yields.

Products		$G_{(calc)}$	$G_{(obs)}$
C_2H_6	$= \dfrac{a^2}{2R}$	~0	0.27
C_3H_8	$= \dfrac{(a)(b)}{R}$	~0.01	0.33
C_4H_{10}	$= \dfrac{b^2}{2R} + \dfrac{(a)(c)}{R}$	~0.06	0.09
C_5H_{12}	$= \dfrac{(b)(c)}{R} + \dfrac{(a)(d)}{R}$	~0.11	—
$iso\text{-}C_6H_{14}$	$= \dfrac{(a)(e)}{R}$	~0.05	0.03
$n\text{-}C_6H_{14}$	$= \dfrac{(a)\,(f)}{R} + \dfrac{(b)(d)}{R} + \dfrac{(c)^2}{2R}$	0.11	0.14
$iso\text{-}C_7H_{16}$	$= \dfrac{(b)(e)}{R}$	0.57	0.41
$n\text{-}C_7H_{16}$	$= \dfrac{(c)(d)}{R} + \dfrac{(b)\,(f)}{R}$	0.28	0.45
$iso\text{-}C_8H_{18}$	$= \dfrac{(c)(e)}{R}$	0.52	0.59
$n\text{-}C_8H_{18}$	$= \dfrac{d^2}{2R} + \dfrac{(e)\,(f)}{R}$	0.23	0.20
$iso\text{-}C_9H_{20}$	$= \dfrac{(d)(e)}{R}$	0.15	0.21
$n\text{-}C_9H_{20}$	$= \dfrac{(d)\,(f)}{R}$	0.07	~0
$iso\text{-}C_{10}H_{22}$	$= \dfrac{(e)^2}{2R} + \dfrac{(e)\,(f)}{R}$	2.42	2.40
$n\text{-}C_{10}H_{22}$	$= \dfrac{(f)^2}{2R}$	0.28	0.28

This method adequately accounts for the high molecular weight products but not for those of lower molecular weight. Many of these low molecular weight compounds are formed by complex secondary reactions such as the production of C_2H_4 with subsequent H atom scavenging to yield C_2H_5 radicals.

In the radiolysis of *n*-hexane the two principal primary reactions are:

$$C_6H_{14} \xrightarrow{} C_6H_{13} + H$$

$$\xrightarrow{} C_6H_{12} + H_2$$

Bond cleavage also occurs, yielding low molecular weight radicals such as methyl, ethyl, propyl, and butyl, and their subsequent reaction products. Carbon-hydrogen bond cleavage occurs predominantly at methylene carbons, hence branched chain products are found as a result of radical combination at these sites.

9-12 EFFECT OF HIGH ABSORBED DOSE

When the total absorbed dose is high, the final products will be appreciably different from the initial products, since the products may also react with the active species as their concentration becomes significant.

For example, ESR experiments have indicated that H atoms are only observed in liquid methane radiolysis, yet it is well known from scavenger experiments (such as the addition of an olefin) that they are formed in most hydrocarbon systems. In the radiolysis of liquid ethane, for example, the ethyl radical is observed by ESR techniques, but H atoms are not. The addition of 5 percent C_2D_4 produces C_2D_4H radicals in a concentration nearly equal to the C_2H_5 radical concentration. The conclusion reached from this observation is that olefins must be produced in excess of hydrogen atoms, and are scavenging the H atoms to form radicals. This effect would be enhanced at high absorbed dose.

9-13 MATERIAL BALANCE

The best method of establishing a material balance is to inventory the products. This is often not convenient because in most hydrocarbon radiolysis a certain amount of polymer is formed. A method which has been found generally useful is to obtain the ratio of the total H and C atoms appearing in the products, and to compare this with the parent compound. For example, in *n*-pentane the ratio of H atoms to C atoms in the parent compound is 2.40. This value could be compared with the ratio of the total H atoms produced per 100 ev and total carbon atoms produced per 100 ev in the products.

Another method compares the hydrogen evolved with the total unsaturation. The hydrogen evolved should be greater than the total unsaturation since reactions such as RH → R + H followed by R + R → RR and H + H → H_2 are also sources of hydrogen. The unsaturation present in a polymer formed is usually determined by iodine titration, a method which is only approximate, but serves as a quick check on any material balance method employed.

9-14 EFFECT OF TEMPERATURE ON THE RADIOLYSIS

In general, the effect of temperature is to favor those reactions which require thermal activation, such as abstraction and bond cleavage. Unimolecular decomposition of the parent ion (see Sec. 9-5 and Example 9-1) should be favored as should also *disproportionation* and radical decomposition reactions. Chemical reactions generally have positive temperature coefficients and hence it is expected that irradiation at higher temperatures should facilitate certain reactions.

The *thermal* decomposition of hydrocarbon molecules has been explained, in general, by initial carbon-carbon bond cleavage, with subsequent reaction of the radicals to produce chain reactions of varying length. The activation energy for carbon-carbon bond cleavage is about 80 kcal per mole. Hence, for a pure thermal reaction to occur at a measurable rate, temperatures of the order of 500°C-600°C must be used. The activation energy for radical or parent ion decompositions are very much less than this and therefore acceleration in the radiolytic decomposition should occur at considerably lower temperatures.

In the normal room temperature radiolytic process, as for example *n*-hexane radiolysis, large radicals (hexyl in this case) are produced. Because of steric and energy factors these radicals normally do not undergo hydrogen abstraction reactions; the principal reaction is radical combination. Smaller radicals such as methyl, ethyl, or propyl undergo abstraction reactions providing the necessary thermal activation is available. Another reaction favored at higher temperatures is decomposition of the larger radicals (plus parent ions) to yield smaller radicals which then abstract hydrogen from the parent molecule to give another large radical which then may decompose.

Schematically this chain process would occur as follows:

(1) RH $\longrightarrow$ R + H

(2) R $\xrightarrow{\Delta}$ R' + stable molecule

(3) R' + RH $\longrightarrow$ R'H + R

Radical combinations and disproportionation will still occur, however the presence of sufficient thermal activation makes the abstraction reaction competitive with the combination reaction.

The effect of temperature will be not only to increase the amount of decomposition per unit of energy absorbed (in terms of absorbed dose) but there may also be a significant change in the relative yields of the different products. As the temperature is increased to about 600°C, the thermally induced rate becomes significant, and if the temperature is raised still higher, the contribution of the thermally induced reaction becomes most significant. If the rate of the thermally induced radical or ion decompositions are ignored, a measure of the ratio of the rates of the thermally induced radical initiation rate to the radiation induced radical initiation rate may be obtained simply from consideration of the number of radicals produced per 100 ev and a rough estimate of the activation energy for the thermally initiated rate. The ratio is only approximate but it is useful in determining the limits of the effect of radiation on thermal reactions. An exercise in this type of calculation is given in Example 9-8.

EXAMPLE 9-8: Calculate the ratio of thermal and radiation initiation rates at 600°C in n-heptane if the dose rate is 10^{16} ev/sec/cm^3 and G(radical) = 6. Assume an activation energy of 80 kcal per mole for the thermal initiation of radicals.

SOLUTION:

Rate of thermal initiation = $k[RH]$

Assuming k is given by $k = 10^{13}\, e^{-\Delta E/RT}$ sec^{-1} and $RH = 5 \times 10^{21}$ molecules/cm^3, the rate of thermal initiation is:

Rate of thermal initiation = $5 \times 10^{34} \times e^{-45}$

$$\text{Rate of radiation initiation} = \frac{10^{16}\ \text{ev}}{\text{sec-cm}^3} \times \frac{6\ \text{radicals}}{100\ \text{ev}}$$

$$= 6 \times 10^{14}\ \text{sec}^{-1}\ (\text{cm}^3)^{-1}$$

$$\frac{\text{Rate of thermal initiation}}{\text{Rate of radiation initiation}} = \frac{5 \times 10^{34}\ e^{-45}}{6 \times 10^{14}} = 2$$

At higher temperatures the ratio will increase until at about 800°C the contribution of the absorbed radiation to the rate of decomposition will be negligible.

A similar type of calculation may be made to determine at what temperature one may anticipate the onset of an increase in the radiation induced rate, assuming an overall activation energy for hydrogen abstraction, parent ion, and radical decompositions.

PROBLEMS

9-1   In the radiolysis of ethylene account for the presence of the $CH_2 = CHCH_2CH_2$ radical as observed by ESR techniques.

9-2   Using the values of the rate constants and concentrations given in Example 9-5, determine the value of $k_1 \, kI/ \, k_s^2 \, C_s^2$ when $\bar{N} = 0.2$ in Eq. (9-23).

9-3   If the activation energy for hydrogen abstraction reactions are of the order of 8 kcal/mole, estimate the relative probability for abstraction versus combination for methyl radicals ($G = 4$) at a dose rate of 10^{13} rads per minute, 10^5 rads per minute, and 10^7 rads per minute.

9-4   Calculate the onset of a dose rate effect for competition by methyl radicals for abstraction versus combination, given $G(CH_3) = 0.1$, $k_s = 6.8 \times 10^4$ liter/mol/sec, $k = 3 \times 10^8$ liter/mol/sec.

9-5   Calculate the rate constant for methyl radical combination assuming $\bar{D} = 2 \times 10^{-5}$ cm^2 sec^{-1} and an encounter parameter of 2 Å.

9-6   If the activation energy for parent ion decomposition is 30 kcal per mole, estimate the temperature at which acceleration in the rate of pentane decomposition would become critical.

9-7   What will be the effect of increasing the temperature on diffusion controlled reactions? Will the change in rate be significant for a twenty degree rise in temperature for a reaction occurring in a liquid?

9-8   Using the electron fraction law calculate the yield of hydrogen expected from a 5 mole percent solution of benzene in n-hexane $G(H_2, benz) = 0.04$, $G(H_2, hex) = 5.8$.

9-9   Assuming the pre-exponential factors are equal, at what temperatures will abstraction be competitive with combination if the activation energy for abstraction is 6 kcal per mol and for combination 1 kcal per mol?

9-10 Using the *G* values for the radicals given in Table 9-5 for *n*-hexane, predict the products and their respective *G* values for *n*-hexane radiolysis.

9-11 Using the formula for methyl radical yields [Eq. (9-23)] determine methyl radical yields of the compounds shown in Table 9-5 and compare with the experimentally determined values.

REFERENCES

1. G. L. Clark and L. W. Pickett, *J.A.C.S.*, **52**:465 (1930).

2. P.W. Baumeister and G. Glocker, *Z. Physik. Chem.*, **97**:368 (1921).

3. A. O. Allen and A. Hummel, *Disc. Far. Soc.*, No. 36:147 (1963).

4. A. Hummel and A. O. Allen, *J. Chem. Phys.*, **44**:3426 (1966).

5. G. Freeman, *J. Chem. Phys.*, **34**:988 (1963).

6. M. C. Sauer, S. Arai, and L. M. Dorfman, *J. Chem. Phys.*, **42**:708 (1965).

7. M. Anbar and E. J. Hart, *J. Phys. Chem.*, **69**:1244 (1965).

8. S. Arai and L. M. Dorfman, *J. Chem. Phys.*, **41**:2754 (1964).

9. V. Voevodsky and Y. N. Molin, *Rad. Res.*, **17**:366 (1962).

10. H. Okabe and J. R. McNesby, *J. Chem. Phys.*, **37**:1340 (1962).

11. P. J. Dyne, J. Denhartog, and D. R. Smith, *Disc. Far. Soc.*, No. 36:135 (1963).

12. W. G. Burns and J. A. Winter, *Disc. Far. Soc.*, No. 36:124 (1963).

13. D. L. Dugle and G. R. Freeman, *Trans. Far. Soc.*, **61**:1174 (1965).

14. T. J. Hardwick, *J. Phys. Chem.*, **64**:1623 (1960).

15. L. Kevan and W. F. Libby, *J. Chem. Phys.*, **19**:1283 (1963).

16. S. J. Rzad and R. H. Shuler, paper presented at the 154th meeting of the ACS, Sept. 1967. Abstract No. 74, Division of Physical Chemistry. (To be published)

17. R. A. Holroyd, "Radical Yields in Hydrocarbon Radiolysis." (In press)

18. T. D. Nevitt and L. P. Remsberg, *J. Phys. Chem.*, **64**:969 (1960).

19. J. Roberts and W. Hamill, *J. Phys. Chem.*, **70**:910 (1966).

20. R. W. Halroyd *et al.*, *J. Phys. Chem.*, **70**:910 (1966).

21. M. B. Fallgatter and R. J. Hanrahan, paper presented at the 154th meeting of the ACS, Sept. 1967. Abstract No. 75, Division of Physical Chemistry.

22. R. R. Williams and W. H. Hamill, *Rad. Res.*, **7**:158 (1954).

23. R. W. Fessenden and R. H. Shuler, *J. Chem. Phys.*, **39**:2147 (1963).

24. R. H. Shuler, *J. Phys. Chem.*, **62**:37 (1958).

25. J. P. Adloff and P. Guequeniat, *J. Chromatog.*, **12**:96 (1963).

26. D. Perner and D. Gnarra, Mellon Inst. Report RRL-147 (1964).

27. D. Perner and R. M. Shuler, *J. Phys. Chem.*, **70**:2224 (1966).

28. I. Mani and R. J. Hanrahan, *J. Phys. Chem.*, **70**:2233 (1966).

29. R. H. Shuler, *J. Phys. Chem.*, **68**:3873 (1964).

30. E. Collinson, J. J. Conway, and F. S. Dainton, *Disc. Far. Soc.*, **36**:153 (1963).

31. R. A. Holroyd and G. W. Klein, *J.A.C.S.*, **84**:400 (1962).

32. _____ and _____, *J. Appl. Rad. Isotopes*, **13**:493 (1963).

33. _____ and _____, *J. Appl. Rad. Isotopes*, **15**:633 (1964).

34. _____ and _____, *J. Phys. Chem.*, **69**:194 (1965).

35. R. H. Shuler and R. R. Kuntz, *J. Phys. Chem.*, **67**:1004 (1963).

36. J. P. Mannion and M. Burton, *J. Phys. Chem.*, **56**:560 (1952).

37. R. H. Shuler, *J. Phys. Chem.*, **61**:1472 (1957).

38. T. J. Hardwick, *J. Phys. Chem.*, **66**:767 (1962).

39. H. Kallman and M. Furst, *Phys. Rev.*, **79**:857 (1950).

40. S. Lipsky and E. M. Burton, *J. Chem. Phys.*, **31**:1221 (1959).

41. U. Fano, "Comparative Effects of Radiation," M. Burton et al., eds., John Wiley & Sons, New York, 1960

42. P. J. Dyne, J. Denhartog, and D. P. Smith, *Disc. Far. Soc.*, **36**:135 (1963).

43. E. Collinson, J. J. Conway, and F. S. Dainton, *Disc. Far. Soc.*, **36**:153 (1963).

44. M. Burton, J. Chang, S. Lipsky, and M. P. Reddy, *J. Chem. Phys.*, **29**:1337 (1957).

45. J. Burns, *J. Phys. Chem.*, **65**:2261 (1961).

46. R. B. Cundall and P. A. Griffiths, *Disc. Far. Soc.*, **36**:111 (1963).

47. E. Collinson, J. F. J. Todd, and F. Wilkinson, *Disc. Far. Soc.*, **36**:83 (1963).

48. R. A. Caldwell, D. G. Whitten, and G. S. Hammond, *J.A.C.S.*, **88**:2659 (1966).

49. R. R. Hentz, D. B. Peterson, S. B. Srivastava, S. B. Barzynski, and M. Burton, *J. Phys. Chem.*, **70**:2362 (1966).

50. M. A. Golub, C. L. Stephens, and J. L. Brash, *J. Chem. Phys.*, **45**:1503 (1966).

51. J. W. Falconer and M. Burton, *J. Phys. Chem.*, **67**:1743 (1963).

52. W. G. Burns, *Trans. Far. Soc.*, **58**:961 (1962).

53. _____, *Trans. Far. Soc.*, **59**:101 (1963).

54. C. D. Wagner, *J. Phys. Chem.*, **64**:231 (1960).

55. R. W. Fessenden and R. H. Shuler, *Disc. Far. Soc.*, **36**:149 (1963).

56. A. E. de Vries and A. O. Allen, *J. Phys. Chem.*, **53**:879 (1959).

10

RADIATION CHEMISTRY OF SOLIDS

10-1 INTRODUCTION

Radiation effects in solids may be viewed as producing defects and these defects in turn may be classified as primarily atom displacement or an altered electronic configuration. These two categories of damage are by no means independent of each other, since an altered electronic configuration will certainly affect the position of neighboring atoms and, of course, vice versa. However in some materials, metals for example, radiation damage is primarily atom displacement since changes in electronic configuration are rapidly adjusted. It is necessary therefore to obtain some understanding of the defect solid state in order to fully appreciate what properties of the substance are affected when solids are exposed to nuclear radiation. Consequently the characteristics of defects in solids, how they are produced, and the properties they affect will be discussed here in limited fashion (see Ref. 1 for a more complete discussion). In this chapter we limit ourselves primarily to those substances which undergo chemical change or are of interest to chemists. This eliminates any discussion of metals, most semiconductors, and many ceramics.

10-2 NATURE OF DEFECTS IN SOLIDS

There is a large variety of defects in solids that are normally present and which have been characterized. The basic structures however may be categorized as point defects and dislocations. Several subcategories give to each a particular identity or name. Point defects include lattice vacancies and interstitial atoms. Dislocations are a volume or linear defect in which the lattice is disturbed a few lattice distances away radial to the dislocation. Point defects are usually termed *Frenkel* and *Shottky defects* and refer to interstitial and vacancy pairs respectively.

10-2.1 Shottky Defects

A perfect ionic lattice* has an equal number of anions and cations. A Shottky defect may be envisaged as an ion leaving a normal

---

*In this section we assume an AB-type lattice.

lattice site and taking up a position on the surface, leaving behind a positive or negative ion vacancy. The number of cation and anion vacancies are always equal (in the absence of impurities). If an excess number of cations migrate to the surface, a positive charge is produced, thus preventing further migration of positive ions, and at the same time creating excess negative charge within the crystal. This latter effect is conducive to migration of the negative charge, so that in the absence of external forces the number of oppositely charged vacancies inside a crystal tends to become equal (Fig. 10-1). Shottky defects are therefore vacancy pairs.

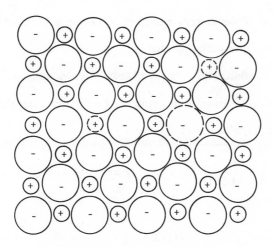

Fig. 10-1. Schematic diagram of
Shottky defects. Broken circles
indicate vacancies.

Shottky defects are always present in a solid. In any normal solid, there exists an equilibrium number of these vacancies which depends on the temperature at which the crystal has been formed. If a crystal contains N atoms, n Shottky defects are produced by removing n cations and n anions from the crystal interior. The different ways in which each kind of ion can be removed is given by

$$\frac{N(N - 1)(N - 2) \ldots (N - n + 1)}{n!} = \frac{N!}{(N - n)\ !n!} \qquad (10\text{-}1)$$

since the number of cation and anion vacancies is the same, the number of ways in which n Shottky defects can be formed is just the square of Eq. (10-1). The creation of n Shottky defects increases the crystal's entropy by

$$S = k \ln \left[\frac{N!}{(N - n) \ ! n!} \right]^2 + nS_p \qquad (10\text{-}2)$$

This increase in the entropy in turn produces a change in the Gibbs free energy

$$G = H - TS \qquad (10\text{-}3)$$

$$G_p = nH_p - nS_p T - kT \ln \left[\frac{N!}{(N - n) \ ! n!} \right]^2 \qquad (10\text{-}4)$$

where G_p = Gibbs energy required to create a vacancy pair

nH_p = total enthalpy change

nS_p = additional entropy change in producing n defects[*]

Equation (10-4) is simplified using Stirling's approximation

$(\ln x \ ! \cong x \ln x - x)$

$$\ln \left[\frac{N!}{(N - n) \ ! n!} \right]^2 = 2 \left[N \ln N - (N - n) \ln (N - n) - n \ln n \right] \qquad (10\text{-}5)$$

or

$$G = nH_p - nTS_p - 2kt \left[N \ln N - (N - n) \ln (N - n) - n \ln n \right] \qquad (10\text{-}6)$$

At equilibrium for a given temperature T, G is constant and therefore its first derivative is zero. Taking the derivative of Eq. (10-6) with respect to n at constant T

$$\left(\frac{\partial G}{\partial n} \right)_T = 0 = (H_p - TS_p) - 2kT \left[\ln (N - n) - \ln n \right] \qquad (10\text{-}7)$$

$$G_p = 2kT \ln \frac{(N - n)}{n} \qquad (10\text{-}7a)$$

$$\frac{N - n}{n} = e^{G_p/2kT} \qquad (10\text{-}8)$$

---

[*]The defects contribute an additional enthalpy term by affecting the vibrational frequencies.

since N is usually $\gg n$, Eq. (10-8) may be simplified to give

$$n \cong N e^{-G_p/2kT} \tag{10-9}$$

This is the number of Shottky defects present at equilibrium at some temperature, T.

EXAMPLE 10-1: If the Gibbs energy required to form a Shottky defect is 2 ev calculate the number of such defects present in KCl at its melting point, $1050°K$. The density of KCl is 1.984 g per cm^3.

SOLUTION: Substituting into Eq. (10-9):

$$n = \frac{1.984\ g}{cm^3} \left|\frac{1\ mol}{74.6\ g}\right| \frac{6 \times 10^{23}\ \text{molecules}}{mol} \left| e^{-2ev/2kT}\right.$$

$$n = 1.62 \times 10^{22} \frac{\text{molecules}}{cm^3}\ \exp -\left[\frac{(2\ ev)1.6 \times 10^{-12}\ \text{ergs}}{ev}\right.$$

$$\times \left(\frac{°K}{2\ \times\ 1.38 \times 10^{-16}\ \text{ergs}}\right)\left(\frac{1}{1050°K}\right)\Big]$$

$$n \cong 15 \times 10^{16}\ \text{vacancies}/cm^3$$

10-2.2 Frenkel Defects

These are characterized by the movement of an ion or atom to an interstitial position, as shown schematically in Fig. 10-2, forming an interstitial vacancy pair. As are Shottky defects, the Frenkel defects are always present; their number is a function of the temperature at which the crystal is formed. The formula expressing the number of Frenkel defects is derived in a manner analogous to Eq. (10-9) and is given by

$$n \cong (NN_i)^{1/2}\ e^{-G_f/2kT} \tag{10-10}$$

where N = number of atoms in the crystal

N_i = number of interstitial positions

G_f = Gibbs energy required to form an interstitial pair

It is seen that even in the absence of radiation there always exists a finite number of vacancies and interstitials and it is therefore,

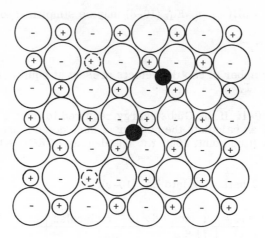

Fig. 10-2. Schematic diagram
of Frenkel defects.

virtually impossible to obtain a crystal which does not contain these
defects.

It must not be construed that the defect concentration produced
at the high temperatures is present in the crystal at room temperature. Diffusional processes rapidly reduce the high temperature
concentration during the cooling process; however, a crystal formed
at the high temperatures and then rapidly quenched will retain a
large fraction of the defects so produced. This is a standard method
for introducing defects into a crystal.

10-2.3 Dislocations

Originally the concept of dislocations was postulated in order to
explain the plastic deformation of solids, and it has now been shown
that dislocations are also very useful in explaining crystal growth
and variations in other properties such as electrical conductivity.

There are basically two types of dislocations, *edge* and *screw*.
The edge dislocations (for monatomic structures) consist of a line
of atoms (or anions or cations) each of which has one atom less
coordinating it than exists in the ideal crystal (Fig. 10-3). Another
way of looking at an edge dislocation is to consider introducing an
extra plane of atoms or, in the case of an ionic lattice, two planes,
one cation, and the other anion into the lattice. The edge dislocation may be looked on as an irregularity which can move under
stress. The plane containing both the dislocation line and the

---

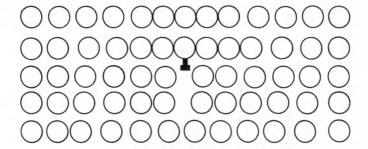

Fig. 10-3. Schematic diagram of an edge dislocation. The symbol ⊥ indicates the dislocation line which is normal to the plane of the paper.

direction of motion is called the *slip* plane. An edge dislocation is only free to move in its slip plane under stress. It can also climb by absorbing or ejecting atoms.

A screw dislocation consists of a line of atoms with the correct number of atoms coordinating it; however, the coordination polyhedron is distorted. Each atom (or anion or cation) in a lattice is connected in a unit cell in a lattice to form a polyhedron such as a cube or a tetrahedron and it is this polyhedron which is distorted (Fig. 10-4). The screw dislocation has in effect a structure similar to a helical staircase. Screw dislocations are often called Burger's dislocations.

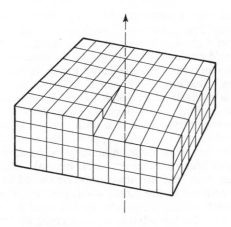

Fig. 10-4. Screw dislocation. The arrow indicates the axis of the distortion.

A wide variety of dislocation types are possible all of which are variants of the two basic types discussed above. A "tilt" boundary for example is composed of a linear array of edge dislocations. Special arrangements of dislocations may be considered as grain boundaries.

A dislocation line can never end within a crystal, it either follows a closed path or ends at the surface. When dislocations move in a crystal it is very likely that they will intersect, this can lead to annihilation of the dislocation. Screw dislocations, when they intersect, most often produce edge dislocations.

10-2.4 Color Centers

Another type of defect in solids is that manifested by color centers. Most organic and inorganic compounds become colored when exposed to ionizing radiation. In some cases the coloration produced is caused by the formation of a new stable compound or relatively stable radical that is absorbing; or the color may be due to the formation of an ion such as the naphthalenide ion that occurs when dilute solutions of naphthalene in 2-methyltetrahydrofuran are irradiated in the glassy state.[2] The color may also be due to a "solvated" electron.[3]

The term *color center* however is usually reserved for a loosely bound electron or hole trapped at a vacancy or other point defect and occurs primarily in ionic, insulating, and semiconducting lattices. The term is used in the literature for radiation induced coloring in all substances, but will be used here in a more restrictive sense, i.e., a loosely bound electron trapped in a vacancy.

Any crystal grown under equilibrium conditions contains defects and dislocations. The presence of such defects alters the charge distribution, and a change in the electronic levels in the vicinity of the defects should be expected. Prior to the general use of ionizing radiation, color centers were produced in alkali halide lattices by the introduction of excess alkali metal or halogen. If alkali metal is deposited on the surface of an alkali halide crystal, a coloration is produced in the crystal. This occurs presumably by an anion migrating through the lattice, reacting with the metal atom, ionizing, and the liberated electron being trapped in the anion vacancy. (See Fig. 10-5.) Such crystals show an absorption band in the visible region (KCl, dark blue; LiF, pink; NaCl, brown). This model was confirmed by the fact that the absorption produced by adding excess metal was independent of the metal used, i.e., addition of sodium metal to KCl produced the same absorption band as if potassium had been used. The model has also been confirmed by ESR techniques; the splitting observed is 1.995 compared to 2.0023 for the free electron.

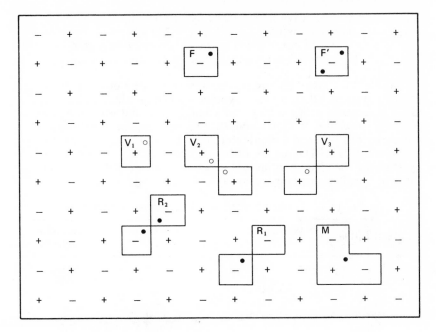

Fig. 10-5. Schematic representation of some color centers. The squares indicate ion vacancies, the black dots electrons and the open circles holes.

The name given to this type of color center is F center (from the German "farbe"). When the F center is irradiated by white light, the trapped electrons can be excited to higher-lying quantum states. The wavelength of light that can excite these trapped electrons is not singular, and it is found that a range of wavelengths can be used; hence an absorption *band* is found which is called an F *band*. When such a crystal is irradiated with light in the F-band region and an electric field is applied to the crystal, photoconductivity is observed. When an F center is bleached by light in the F-band region a new band called an F' band appears and is apparently due to the electron being excited into the conduction band and then trapped in an F center to give two electrons in the vacancy instead of one.

When excess halogen is added to an alkali halide crystal (NaCl) new color bands are produced. These new bands called V bands are formed presumably by the halide ion, occupying normal lattice sites, which produce a positive hole in the lattice and these holes are trapped. Such V centers are complex; electron spin resonance has shown that some of these centers are not spherically symmetrical and may be interpreted as due to the existence of a Cl_2^- molecule ion.

This would be a positive hole shared by two neighboring halogen ions.[4] Similar centers have been found in LiF crystals.[5,6] This type of center would correspond to the V_1 center designated by Seitz.[7] A V_1 center is a hole trapped at a positive ion vacancy.

Table 10-1 gives the approximate wavelengths of the F-band centers in some alkali halide crystals. When an alkali halide crystal is irradiated with ionizing radiation, both F and V centers are formed. However, it is considerably more complex to delineate color centers in more complicated ionic crystals such as nitrates or perchlorates. The nature of these color centers is determined by studying the change in optical properties under different conditions of irradiation (temperatures) and annealing.

Table 10-1. APPROXIMATE WAVELENGTHS OF F BAND

Alkali halide	Position of max, Å	Half-width, ev at 20°C	Oscillator strength
NaF	3400	0.62	—
NaCl	4650	0.47	0.81
NaBr	5400	—	—
NaI	5880	—	—
KF	4550	0.41	—
KCl	5630	0.36	0.90
KBr	6300	0.36	0.80
KI	6850	0.35	—
RbCl	6240	0.31	—
RbBr	7200	0.28	—
RbI	7750	—	—

Color bands vary in their stability, which is a direct measure of the energy of the color center. Annealing studies at different temperatures can provide some knowledge of the temperature coefficient (activation energy) of the processes involved.

The number of color centers may be determined using an equation originally derived by Smakula but simplified by Przibram.[8] The formula can be applied only if the band has a Gaussian or Lorentian shape.

$$fd = 1.31 \times 10^{17} \frac{n}{(n^2 + 2)^2} \alpha_{max} H \qquad (10\text{-}11)$$

where f = oscillator strength

n = index of refraction

d = concentration of absorbing centers

α_{max} = absorption coefficient in cm^{-1} at λ_{max} where λ_{max} is the wavelength at peak absorption

H = half-width of the band in ev

In order to obtain the color center concentration it is first necessary to plot the optical density versus wavelength and determine the shape of the band, and λ_{max}. The absorption coefficient α is equal to the product of the extinction coefficient and the concentration $\alpha = \mathcal{E}C$, hence the optical density at λ_{max} divided by the path length gives α, the absorption coefficient at λ_{max}. The oscillator strength must also be known, however these generally vary between 0.6 and 1. For a single emission electron there is a sum rule which gives a maximum value of 1; hence using an approximate value for f, a rough value of the color center density can be obtained.

10-2.5 Other Defects

Impurities are also defects in a lattice. In a chemically reactive system impurities build up with exposure to radiation. For example, irradiation of KNO_3 produces NO_2^- and O_2, both of which are impurities and can affect energy transfer in the solid. Impurities may also be formed by nuclear mutation.

10-3 RADIATION DAMAGE

Energy may be absorbed in a solid by (1) electron displacement (ionization, excitation), (2) atom displacement, (3) production of an impurity atom and (4) electron trapping. The energy absorption process occurs in about 10^{-17} sec. This is followed by molecular processes (including exciton transfer) such as fluorescence, bond dissociation and so forth, which occur in about $10^{-13} - 10^{-9}$ sec. Phosphorescence, diffusional processes, chemical reactions, color center decay, hole pair interactions and the like complete the time scale of events to restore equilibrium, which may be achieved in from 10^{-8} sec up to times as large as years.

Radiation effects in solids are broadly characterized as those which are primarily crystallographic structural defects, and those which are chemical in nature. The predominant type of damage will depend to a large measure on the material (metals, ionic solids, semiconductors, and such) and on the source of radiation. Heavy particle radiation (fast neutrons, fission fragments, fast protons, and so on) may cause atom displacement and chemical change while photons and electrons produce mostly chemical changes, if they can occur.

10-3.1 Interaction of Neutrons with Solids

Fast neutrons interact primarily by direct collision with nuclei (knock-on collision). The result is a displaced atom which is ionized and behaves as a heavy charged particle, causing some ionization and other displacements. Slow neutrons react almost entirely by capture processes to produce impurity (defect) atoms which may possess sufficient recoil energy to cause ionization and excitation and induce displacements.

The source of fast neutrons is usually a reactor since machine sources in general do not produce a sufficiently high flux for their practical use in most damage studies. Reactor neutrons are always accompanied by gamma rays and the sample is invariably exposed in a reactor in the presence of the gamma field. For a chemically reacting system the effect of decomposition by fast neutrons (via displaced atoms) is usually small compared to the decomposition induced by the gamma field accompanying fission neutrons.

The average number of displacements, N, produced by a fast neutron may be determined approximately by Eq. (10-12).[9]

$$N \approx \frac{E}{4T_m} \left[0.108 - 0.561 \log \frac{E_T}{E} \right] \left[1 + \frac{E_T}{E} \right]^{-1} \qquad (10\text{-}12)$$

where E = the energy of the neutron

E_T = the energy required to displace an atom

T_m = the maximum energy of the primary displaced atom

The value of E_T is estimated for most solids to be about 10 ev,[10] which is large compared to the energy to produce a Frenkel defect. This is because the recoil takes place before the neighboring atoms have a chance to relax. T_m, the maximum energy of the primary knock-on, is given by

$$T_m = \frac{4EMm}{(M + m)^2} \qquad (10\text{-}13)$$

where m = mass of the neutron

M = mass of the struck atom

As an example of the use of this equation the number of displacements produced by 1.5 Mev neutrons in $NaNO_3$ is calculated below.

EXAMPLE 10-2: Calculate the number of displacements in a sample of $NaNO_3$ when irradiated with a fast neutron flux (average energy 1.5 Mev) of $10^{13}/cm^2$-sec for two days.

SOLUTION: From Eq. (10-12)

$$N = \frac{E}{4T_m} \left[0.108 - 0.561 \log \frac{E_T}{E} \right] \left[1 + \frac{E_T}{E} \right]^{-1}$$

In order to determine T_m an average atomic mass for $NaNO_3$ of 17 will be assumed.

$$T_m = \frac{4(1.5 \times 10^6) \; 17}{(18)^2}$$

$$T_m = 31 \times 10^4 \text{ ev}$$

$$N \approx \frac{1.5 \times 10^6}{124 \times 10^4} \{0.108 - 0.561 \log [6.6 \times 10^{-6}]\} [1 + 6.6 \times 10^{-6}]^{-1}$$

$$N \approx 4$$

Total number $= 4 \times 10^{13} \times 3600 \times 24 \times 2$

$$\approx 0.7 \times 10^{19}/cm^3 \text{ or}$$

$$\approx 0.3 \times 10^{19} \text{ displacements/gram}$$

10-3.2 Heavy Charged Particle (Alpha, Protons, Etc.)

For energetic charged particle interactions the collision is coulombic. These particles lose energy by ionization and excitation and also by atom displacement. The maximum energy transferred by atom displacement is given by Eq. (10-14) which is also valid for a hard sphere collision. The mean energy transferred to the primary atom is

$$\bar{E} = E_T \ln \left(\frac{T_m}{E_T} \right) \quad \text{for } T_m \gg E_T \tag{10-14}$$

where the symbols have the same meaning as in Eq. (10-12).

Equation (10-14) gives the mean energy of the primary recoils; the average number of secondaries dislodged from the lattice by the primary atom is

$$N = \left[0.885 + 0.561 \ln \left(\frac{X_m + 1}{4} \right) \right] \frac{X_m + 1}{X_m} \qquad (10\text{-}15)$$

where $X_m + 1 = \dfrac{4Mm}{(M + m)} \dfrac{E}{E_T}$

M = mass of struck atom

m = mass of particle

For example, bombarding copper with 500-kev deuterons, $\bar{E}$ = 195 ev and $\bar{N} \cong 4.5$.

10-3.3 Electrons and Gamma Rays

Irradiation with energetic electrons (~1–2 Mev) or energetic gamma rays (>1 Mev) can produce displacements. An outstanding example is the disordering produced in copper gold alloy by ^{60}Co gamma rays. The number of displacements produced however are so small, compared to chemical damage (in a chemically reacting system) that displacement damage relative to other effects may be ignored. The primary atoms displaced by energetic electrons will have very little energy and hence secondary production is virtually nil. Irradiation with electrons or photons will cause primarily excitation and ionization and in chemically reacting systems, decomposition.

Assuming 35 ev to form an ion pair, a 1 Mev electron will produce about 10^4 ions and about 2–3×10^4 excited species; these would be distributed over the path of the ionizing electron which is a little more than the range of the particle in that medium. An alpha particle of the same energy will, on the other hand, produce a densely ionized path containing the same number of ion pairs, but distributed over a much shorter and more direct path.

10-3.4 Fission Fragments and Recoils

If a fissionable substance is incorporated into a lattice and the material then exposed to a neutron source, the fission fragments produced in the lattice are essentially massive charged particles of high energy which can produce ionization and atom displacements.

Mutations resulting from nuclear reaction are a very common source of recoils. Hot-atom chemists employ this means quite frequently, the elements commonly used being lithium (which becomes a triton) and nitrogen (which becomes carbon 14).

10-3.5 Other Mechanisms for Producing Damage in Solids

As indicated in Secs. 10-3.1, 10-3.2 and 10-3.4 fast neutrons, heavy charged particles, fission fragments or recoils resulting from slow neutron capture produce defects in crystals. These defects include atom displacements, chemical decomposition, and color centers. Irradiation with photons or electrons on the other hand would result primarily in an altered electronic configuration (chemical deeomposition, color centers, radicals, and so forth) and very little or no atom displacement. The mechanism for the production of atom displacement by neutrons or heavy charged particles is considered to be as a result of a knock-on collision.

There are several additional mechanisms which have been postulated for the production of atom displacement in crystals.

10-3.5a Thermal Spikes

There are basically two types of thermal spikes to be considered. One is that caused by a knock-on atom (primary recoil) of energy E, with the deposition of this amount of energy in a small, restricted volume. This sudden deposition of energy may result in very high local temperatures for a short duration of time.[8] For example, using an energy deposition of 10^5 ev in a volume containing about 10^4 atoms and a thermal diffusivity of 10^{-3} cm^2 per second, this number of atoms could be heated to temperatures of about $1000°$K in a time duration of about 10^{-11} sec. The role of this type of thermal spike can only be significant in heavy particle or neutron bombardment.

10-3.5b Electron Spike

The other type of thermal spike is that which is sometimes called an *electron spike*.[8] This is the spike associated with the passage of a charged particle (electron) where the condition exists that little or no energy is lost directly to the lattice, the charged particle energy being dissipated entirely to the electrons and the electronic excitation energy subsequently being transferred (degraded) as heat. The rate at which energy is converted from electronic excitation energy to lattice energy will decide whether sufficiently high lattice temperatures can be achieved to cause change. The magnitude of the energy transferred will depend directly on the degree of coupling between the electronic states and the lattice. For metals where the coupling is very weak, Seitz and Kohler[9] show that lattice temperatures will be of the order of $500°$K for 10 ev electron excitation per atom along the track of the ionizing particle. This temperature is only 1/100 of the electron temperature, and is not considered significant in terms of lattice changes. However, when the coupling is much larger, Seitz and Kohler believe that electron spikes may be significant.

In terms of chemical change produced, conversion of electronic excitation energy to lattice vibration energy may be quite significant however there is as yet no definite theoretical or experimental evidence to support the view that this event plays an important role in the chemical change observed in radiation induced decomposition of inorganic or organic systems. It can only be said that this remains a possibility.

10-3.5c Varley Mechanism

Another method of producing defects is that postulated by Varley[11] which applies to ionic solids. Multiple ionization of an anion to produce a net positive charge will result in the anion finding itself in a highly unstable position by virtue of the crystal potential (it will be surrounded by positive charges). Multiple ionization could occur as a result of an Auger cascade following readjustment of the electron cloud initiated by inner-shell ionization. In the case of neon, for example, multiple ionization will occur in 16 percent of those atoms losing a K electron. Because of this unstable condition the ionized anion could be forced out of its equilibrium position to an interstitial one. The Varley mechanism, however, would be most likely to occur only with simple anions such as the halides; with polyatomic anions it would be expected that decomposition of the anion would occur.

Durup and Platzman[13] have developed methods for calculating absolute yields for inner-shell ionization. The results indicate that the G value for inner-shell ionization falls rapidly when the initial electron energy is less than one hundred times the threshold energy for the pertinent event. At initial electron energy of about 1 Mev, G_K values for K shell ionization for Li, F, K, and Cl are 0.155, 0.00681, 0.00027, and 0.000373 respectively. In fluorine, G_L values for ejection of an electron in the L shell is calculated as 0.3; for potassium and chlorine the L and M subshell yields are significantly larger than K-shell yields (the order of 20 to 100 G_K).

Although the Varley mechanism is still thought to be valid, a more recent mechanism[14] is the formation of excited molecular ions (X_2^{2-} in alkali halides) whose subsequent breakup gives a vacancy and interstitial ion. This latter mechanism is rapidly gaining acceptance.

10-3.6 Summary

The overall picture which depicts the various processes that may occur is shown in Fig. 10-6 and Table 10-2. The electrons

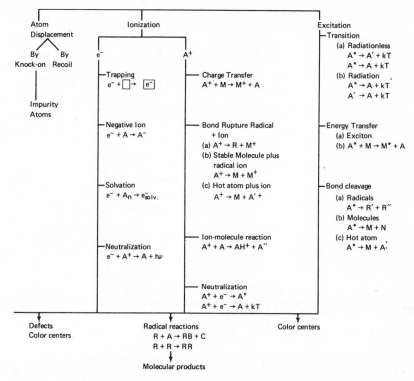

Fig. 10-6. Summary of events in solids. The time scale
is with increasing time toward the bottom of the figure.

ejected in the ionization process (regardless of the radiation source)
will, depending upon the medium, migrate some distance from the
parent ion, but will eventually be captured by a positive ion or be
trapped at some trapping site with possible formation of color
centers.

10-4 PROPERTIES SENSITIVE TO
RADIATION DAMAGE

For the substances of most interest to chemists, the properties
of principal concern are thermal, electromagnetic, physical, and
electrical properties. Mechanical properties are, of course, definitely affected in irradiated solids, but these are of minor importance in inorganic and organic crystals. A significant mechanical
effect in complex inorganic crystals is a general destruction of the
crystal forces producing changes in density and in those cases where
significant chemical change has occurred, pulverization. In some

Table 10-2. SUMMARY OF THE EFFECTS
OF THE VARIOUS RADIATIONS

Radiation	Energy	Electronic defects	Displacements
UV	$10-10^3$ ev	Color centers	None (practically)
X-ray	10^3-10^5 ev	Color centers	None (practically)
Gamma ray	10^5-10^8 ev	Color centers	Few
Neutrons	0.01–0.1 ev	None	None*
Neutrons	> 10 kev	Some	Some
Charged particles (heavy)	10^4-10^7 ev	Excitation, color centers	Some
Electrons	> 10^6 ev	Excitation, color centers	Few
Fission fragments	$\sim 10^8$ ev	Excitation	Very many

*Except by capture and recoil.

simple salts such as LiF hardening may occur and the yield stress may increase (in some cases by as much as a factor of 2).

10-4.1 Thermal Properties

The presence of a large amount of point defects will cause a decrease in the thermal conductivity. This is caused by the scattering of phonons. *Phonons* are vibrational quanta associated with the equilibrium oscillations of an atom (or a complex of atoms) to produce lattice waves. Heat is transferred through a crystal by phonons and, therefore, if there exist large numbers of defects, the phonons will be scattered producing a decrease in the thermal conductivity.

Stored energy in the form of defects in crystal lattices is an important thermal property. Frenkel defects require the expenditure of about 2 to 5 ev; hence these defects represent stored energy in a crystal. A particular example of this is the stored energy due to defects in carbon moderators in nuclear reactors. If this energy should be released suddenly, serious damage may result.*

The stored energy in crystals (which may represent a variety of defects) of interest to the chemist can be determined by heats of solution measurement. Modern techniques for this type of study will detect at least 0.01 cal per gram of stored energy.

*This was the basic cause of the severe reactor accident which resulted in the closing down of the reactor at Windscale, Lancashire, England.

10-4.2 Electromagnetic Properties

The electric potential is altered in the vicinity of point defects and these defects then may act as electron scattering centers which produce an increase in electrical resistivity.

The effect on the electric potential by the defect often results in the introduction of localized electronic states producing optical absorption bands (F, F', V centers, and so on) which are manifested by a coloring of the crystal, luminescence, and photoconductivity.

The determination of the nature of the species that gives rise to a color center is often very difficult to resolve for complex molecules, and may require a combination of EPR (or NMR), optical spectroscopy, radical scavenging (isotopic labeling), thermal annealing, optical bleaching, or other techniques for identification.

The irradiation of methanol and ethanol (glassy state) provides an excellent example of the difficulties in determining the nature of the color center. Pulsed radiolysis studies show the spectrum of the solvated electron, in ethanol (298°K) to be a broad peak at 7000 Å with a shoulder at 5200 Å. Irradiation in the glassy state (77°K) produces an optical spectra with an absorption peak at about 5200 Å and an ultraviolet absorption beginning below 3000 Å. If the band at 5200 Å is bleached by white light or thermally annealed, the central region of the ESR spectrum changes slightly and the side bands grow, finally producing the spectrum of the CH_2CHOH radical. The unpaired spin associated with the color center is the precursor of the radical and in all probability is a solvated electron in the glassy matrix.

10-4.3 Electrical Properties

There are several electrical property measurements which can be made which are of value to the radiation chemist; however of these there are only two which are tractable. These are conductivity (or resistivity) and photoconductivity. These measurements give a very good indication of the number of free-charge carriers (indicative of the number of electrons which escape the parent positive ion), the number and energy distribution of electron trapping sites, depth of traps, and the ability of the free-charge carriers to transfer energy to the surrounding molecules.

In an irradiated system the number of free electrons per cm^3 equals the number formed per cm^3 per unit time multiplied by the lifetime

$$G_e \, R\tau = n = \frac{\sigma}{e\mu} \tag{10-16}$$

where G_e = number of electrons separated per 100 ev

R = absorbed radiation intensity in units of 100 ev per second

σ = conductivity (ohm cm)$^{-1}$

e = electronic charge

μ = electron mobility in cm^2/V-sec

τ = lifetime

Photoconductivity is the conductivity observed when a sample is illuminated with light (in a strict definition this could be extended to irradiation with X- or gamma-rays).

By studying the conductivity as a function of temperature, wavelength and combinations of these, valuable information can be obtained concerning the centers responsible for the supply of conduction electrons. This technique is often used in conjunction with ESR. For example, in the iodine complexes of pyrene and perylene it has been found that the number of paramagnetic species had the same temperature dependence as the conductivity.[15] Conductivity measurements have provided information on the effect of impurities or the trapping of electrons and holes in anthracene.[16]

10-4.4 Other Properties

In almost all cases of irradiated inorganic materials that undergo chemical decomposition (including alkali halides) a change in density is observed. Such a change in density is often accompanied by changes in X-ray pattern and infrared absorption curve. X-ray studies of irradiated inorganic crystals will, in general, show line broadening, and if the crystal is nearly perfect, general distortion of peak reflections. Infrared studies on irradiated crystals may show broadening of the principal bands and the production of many side bands which are probably due to general distortion of the lattice planes.

There may also be changes in properties such as solubility, melting point, and surface characteristics. Any property or physical measurement that is dependent on diffusion in the solid may be affected because diffusion in crystals is sensitive to the defect concentration.[17]

10-5 ROLE OF LATTICE ORIENTATION

It appears from most of the evidence accumulated to date that the mode (product distribution) and extent of decomposition of both organic and inorganic substances is often dependent on the crystal environment.

Irradiation of crystalline choline chloride at room temperature results in decomposition with *G* values as high as 55,000. The decomposition may be expressed as

$$[(CH_3)_2NCH_2CH_2OH]^+ Cl^- \xrightarrow{\sim\!\!\sim} (CH_3)_2NH^+Cl^- + CH_3CHO$$

$$(10\text{-}17)$$

At about 73–78°C choline chloride undergoes a phase transition from orthorhombic to face-centered cubic. Irradiation at this temperature gives a very significant decrease in product yield.[19]

Irradiation of alkyl halides in the glassy state produces significant differences in product yields than when the identical material is irradiated in the polycrystalline form.[20]

The polymerization of *n*-alkyl-*n*-vinylsulfonamides induced by ionizing radiation occurs with a much higher yield in the solid than in the liquid. Most spectacularly, irradiation at -75°C induces polymerization in the crystalline state, but not in the glassy state.[21]

Barium bromate decomposes during irradiation to yield BrO_2^-, BrO^- and Br^- (and possibly some BrO_2). At 180°C there is a marked change in product yields and this is directly attributed to a phase change which $Ba(BrO_3)_2$ undergoes at this temperature.[22] Numerous other examples may be found where a change in phase has resulted in very marked changes in behavior when the material is exposed to ionizing radiation.[23]

It is therefore a very important part of solid state radiation chemistry to have knowledge of the crystal structure and the orientation of the molecules in the lattice. It may also be added that spatial orientation has been used to explain the observed dimer products in the radiolysis of solid hexane.[24]

10-6 ENERGY TRANSFER

In pure crystalline solids there is strong coupling of the electronic states, and an excited state should not be considered as confined to a single molecule.* This is in contrast to a molecule in the gas phase, solution or rigid glasses. In these systems the energy levels are essentially those of an isolated molecule. In rigid glasses such as boric acid and in frozen solutions as for example those of aromatic hydrocarbons, fluorescence when exhibited shows no change in lifetime from that observed in the gas phase or liquid solution.

---

*This is not true of deep lying levels such as $\underline{f}$ states of rare earths.

Energy transfer occurs by two basic processes: electronic and thermal. The transfer of electronic excitation may take a variety of forms depending on the system. Many of the mechanisms for the transfer of excitation energy have been discussed in Chap. 5 (these apply largely to organic systems). Some mechanisms are unique to solids such as exciton transfer and the transfer of electronic excitation energy to lattice vibrational energy. Thermal effects are also different in solids because of the lack of mobility of the components of the lattice.

10-6.1 Excitons

The transfer of energy by excitons is limited entirely to semi-conducting or insulating crystals. This would include molecular crystals, ionic crystals, ceramics, most polymers, semiconductors, and so forth. Excitons are the excited electronic states in these crystals. The exciton is in principle an electron hole pair, and may be considered as a conduction-band electron and valence-band hole bound together but with separation, the pair traveling through the crystal. The movement of the exciton through a crystal may be envisioned as occurring by a process of recombination, and subsequent reabsorption of the liberated energy. The excited molecule finds itself surrounded by others that are capable of accepting and re-emitting the excitation. The exciton wanders throughout the crystal until some event occurs such as interaction with phonons (scattering) or with impurity atoms, dislocations, or point defects, which results in a loss of the exciton energy. The exciton can no longer wander and remains trapped and localized; the energy of the exciton being dispersed by fluorescence or even chemical decomposition of the species where trapping has occurred. The role of excitons has not been established with any certainty in inorganic (ionic) solids except alkali halides and some oxides, but it is important in some organic systems.

The principal contribution of exciton-type transfer of energy is the ability to transport energy to another site far removed from the initial point of absorption. The importance of exciton transfer in crystals may be studied by observing the effect of the addition of well characterized impurity atoms or of increasing the defect concentration. For example, in a system containing 1 part in 10,000 of tetracene in anthracene, the exciton becomes trapped on the tetracene because the base of the electronic state of tetracene is lower than that of anthracene. The energy of the exciton is emitted as fluorescence from the tetracene molecule.

The energy of excitons varies with the nature of the crystal. In a semiconductor the ground state of the crystal corresponds to an integral number of valence bands completely full, and separated by an energy gap from completely empty conduction bands.[25,26] In the excited states electrons are excited across the gap.

Exciton energies can be determined from the absorption spectra of the solid. In ionic lattices, band-to-band transitions are estimated to occur approximately 1 ev beyond the first absorption peak. When an exciton recombines, the heat generated may be quite large; in KCl for example this is about 6 ev. Irradiation of a chemically decomposable substance such as KNO_3 in a matrix of KBr, and irradiation in heterogeneous systems (see Sec. 10-16) provide excellent examples of energy transfer. For KNO_3, $KBrO_2$, or KNO_2 (0.03 mol %) in KBr matrix it has been found that — based on the electron fraction — the amount of KNO_3, $KBrO_3$, or KNO_2 decomposed is in enormous excess and can only be accounted for by a portion of the energy absorbed in the KBr being transferred to the dispersed salts.[27]

An approximate idea of the range of energy transfer is obtained when it is realized that an impurity of 1 ppm can appreciably quench luminescence in a host lattice.

10-7 RADIATION EFFECTS IN ORGANIC COMPOUNDS

Irradiation of organic systems will produce radicals, new stable molecular species, trapped electrons, various excited states, holes, interstitials, and so forth. These are detected by the usual techniques of EPR, NMR, optical spectroscopy, X-ray, infrared, photo conductivity, and conductivity measurements. It must be remembered however that detection of the various primary species will depend in most cases on the temperatures of irradiation.

10-7.1 Radical Yields

By far the most important intermediate species identified in organic radiolysis are free radicals. Voedvodskii and Molin[28] have irradiated a series of organic compounds and obtain linear plots of radical concentrations (as determined by ESR techniques) versus dose at low temperatures and find that radical yields in compounds containing no conjugated multiple bonds are very much greater than those found in aromatic compounds. For example $G(R)$ in cyclohexane is ~4.2, in benzene $G(R) = 0.2$, diphenyl $G(R) = 0.045$, and in aniline $G(R) = 0.05$. (See Table 10-3.) The more highly conjugated the system the smaller is $G(R)$. To account for this large variation in radical yields they advance the hypothesis that the radical yields may be associated with the position of the lowest excited level. The thesis advanced is essentially that when aromatic molecules are excited to some high lying state (adjacent to the ionization boundary) they will decay very rapidly (10^{-13} sec) by a radiationless transition to the first excited state. This statement is supported by the fact that the appearance of luminescence spectrum is independent of the wavelength of the absorbed light. They observe that radical yields appear to fall considerably when E_1 (energy of the first singlet) becomes roughly equal to the bond dissociation energy.

Table 10-3. NATURE AND SOME G VALUES OF RADICALS
IDENTIFIED IN SOME ORGANIC MOLECULES

Substance	Radical	G(R)
Malonic acid	$CH(COOH)_2$	—
Cyclohexane	C_6H_{11}	4.2–4.6
Benzene	C_6H_5	0.2
Cyclopentane	C_5H_9	4.2
CH_3OH	CH_2OH	12
CH_3CH_2OH	CH_3CHOH	8.3
$CH_3CH_2CH_2OH$	CH_3CH_2CHOH	8.4
$RCONHCH_2CH_3$	$RCONHCHCH_3$	—
CH_3COOH	CH_2COOH	—
CH_4	CH_3, H	4.2
C_2H_5I	C_2H_5	—
CCl_4	CCl_3	—
CF_4	CF_3	—
$C_6H_5CH_3$	$C_6H_5CH_2$	—
$C_6H_{11}OH$	$\alpha-C_6H_{10}OH$	—

Magee[29] has shown in the case of coupling between linear molecules (H_2^+ in this calculation) for weak coupling an initially excited molecule dissociates. In strong coupling however the electronic excitation spreads out so fast that dissociation is impossible. Whether or not these ideas may be extended to other types of solids remains to be seen; however, it can be said that G values for decomposition for ionic solids are usually very much less than in organic solids.

A large number of radicals have been detected in the organic solid state. Small radicals such as hydrogen atoms are not easily detected because of their mobility even at low temperatures. Hydrogen atoms are detected when methane is irradiated at $4°K$ however they rapidly disappear on slight warming. A rough rule-of-thumb for the stabilization temperature of small radicals is 0.4 to 0.6 times the melting point of the pure matrix material.[30]

Almost all organic materials when irradiated will show the presence of unpaired spins. Unfortunately many of the spectra cannot be resolved because of the complicated nature of the total spin spectrum.

The radical concentration in both organic and inorganic solids appears to saturate, i.e., there is a concentration beyond which further irradiation produces only a slight increase. The saturation concentration is a function of temperature but a point is usually reached when the rate of radical disappearance roughly equals the rate of appearance. Saturation concentrations only reach a few tenths percent. A distortion in the lattice results when radicals are formed and this may be at least in part responsible, since such distortion would aid diffusional processes facilitating radical reactions. A discussion of the theoretical approaches to this problem is given in Ref. 25.

10-7.2 Glasses

Radiation effects on organic glasses have been particularly valuable in revealing the predominance of certain types of reactions in classes of compounds. The information accumulated is in general more applicable to the liquid state than to the crystalline state. For example, aromatic hydrocarbons in methanol glasses when irradiated form anion radicals[31] which can subsequently react with the alcohol matrix by transfer of a proton from the alcohol:

$$Ar^- + ROH \longrightarrow ArH + RO^-$$

In methyltetrahydrofuran glasses, aromatic compounds readily form a negative ion, Ar^-. The reaction to form the aromatic anion shown above has been observed in the liquid state for dilute solutions of naphthalene in several alcohols.[32] In butyl chloride glasses, however, the aromatic hydrocarbons appear to be effective traps for the positive hole and only the cation is observed.

10-8 RADIATION EFFECTS IN INORGANIC COMPOUNDS

Radiation effects on inorganic compounds with the exception of the alkali halides have not been studied extensively. In most cases only the room temperature chemistry has been determined, i.e., the products and their relative yields. Several attempts at correlating yields of a homologous series of inorganic salts with such factors as free space, free energies of formation of products, temperatures of thermal decomposition, densities, polarizabilities of the cations, melting points, and lattice energies have been unsuccessful. It is now generally accepted that the factors influencing relative G values in a series of compounds such as the nitrates, bromates, or perchlorates are very complex and are probably related to crystal structure, degree of coupling of electronic states to lattice vibrations, densities, and average energies of vibrational states, cage effects, and so forth. There is too little information available on these parameters to permit speculation as to their relative role in inorganic decompositions.

It must be borne in mind that radiolysis of systems that show chemical decomposition extensive lattice damage will occur, affecting energy transfer and diffusional processes. This will be especially evident in those compounds that produce gaseous products such as oxygen or nitrogen.

The G values may in some cases be affected by "doping" the parent salt with traces of other elements. This technique has been found very valuable in studying exciton trapping and general photochemical investigations in organic crystals. The use of doping in the radiolysis of inorganic crystals has not been exploited to the extent it deserves. It has been found for example that adding small amounts of silver to KNO_3 affects the nitrite yields.

The radiolysis of inorganic compounds is usually studied by dissolution of the irradiated salt in water and subsequent chemical analysis. Criticism against this method is that the products analyzed may be a result of solvent reaction with the irradiated salt and are not truly representative of the radiolysis products. X-ray, infrared, and UV spectra and heats-of-solution measurements can in most cases dispel any doubts about the nature of the radiolysis products for room temperature irradiations. There is some evidence however that KNO_3 irradiated at -195°C and added to ceric sulfate solutions, produces different results than if the same experiment took place at room temperature.[33]

In those few salts that have been studied, we find a direct relationship between decomposition and temperature, indicating the importance of thermal activation for some of the reactions.

Since increasing the temperature, which certainly expands the lattice, appears to facilitate decomposition it would seem likely that high pressure should achieve the opposite. In some of the salts studied this has been true; but in other salts (over the pressure range studied) no effect has been observed. The effects of temperature and pressure for the specific salts are discussed in the appropriate sections that follow.

10-8.1 Cage Effects

In a solid, decomposition fragments are not as free to escape from the parent molecule as they are for example in a liquid, because of the restrictions of the crystal lattice. The decomposition fragment finds itself in a cage so to speak, and this cage will favor recombination processes. Small fragments such as hydrogen atoms will have a much better opportunity to escape than large fragments such as oxygen atoms, nitrogen atoms, and so forth. This process will affect G values, not product distribution.

Cage effects have been used to explain the isotope effect observed in nitrate radiolysis[34] and in the high temperature coefficients of ionic salt radiolysis.[34]

10-8.2 LET Effects

There has been relatively little work on LET effects in most solids. Irradiation of nitrates with heavy particles shows an increase in G value, and this increase in G value roughly parallels the increase in G values with temperature for irradiation in the solid state.[35] The LET effect does not appear to be accounted for by an overlapping of tracks as in liquids, but rather a general heating and high local disordering. In KNO_3, irradiation of the solid at $60°C$ shows a G value of 1.46 and at $190°C$ a G value of 2.84; irradiation with alpha rays at $30°C$ gives a G value of 2.2 (Table 10-4). The G value for KNO_3 decomposition using fission recoils[36] is about 6. The LET for fission recoils in KNO_3 is about 600 ev per angstrom compared to about 34 ev per angstrom with alpha particles and 0.06 ev per angstrom with cobalt gamma rays.

Table 10-4. INITIAL G VALUES FOR
THE DECOMPOSITION OF NITRATES

| Salt | $^{60}Co\,\gamma$-rays | | | | | α-rays |
	$-110°$	$25°$	$60°$	$190°$	$330°$	$30°$
$LiNO_3$	—	0.02	—	—	3.73(L)*	0.7
$NaNO_3$	0.341	0.15	0.308	1.04	5.1 (L)	1.3
KNO_3	1.472	1.38	1.46	2.84	5.8 (L)	2.2
$RbNO_3$	0.79	0.79	0.78	2.54	4.5 (L)	—
$CsNO_3$	1.364	1.65	1.66	3.13	7.0 (L)	1.4
$Ba(NO_3)_2$	1.462	1.90	1.78	1.81	0.8 (S)	1.6
$Sr(NO_3)_2$	—	~0.5	—	—	—	—
$Ag(NO_3)$	—	0.18	—	—	—	—
$Pb(NO_3)_2$	—	0.45	—	—	—	—

*Initial G value at $270°C$, personal communication from G. Boyd, Chem. Dept., Oak Ridge National Laboratory.

There are no extensive studies of LET effects on inorganic or organic crystals which can permit reasonable predictions as in liquids (especially water). However, mixed pile irradiation gives the same product distribution in bromates, chlorates, and nitrates as does gamma irradiation and this also appears to be the case in organic compounds, where mutation processes are not of importance. The increased decomposition of azides and nitrates as a result of the $^{14}N\,(n,\,p)\;^{14}C$ reaction when the samples are exposed to mixed pile irradiation is attributed to (1) competition between first order and second order processes, as $X + X \rightarrow$ products and $X + M \rightarrow$ products, where X is a radical or excited species and M is a stable molecule and (2) "charge displacement" caused by electron capture loss between the medium and low velocity ions.[37] These findings are not in accord with those of Hennig, Lees, and Matheson[38] who were able to account for the increased decomposition of $NaNO_3$ when exposed to reactor radiation without evoking LET effects.

10-9   NITRATES

The radiation induced decomposition of the alkali and alkaline earth nitrates appears to yield nitrite ion and oxygen as the sole products. This however is not true for some of the transition metal salts. Both lead nitrate and silver nitrate appear to decompose to yield some oxide. Low temperature ESR studies indicate the presence of a variety of primary species in these salts, however it has not been possible to delineate the role of these species in any overall kinetic mechanism. The room temperature radiolysis of several nitrates appears to follow the following rate law[39], where Φ is intensity.

$$NO_3^- \xrightarrow{\quad} NO_2^- + O \qquad\qquad k_1\,\Phi \qquad\qquad\qquad (10\text{-}18)$$

$$O + NO_2^- \longrightarrow NO_3^- \qquad\qquad k_2 \qquad\qquad\qquad\qquad (10\text{-}19)$$

$$O + NO_3^- \longrightarrow NO_2^- + O_2 \qquad k_3 \qquad\qquad\qquad\qquad (10\text{-}20)$$

The rate of formation of nitrite ion is given by

$$\frac{d[NO_2^-]}{dt} = k_1\,\Phi[NO_3^-] - k_2[NO_2^-][O] + k_3[NO_3^-][O] \qquad (10\text{-}21)$$

employing the usual steady state approximation

$$\frac{d[NO_2^-]}{dt} = \frac{2k_1\,k_3\,\Phi[NO_3^-]^2}{k_2[NO_2^-] + k_3[NO_3^-]} \qquad\qquad (10\text{-}22)$$

For small conversions the $[NO_3^-]$ remains essentially constant and integration gives

$$\frac{1}{2}\,\frac{k_2}{k_3}\,\frac{1}{[NO_3^-]}\,[NO_2^-]^2 + [NO_2^-] = 2k_1\,\Phi[NO_3^-]t \qquad (10\text{-}23)$$

or

$$aX^2 + X = bT \qquad\qquad\qquad\qquad\qquad\qquad\qquad (10\text{-}24)$$

where

$$X = \frac{\text{molecules } NO_2^-}{g \times 10^{-19}}$$

$$T = \frac{\text{dose in ev}}{g \times 10^{-21}}$$

The constants a and b are evaluated from the appropriate nitrite yield versus dose curves. The rate law, which indicates a nonlinear dependence of nitrite yield on dose, reproduces the nitrite yield curves for $NaNO_3$, KNO_3, $CsNO_3$, $Ba(NO_3)_2$, $Pb(NO_3)_2$ but does not for $AgNO_3$. This latter salt decomposes to yield oxide in addition to NO_2^-. The decomposition of $Pb(NO_3)_2$ is also complex; and though the NO_2^- yield versus dose curve follows the rate law as expressed in Eq. (10-24), the detailed mechanism is considerably more complex than that shown in Eqs. (10-19) to (10-21). No effect of intensity on the rate of decomposition over a dose rate difference of five orders of magnitude for irradiation of the solid nitrates have been found. This is to be expected since free bimolecular reactions of radicals with each other cannot play a significant role in solids due to the restrictions of the diffusional process.

The G values for the decomposition of the different nitrates are shown in Table 10-4.

10-9.1 Color Centers in Nitrates

Pringsheim[40] has identified a strong absorption band at 3500 Å in irradiated $NaNO_3$ which is believed to be due to an NO_2^- ion perturbed by the proximity of another electron. The actual species observed may possibly be $NO_2^=$. Subsequently several more optical absorption bands have been identified in KNO_3 which have been correlated with EPR spectra. Bands associated with $(NO_2^=)$, NO_3, NO_2, and $NO_3^=$ have been postulated but not confirmed.[41] The band believed to correspond to $(NO_2^=)$ purportedly has maxima at 2900 Å and 5100 Å.

10-9.2 EPR Spectra

Some conflict in the literature exists concerning the EPR spectra of irradiated nitrates.[42-44] EPR spectra have revealed the presence of NO_3, NO_2, $NO_3^=$, and O_2^-. NO_2 is observed in the room temperature radiolysis of $Pb(NO_3)_2$ and $Sr(NO_3)_2$, but is observed in the alkali nitrates only at low temperatures. There is some evidence that NO_2^- is the precursor of the NO_2 radical.[44] NO has been postulated as a product in the decomposition of nitrates but no direct chemical evidence for the existence of this species has been found.

$NO_2^=$ has been found to occur with high efficiencies in $NaNO_3$ irradiated at $77°K$ with X rays.[45]

10-9.3 Effect of Pressure

An effect of pressure on the radiolysis of several nitrates has been observed.[46-47] The effect of pressure appears to depend on the salt, temperature, and region of absorbed dose, i.e., percent decomposition. There is some disagreement in the literature concerning the effect of pressure on KNO_3 and it is apparent from the evidence presented in Ref. 46 that pressure effects are complex in these systems.

10-9.4 Effect of Temperature

The effect of temperature on the decomposition yield of the nitrates is summarized in Table 10-4. As can be seen there is a general increase in G value with temperature except for $Ba(NO_3)_2$ which shows a dramatic decrease. It is possible that this decrease is due to a phase change. As is expected, there is a large increase in G values when the salts are irradiated in the liquid state.

10-10 PERCHLORATES

The alkali and alkaline perchlorates decompose at room temperature to yield ClO_3^-, ClO_2^-, ClO^-, Cl^-, ClO_2, and O_2 and possibly trace amounts of metal oxide, and ClO_3.[48-51] There is some evidence that ClO^- is a secondary product resulting from some complex interaction of the primary products.

All of the perchlorates become colored upon irradiation and the color appears to be associated with the ClO_2 concentration. Both ClO_3^- and Cl^-, the major products, have been identified in the dry powders by X-ray and infrared analysis; ClO_2^-, ClO^- and ClO_2 have been identified by wet chemical analysis. The G values for the decomposition of these perchlorates are summarized in Table 10-5.

10-10.1 Effect of Temperature

The principal effect of increasing temperature on the radiolysis of the perchlorates is decomposition of ClO_2^- and ClO^- to yield Cl^-. The concentration of ClO_2 is also considerably decreased when these salts are irradiated at higher temperatures $(25-300°C)$ however the decrease of ClO_2 is not accompanied by a corresponding increase in Cl^-. The ClO_2 is believed to react with a metal oxide formed in the radiolysis to yield ClO_4.[49]

The products, ClO_2^-, ClO^-, and ClO_2 show varying degrees of thermal stability in the different lattices. The ClO^- for example, is

Table 10-5. G VALUES OF ALKALI AND
ALKALINE EARTH PERCHLORATES

Salt	$-ClO_4$	ClO_3^-	ClO_2^-	ClO_2	ClO^-	Cl^-	O_2
Li	3.76	2.80	0.15	0.59	0.10	0.12	2.15
Na	4.36	3.57	0.17	0.11	0.09	0.42	2.96
K	3.83	2.99	0.18	0.12	0.09	0.45	2.68
Rb	5.27	4.06	0.20	0.12	0.14	0.75	3.84
Cs	6.84	5.28	0.22	0.10	0.17	1.07	5.28
Mg	4.67	4.29	0.14	0.07	0.03	0.15	2.62
Ca	4.15	3.44	0.00	0.51	0.08	0.12	1.99
Sr	4.53	3.90	0.19	0.14	0.11	0.19	2.61
Ba	3.20	1.76	0.84	0.42	0.12	0.06	2.18

Table 10-6. G VALUES OF $KClO_4$ IRRADIATED
AT VARIOUS TEMPERATURES

Temp., °C	$-ClO_4$	ClO_3^-	ClO_2^-	ClO_2	ClO^-	Cl^-	O_2
-196	4.0	2.7	0.58	0.18	0.00	0.5	3.0
-80	4.0	2.8	0.49	0.17	0.00	0.6	2.7
-16	3.7	2.8	0.26	0.06	0.06	0.5	2.4
-8	3.5	2.6	0.26	0.09	0.06	0.5	2.6
0	3.4	2.6	0.20	0.07	0.06	0.5	2.2
72	4.1	3.3	0.19	0.09	0.00	0.5	2.7
295	3.8	2.9	0.00	0.00	0.00	0.7	1.0

generally more stable in the alkaline earth lattices than in the alkali
lattices. The G values for the different products when $KClO_4$ is irradiated at various temperatures are shown in Table 10-6.

10-10.2 EPR Spectra

The EPR spectra of irradiated perchlorates are extremely
complex and have not been satisfactorily resolved. Evidence has
been presented for the occurrence of ClO_2 and ClO_3 in these crystals by EPR spectra studies,[52] supported by chemical evidence.

10-10.3 Kinetics

The kinetics of the decomposition are complex and do not even
approximate first order reactions.

The principal products are ClO_3^- and Cl^- and the yields of these
products are not appreciably affected by temperature. Furthermore,
the yields of ClO_3^- are not linear with dose. These facts together
with thermal decomposition studies on the irradiated salts support
the following general mechanism:

$$ClO_4^- \xrightarrow{\sim\!\!\sim} ClO_3^- + O \tag{10-25}$$

$$O + ClO_4^- \longrightarrow ClO_3^- + O_2 \tag{10-26}$$

$$O + ClO_3^- \longrightarrow ClO_4^- \tag{10-27}$$

$$ClO_4^- \xrightarrow{\sim\!\!\sim} Cl^- + 2O_2 \tag{10-28}$$

$$ClO_4^- \xrightarrow{\sim\!\!\sim} (ClO_4^-)^* \tag{10-29}$$

where $(ClO_4^-)^*$ is an excited state of ClO_4^- which could also be $(ClO_4^=)$ the decomposition of $(ClO_4^-)^*$ occurring as follows:

$$(ClO_4^-)^* \longrightarrow ClO_2^- + O_2 \tag{10-30}$$

or $$\longrightarrow ClO_2 + O_2^- \tag{10-31}$$

or $$\longrightarrow ClO_2 + O + O^- \tag{10-32}$$

$$(ClO_4^-)^* + \text{thermal activation} \longrightarrow ClO^- + O_2 + O \tag{10-33}$$

10-10.4 Effect of Pressure

No detectable effect of pressure (up to 2000 psi of argon) has been observed on the G values in the radiolysis of the alkali or alkaline earth perchlorates. The only detectable effect was a decrease in weight (escape of O_2 from the lattice) in the Sr, Rb, and Cs salts.

10-11 BROMATES

The alkali and alkaline earth bromates appear to decompose to yield Br^-, O_2, BrO_2^-, and BrO^- and possibly, with analogy to the perchlorates, some BrO_2.[53-56] Irradiations have been done with ^{60}Co gamma rays, with mixed pile radiation, ultraviolet light,[57] and in the special case of $LiBrO_3$ tritons and α's from [6]Li fission.

At large doses the oxidizing fragments appear to reach a steady state whose concentration is dependent on the irradiation temperature. The steady state values arise as a result of an apparent equilibrium between rate of production and back reaction to form bromate ion, and some thermal decomposition. There is no effect of intensity over a tenfold variation in gamma ray intensity.

The irradiated salts are all colored (yellow-brown) and produce a weakly alkaline reaction when dissolved in H_2O, the alkalinity being ascribed to hydrolysis of the BrO^- ion. The color and alkaline reaction disappeared by annealing the crystals below the melting point. Br^- and BrO^- and BrO_2^- are believed to have been observed in the irradiated dry powders by X-ray and infrared analysis.

The initial G values are summarized in Table 10-7.

Table 10-7. INITIAL G VALUES FOR RADIOLYTIC PRODUCTS OF THE CRYSTALLINE ALKALI AND ALKALINE EARTH BROMATES AT $35°C$

	$LiBrO_3$	$NaBrO_3$	$KBrO_3$	$RbBrO_3$	$CsBrO_3$	$Ca(BrO_3)_2$	$Sr(BrO_3)_2$
$G(-BrO_3^-)$	0.31	1.4	1.3	2.3	5.6	2.4	2.9
$G(Br^-)$	0.10	(0.59)	0.63	(0.96)	0.48	0.33	0.51
$G("Ox")$	0.21	0.83	0.69	1.4	5.2	2.0	2.4
$G(O_2)$	—	—	—	—	2.4	1.5	2.0

10-11.1 Effect of Temperature

The dependence of the radiolytic yields on temperature has been investigated for $CsBrO_3$. At constant absorbed dose the yield of oxidizing fragments decreased steadily above $-86°C$ to $300°C$ at which temperature the oxidizing fragment concentration was zero.

10-11.2 ESR Spectra

Several paramagnetic bromine-containing centers have been detected in KB_2O_3 irradiated at $77°K$ but have not been resolved.[58]

10-11.3 Kinetics and Mechanism

Boyd and co-workers[53-56] provide evidence for the following mechanism for the irradiation induced decomposition of the bromates:

$$BrO_3^- \longrightarrow\!\!\!\!\sim\!\!\!\!\longrightarrow BrO_3^* + e^- \tag{10-34}$$

$$\longrightarrow\!\!\!\!\sim\!\!\!\!\longrightarrow BrO_3^{-*} \tag{10-35}$$

$$BrO_3^{-*} \longrightarrow BrO_2^- + O \tag{10-36}$$

$$\longrightarrow BrO^- + O + O \tag{10-37}$$

$$BrO_3^* \longrightarrow BrO_2 + O \tag{10-38}$$

$$BrO_2 + e^- \longrightarrow BrO_2^- \tag{10-39}$$

$$\longrightarrow BrO_2^{-*} \tag{10-40}$$

$$BrO_2^{-*} \longrightarrow BrO^- + O \tag{10-41}$$

$$BrO_2^- + O \longrightarrow BrO_3^- \tag{10-42}$$

The reaction

$$BrO_3^- + O \longrightarrow BrO_2^- + O_2 \tag{10-43}$$

is excluded because the BrO_2^- concentration tends to reach a steady state and inclusion of Eq. (10-43) would give a BrO_2^- yield versus dose curve contrary to this.

The oxygen forming reaction is given as

$$BrO_3^- + O \longrightarrow Br^- + 2O_2 \tag{10-44}$$

10-12 SULFATES

The $SO_4^=$ appears to be quite resistant toward decomposition. Irradiation of solid $FeSO_4$ and $NiSO_4$ hydrates at room temperature causes oxidation of the cation and reduction of the $SO_4^=$ group to give $SO_3^=$ and of the water of hydration to give $H_2+ OH^-$ with low G values. $CoSO_4$, $Cr_2(SO_4)_3$, $CuSO_4$ and $ZnSO_4$ hydrates however show no oxidation of the cation or reduction of the $SO_4^=$ anion and only minor decomposition of the water of hydration. In $MnSO_4H_2O$ the manganous ion is oxidized and the H_2O reduced but there is no reduction of the sulfate group.

The alkali and alkaline earth sulfates are very resistant to decomposition by ionizing radiation. Irradiation of Na_2SO_4 to a total absorbed dose of greater than 10^{22} ev per gram shows no detectable decomposition. This is also true for a sample irradiated at 300°C for a total absorbed dose of 3×10^{21} ev per gram. The stability of the sulfate group in cobalt sulfate hydrate appears to be related to the oxidation potential of the cobaltic ion relative to water, however the stability of the sulfite ion in the nickel and ferrous salts is difficult to explain.

The overall mechanism postulated in the hydrates is:

$$(MSO_4)(H_2O)_n \xrightarrow{} H_2O^+ + e^- \tag{10-45}$$

$$e^- + H_2O \longrightarrow H_2O^- \tag{10-46}$$

$$H_2O^+ + M^{n+} \longrightarrow M^{n+1} + H_2O \tag{10-47}$$

$$H_2O^- + H_2O^+ \longrightarrow 2H_2O \tag{10-48}$$

$$H_2O^- + SO_4^= \longrightarrow SO_3^= + 2OH^- \tag{10-49}$$

$$2H_2O^- \longrightarrow H_2 + 2OH^- \tag{10-50}$$

$$2H_2O^+ \longrightarrow O_2 + 2H^+ + H_2 \tag{10-51}$$

where M^{n+} is a metal cation. Reaction (10-48) is considered to be competitive with Reaction (10-47). In the event Reaction (10-47) is favored this is usually followed by Reaction (10-50) or, in the few cases observed, Reactions (10-49) and (10-50). In the absence of any reaction with the cation or anion a small amount of decomposition occurs via Reactions (10-50) and (10-51).[59]

10-13 CHLORATES

The radiation-induced decomposition of several of the chlorates have been studied by X irradiation,[50] [60]Co gamma irradiation,[58,60] and mixed pile irradiation.[61,62] The products identified have been Cl^-, ClO^-, ClO_2^-, O_2, ClO_2, Cl_2O_6, and ClO_4^-.

Identification of Cl_2O_6 was based on a weak absorption band at 450 mμ in crystals irradiated at room temperature, and ClO_2 by the absorption at 330–400 mμ of irradiated crystals dissolved in dilute Na_2CO_3 solution. Chloride, chlorite and hypochlorite were identified by wet chemical methods.

Reported G values are summarized in Table 10-8.

Table 10-8. G VALUES OF SOME ALKALI CHLORATES

Substance	Cl^-	ClO^-	ClO_2^-	O_2	ClO_2	Cl_2O_6	ClO_4^-	Reference
$KClO_3$	1.9	0.7	2.6	2.9	0.2	1.4	—	50
$KClO_3$	—	—	1.2	—	—	—	—	58
$KClO_3$	—	—	—	1.57	—	—	—	62
$NaClO_3$	0.23	0.21	1.34	1.95	0.95	—	0.22	60

10-13.1 Effect of Temperature

Irradiation of $KClO_3$ at low temperatures (77°K) produced a significant decrease in the radiolytic yield of O_2, ClO^-, ClO_2^-, and Cl^-. Annealing of irradiated chlorates (100–210°C) increases the Cl^- content which presumably arises from the thermal decomposition of ClO^- and ClO_2^-.

10-13.2 Mechanism

There is very little experimental support for any kinetic mechanism. For large absorbed doses the rates of formation of chlorite and hypochlorite decrease — indicating decomposition, back reaction, or some other complex reaction. Heal[50] reports an effect of intensity on the radiolysis of $KClO_3$. When the intensity is reduced by a factor of three, Heal observes a significant decrease in the major products. This result is very much in disagreement with that found for other salts.

10-14 ALKALI HALIDES

The alkali halides are the simplest of the inorganic salts since the only chemical products that can be formed are the alkali metal and the halogen. The color centers formed are discussed in Sec. 10-2.4. These color centers are definitely related to either electron excess bands formed when electrons are trapped at crystal imperfections, or hole-type bands resulting from similarly trapped holes. The molecular species formed have been postulated as Na_2, Br_2, or Cl_2 and the ions, Cl_2^-, Cl_3^-, I_3^-, and Br_3^-.

It has been shown chemically that electron excess and deficient centers are produced in alkali chloride in equal amounts.[63] This was done by dissolving the irradiated salt in water and determining the H_2 liberated and the hypochlorite formed. The reactions may be viewed as follows:

$$Na + H_2O \longrightarrow NaOH + 1/2\ H_2 \qquad (10\text{-}52)$$

or $\quad e^- + H_2O \longrightarrow OH^- + 1/2\ H_2 \qquad\qquad (10\text{-}53)$

$$Cl + H_2O \longrightarrow ClO^- + 2H^+ \qquad\qquad (10\text{-}54)$$

Although a limiting concentration of centers of 10^{17} per cm^3 has been reported in samples irradiated at low temperatures, irradiation of KCl at room temperature will produce an amount of ClO^- equivalent to at least 8 mol percent decomposition.[48]

The most important results of the irradiation of these crystals are those related to color centers, their mode of formation, identification and characterization. For a comprehensive review of this subject see Refs. 64-66.

10-15 AZIDES

Sodium azide when irradiated with X-rays[67] decomposes to yield, upon dissolution of the irradiated salt in water, NH_3, OH^-, and N_2 in the stoichiometric ratio 1:3:4. The NH_3 and OH^- possibly arise from hydrolysis of the nitride ion.

$$3N_3^- \xrightarrow{\hspace{0.8cm}} N^3 + 4N_2 \qquad\qquad (10\text{-}55)$$

$$N^{3-} + 3H_2O \longrightarrow NH_3 + 3OH^- \qquad\qquad (10\text{-}56)$$

Pile irradiation and subsequent dissolution of the irradiated salt in water indicates that hydrogen is also a product, presumably arising from the reaction of sodium atoms with the water.[68] Dissolution of the irradiated salt in liquid ammonia produces a coloration similar to that found when sodium is dissolved in liquid ammonia.

Furthermore, aqueous solutions of the irradiated salt yield traces of hydrazine.

Photolysis with 2537 Å light causes decomposition with the liberation of nitrogen; because of this it is postulated that mobile positive holes and F centers are produced in equal amounts by exciton interaction with anion vacancies, or of the V center with an exciton to give an F center and a double vacancy.[69] Optical irradiation at $573°K$ produces colloidal sodium in addition to nitrogen gas.

Although strong F bands, V bands and R bands have been reported from photochemical studies, only weak F bands are formed when NaN_3 is irradiated with X-rays or gamma rays. There is evidence therefore that significant differences exist in photochemical decomposition compared to decomposition induced by high energy radiation.

10-16 HETEROGENEOUS SYSTEMS

It has been shown that when a chemically decomposable substance adsorbed on the surface of an inert matrix such as silica gel, magnesium oxide, or other solids is irradiated, a part of the excitation energy delivered to the solid by the radiation is transferred to the surface causing decomposition of the adsorbate.[70,71] This is based on the fact that the amount of decomposition of the adsorbate relative to the amount of energy absorbed by it, is far in excess of that found for the pure adsorbate on an electron fraction basis. The conclusion drawn is that a good portion of the energy absorbed by the inert matrix must have been transferred to the surface causing decomposition.

When silica gel or microporous $SiO_2-Al_2O_3$ are irradiated in the absence of the absorbate, a blue color develops which is bleached by simple post-irradiation exposure to the adsorbate. The disappearance of the color is accompanied by decomposition of the adsorbate.

The efficiency of the energy transferred to the surface in these heterogeneous systems depends on the total absorbed dose, i.e., G is not linear with dose. The explanation offered for this effect is that defects are produced in the solid during irradiation which affect the energy transfer process. A solid therefore with a previous history of irradiation is less efficient at energy transport than an unirradiated solid. Support for this thesis also comes from the fact that when MgO is used as the solid, the more perfect crystalline preparations are appreciably more efficient in energy transfer than in the more imperfect crystals.

Another important aspect is that of the energy states on the surface of the solid which are available to the adsorbate molecule. Product distribution is affected in at least some cases by the extent of the surface coverage.

In summary the available information appears to suggest that:

(1) Energy is transferred through the solid to the surface.

(2) The efficiency of this process appears to depend on the material, the number of defects present, the energy gap, degree of crystallinity and surface coverage.

PROBLEMS

10-1 Starting with Eq. (10-21) derive Eq. (10-23).

10-2 Calculate the number of Frenkel defects in a sample of KNO_3 quenched at its melting point in liquid nitrogen.

10-3 What is the color center density of a sample of sodium azide that shows an absorption peak at 3400 Å if the absorption coefficient is 0.4, and if half width is 740 Å at λ_{max}.

10-4 If the activation energy for diffusion of a particular atom in a lattice is very low what can be said about the probable radiation decomposition mechanism.

10-5 Derive a probable mechanism for the decomposition of the alkali chlorates.

REFERENCES

1. H. G. Van Bueren, "Imperfections in Crystals," North Holland Publishing Co., Amsterdam, 1961.

2. M. R. Ronayne, W. H. Hamill, and J. P. Guarino, *J.A.C.S.*, 84:4230 (1962).

3. W. H. Hamill, J. P. Guarino, M. R. Ronayne, and J. A. Ward, *Disc. Far. Soc.*, No. 36:169 (1963).

4. W. Känzig, *Phys. Rev.*, 99:1890 (1955).

5. W. Känzig and T. O. Woodruff, *Phys. Rev.*, 109:220 (1958).

6. W. Känzig, *Phys. Rev. Letters*, 4:117 (1960).

7. F. Seitz, *Rev. Mod. Phys.*, **26**:7 (1954).

8. K. Przibram, "Irradiation Colours and Luminescence," Pergamon Press, London, 1956.

9. F. Seitz and J. S. Koehler in F. Seitz and D. Turnbull (eds.), "Solid State Physics," vol. 2, Academic Press Inc., New York, 1956.

10. Y. Querre, in M. Haissinsky (ed.), "Action Chimique et Biologiques des Radiations," Masson, Paris, 1964.

11. J. H. O. Varley, *Nature*, **174**:886 (1954).

12. T. A. Carlson and M. O. Krause, *Phys. Rev.*, **140A**:1057 (1965).

13. J. Durup and R. L. Platzman, *Disc. Far. Soc.*, **31**:156 (1961).

14. D. Pooley, Color Center Conferences, U. of Ill., 1965.

15. L. S. Singer and J. Kommandeur, *J. Chem. Phys.*, **32**:1013 (1961).

16. D. C. Hoosterey and G. M. Leston, *J. Phys. Chem. Solids*, **24**:1609 (1963).

17. G. J. Dienes and A. C. Damas, in G. M. Schwab (ed.), *5th International Symposium on the Reactivity of Solids*, Elsevier Publishing Co., New York, 1965.

18. A. Rose, "Concepts in Photoconductivity," Chap. 4, Interscience Publishers, New York, 1963.

19. I. Serlin, *Science*, **126**:261 (1957).

20. H. W. Fenrick, S. U. Filseth, A. L. Hanson, and J. E. Willard, *J.A.C.S.*, **85**:3731 (1963).

21. F. W. Stacey, J. C. Sauer, and B. C. McKusick, *J.A.C.S.*, **81**:987 (1959).

22. G. Boyd, private communication.

23. S. Okamura, K. Hayashi, and Y. Kitanishi, *J. Polym. Sci.*, **58**:927 (1962).

24. L. Kevan and W. F. Libby, *Recent Advances in Photochemistry*, 183 (1963).

25. R. S. Knox, "Theory of Excitons," Solid State Physics Supplement 3, F. Seitz and D. Turnbull (eds.), Academic Press, New York, 1963.

26. A. S. Davydov, "Theory of Molecular Excitons," M. Kasha and M. Oppenheimer (trans.), McGraw-Hill Book Company, New York, 1962.

27. A. R. Jones, *J. Chem. Phys.*, **35**:751 (1961).

28. V. V. Voedvoskii and Y. N. Molin, *Rad. Res.*, **17**:366 (1962).

29. J. L. Magee, *Rad. Res.*, **20**:71 (1963).

30. A. M. Bass and H. P. Broida, "Stabilization of Free Radicals at Low Temperatures," NBS Monograph 12, 1960.

31. T. Shida and W. H. Hamill, *J.A.C.S.*, **88**:2369, 2375, 3683, 3689, 4372, 5371, 5376 (1966).

32. S. Arai and L. M. Dorfman, *J. Chem. Phys.*, **41**:2190 (1964).

33. J. Cunningham, *J. Phys. Chem.*, **67**:1772 (1963).

34. ——, *J. Phys. Chem.*, **65**:628 (1961).

35. C. J. Hochanadel, *Rad. Res.*, **16**:3, 286 (1962).

36. D. Hall and G. N. Walton, *J. Inorg. Nuclear Chem.*, **10**:215 (1959).

37. J. Cunningham, *Trans. Far. Soc.*, No. 525, **62**(part 9):2423 (1966).

38. G. Hennig, R. Lees, and M. Matheson, *J. Chem. Phys.*, **21**:664 (1955).

39. T. Chen and E. R. Johnson, *J. Phys. Chem.*, **66**:2249 (1962).

40. P. Pringsheim, *J. Chem. Phys.*, **23**:369 (1953).

41. J. Cunningham, *J. Phys. Chem. Solids*, **23**:843 (1962).

42. C. Jacard, *Phys. Rev.*, **124**:60 (1961).

43. R. M. Golding and M. Henchman, *J. Chem. Phys.*, **40**:1554 (1964).

44. H. Zeldes and R. Livingston, *J. Chem. Phys.*, **35**:563 (1961).

45. J. Cunningham, *J. Phys. Chem.*, **71**:1967 (1967).

46. ——, *J. Phys. Chem.*, **70**:30 (1966).

47. T. H. Chen and E. R. Johnson, *J. Phys. Chem.*, **66**:2068 (1962).

48. L. A. Prince, Dissertation, Stevens Institute of Technology, Hoboken, N.J.

49. ——— and E. R. Johnson, *J. Phys. Chem.*, **69**:359, 369, 377 (1965).

50. H. G. Heal, *Can. J. Chem.*, **37**:979 (1959).

51. A. S. Baberkin, Akad Nauk, SSSR Otd. Khim. Nauk 1957, 167 (1958).

52. T. Cole, *Proc. Natl. Acad. Sci. U.S.*, **46**:506 (1960).

53. G. E. Boyd, *et al.*, *J. Phys. Chem.*, **66**:300 (1962).

54. ———, *J. Phys. Chem.*, **69**:1413 (1965).

55. ———, *J. Phys. Chem.*, **70**:1031 (1966).

56. J. W. Chase and G. E. Boyd, "Symposium on the Chemical and Physical Effects of High Energy Radiation," p. 17, ASTM STP 400 (1966).

57. P. J. Herley and P. Levy, *J. Chem. Phys.*, **46**:627 (1967).

58. A. S. Baberkin, Moscow Acad. of Sci. USSR Press, p. 187 (1958).

59. S. Huang and E. R. Johnson, Radiation Effects Symposium, ASTM Committee E-10, Seattle, Washington, Nov. 2-5, 1965.

60. C. E. Burchill, *Nature*, **194** (1962). Reported by P. F. Patrick and K. J. McCallum.

61. L. J. Sherman and K. J. McCallum, *J. Chem. Phys.*, **23**:597 (1955).

62. G. Hennig, R. Lees, and M. S. Matheson, *J. Chem. Phys.*, **21**:664 (1953).

63. W. G. Burns and T. F. Williams, *Nature (London)*, **175**:1043 (1955).

64. D. A. Wiegand and R. Smoluchowski, The Production of Defects in Alkali Halides, "Actions Chemiques and Biologiques des Radiation," M. Haisainsky (ed.), 7, Masson, Paris, 1964.

65. W. D. Compton and H. Rabin, F Aggregate Centers in Alkali Halide Crystals, in F. Seitz and D. Turnbull (eds.), Solid State Physics, Vol. 16, Academic Press, New York, 1964.

66. C. F. Gibbon and G. C. Kuczynski, "Materials Science Research," vol. 3, p. 131, Plenum Press, New York, 1966.

67. H. G. Heal, *Can. J. Chem.*, 31:1153 (1953).

68. J. Cunningham, *Trans. Far. Soc.*, 62(Part 9):2423 (1966).

69. J. C. Cunningham and F. C. Tompkins, *Proc. Roy. Soc.*, A251: 27 (1959).

70. A. O. Allen, *et al.*, *J.A.C.S.*, 86:3887 (1964).

71. R. R. Hentz, *J. Phys. Chem.*, 66:1625 (1962).

RADIATION-INDUCED POLYMERIZATIONS

Before discussing the unique aspects of radiation polymerizations, we will describe in brief detail the nature of polymers and the
properties by which they are characterized. In general these properties arise from the high molecular weights, the chemical structure of the individual molecules, and their morphological arrangement.

11-1 SOLID STATE PROPERTIES OF POLYMERS

With few exceptions, one may classify polymers as (1) consisting of long chain, one-dimensional repeating units of molecular
weight $10^4 - 10^7$ where the chains are held together by weak secondary forces, or (2) three-dimensional crosslinked network polymers
where chains are linked to each other by primary bonds. Examples
of one-dimensional molecules include plastics such as polyethylene
and Teflon, fibers such as cellulose, and rubbers such as (uncured)
butadiene-styrene. Three-dimensional, densely crosslinked polymers include phenolformaldehyde, urea-formaldehyde, and vulcan-
ized rubber. Polymers exist which are lightly crosslinked network
structures, an example being partially cured rubber. Polymers,
like all solids, can be characterized in terms of response to an applied stress, a typical stress-strain curve being shown in Fig. 11-1.
The region between the yield and break points is CD and at D the
polymer breaks. The initial, linear, elastic response portion of the
curve is the *Hooke's law region*.

$$F/A = Y(\Delta l/l)$$

where F = force

A = cross sectional area

Y = Young's modulus

l = length

The effect of increasing crosslinking, in general, is to increase
Young's modulus, and to decrease the elongation at break.

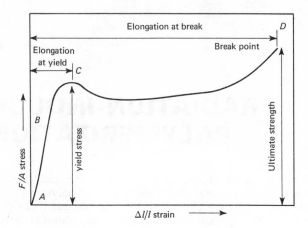

Fig. 11-1. Polymer stress–strain curve.
AB = elastic response; BC = viscoelastic
response; CD = viscous or plastic flow.

Various adjuncts to stress-strain measurements may be made.
These include:

Thermochemical Curves. The polymer, in tension, is heated at
a slow rate. The temperature at which the polymer increases
sharply in length is called the fusion temperature. Fusion points
increase with degree of crosslinking, all other things being equal.

Impact Strength. If the load is applied over a time interval
which is short compared to the viscoelastic response time, the
specimen will fracture. Many different versions of impact tests
exist; most of them are carried out with notched samples to concen-
trate the stress and assure fracture.

11-1.1 Electrical Properties of Polymers

Among the important electrical properties of polymers are:

The dielectric constant — the ability of a material to increase
the energy which can be stored in an electric field, or to reduce the
force between charges in the medium. Most rigid polymers have
dielectric constants between 2 and 4.

The dielectric strength — defines the ability of a material to
withstand an applied field without breakdown. The dielectric strength
for polymers is in the range of a few hundred volts per mil.

The loss factor — related to the speed with which the permanent dipoles accommodate to the field. The loss factor is a measure of the energy dissipated by charge migration and friction losses.

The electrical conductivity — for polymers is very low, the resistivities are generally above 10^{10} ohm-cm.

It should be noted that all of the above listed properties are complicated functions of the frequency, temperature, and environmental factors.

11-1.2 Molecular Weight

A polymeric material is usually a mixture of long chain molecules of various lengths whose molecular weights must be stated in terms of averages. These averages include:

(1) Number average molecular weights and number average degrees of polymerization

$$\bar{M}_n = \frac{\Sigma n_i M_i}{\Sigma n_i}$$

$$\overline{DP}_n = \frac{\Sigma n_i \overline{DP}_i}{\Sigma n_i}$$

The number of molecules belonging to any one species is represented by n_i; and $\bar{M}_i$ and $\overline{DP}_i$ are the corresponding molecular weights and degrees of polymerization of the chain, the latter being defined in terms of the number of repeating units per chain. Number averages are determined by osmotic measurements or by the analytical determination of end groups, since only the number of chains are measured by these techniques.

(2) Weight average molecular weight $\bar{M}_W$ and weight average degree of polymerization $\overline{DP}_W$

$$\bar{M}_W = \frac{\Sigma n_i M_i^2}{\Sigma n_i M_i}$$

$$\overline{DP}_W = \frac{\Sigma n_i \overline{DP}_i^2}{\Sigma n_i \overline{DP}_i}$$

In calculating weight average molecular weights, the molecular weight of the species is weighed by its weight fraction (not the number of chains), hence the square term. The $\bar{M}_W$ can be determined

by light scattering, viscosity, diffusion, or sedimentation. The latter
three methods may, however, also lead to more complicated averages.

11-1.3 Solution Properties

When linear polymers are put in solution the molecules separate, and thus can be studied individually. Such properties as osmotic pressure, freezing-point depression, boiling-point elevation,
light scattering, diffusivities, and viscosities are all useful for determining molecular weights, as well as shapes of individual molecules.

Crosslinked polymers, although they do not dissolve, often swell
in solvents; the degree of swelling is related to the degree of crosslinking.

11-1.4 Transition Properties

Polymers, composed as they are of a mixture of different molecular weight molecules, have no sharp melting points (in the sense
that ice melts at $32°$ F). On heating, the amorphous polymers behave like a supercooled liquid such as glass in that they pass through
a rubbery stage prior to softening, and melting into a viscous liquid.
True melting can occur only in the uncrosslinked portion of the
polymer.

11-1.5 Crystallinity and Orientation

Polymers generally do not form perfect crystals because they
contain a distribution of molecular weights, and because of the very
poor mobility of the polymer molecules at the temperature at which
crystallization would normally occur.

The degree of crystallinity varies with the chemical structure
of the polymer, as well as rate of cooling from melt to solid. Some,
such as nylon, crystallize easily. Additional crystallite properties
can then be obtained by orientation (stretching) along the crystal
axis, as shown in Fig. 11-2. Orientation can also be achieved in
noncrystalline polymers such as rubber, in which case the individual
oriented molecules combine to give a crystal-like, X-ray pattern.

A special type of morphological orientation can be obtained by a
stereospecific polymerization in which the polymer chains are made
to conform to certain shapes. Consider a vinyl polymer such as
$-CH_2-CHR-CH_2-CHR-CH_2-CHR$ where R may be a phenyl group
(polystyrene) or a methyl group (polypropylene). A chain such as
this may align randomly in an *atactic* fashion, or stereospecifically
in the *isotactic* or *syndiotactic* arrangements shown.

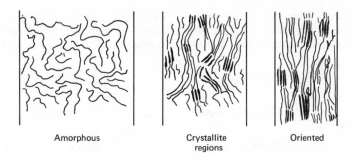

Amorphous   Crystallite   Oriented
regions

Fig. 11-2. Arrangements of polymer
molecules with respect to each other.

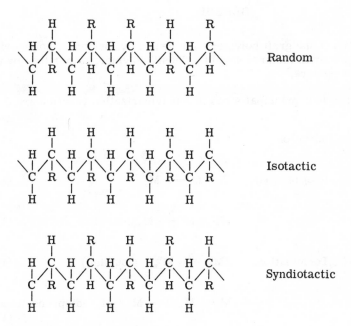

Random

Isotactic

Syndiotactic

11-2 ADDITION POLYMERIZATIONS

In addition polymerizations the monomer ⟶ polymer reaction
occurs without elimination of byproduct. During the course of the
reaction no stable compounds are formed, the intermediates being
short-lived radicals, or ions. The formation of the polymer chain
usually takes place in fractions of seconds unless there are retard-
ing steric or viscosity factors. Although addition polymerization
reactions generally involve a single vinyl species, they may take

place with mixtures of monomers. Reactions involving mixtures of monomers are called *copolymerizations* and will lead to the different types of chains shown below for mixtures of monomer A and B:

AABAAABBBBABA	Random
ABABABABABABAB	Alternating
AAAABBBBAAAA	Block

$$\begin{array}{ccc} \text{BBBBB} & & \text{BBB} \\ {\diagup} & & {\mid} \\ \text{AAAAAAAAAAAAAAAA} & & \text{Graft} \\ {\diagdown} & & \\ & \text{BBBBBB} & \end{array}$$

Block and graft polymers are generally formed by polymerizing a monomer in the presence of a "host" polymer, rather than by using two monomers.

The four principal steps in a polymerization reaction are

R_i, Initiation: $\quad\quad\quad C \xrightarrow{k_i} C\cdot$ $\hfill$ (11-1)

R_p, Propagation: $\quad\quad C\cdot + M \xrightarrow{k_p} M\cdot$ $\hfill$ (11-2)

$\quad\quad\quad\quad\quad\quad\quad M_n\cdot + M \xrightarrow{k_p} M_{n+1}\cdot$ $\hfill$ (11-3)

R_t, Termination: $\quad 2M_n\cdot \xrightarrow{k_t} M_{2n}$ (coupling) $\hfill$ (11-4)

$\quad\quad\quad\quad\quad\quad M_n\cdot + M_m\cdot \xrightarrow{k_t} M_n + M_m$ (disproportionation) $\hfill$ (11-5)

R_s, Chain transfer: $M_n\cdot + M \xrightarrow{k_s'} M_n + M\cdot$ (with monomer) $\hfill$ (11-6)

$\quad\quad\quad\quad\quad\quad M_n\cdot + M_m \xrightarrow{k_s''} M_n + M_m\cdot$ (with polymer) $\hfill$ (11-7)

$\quad\quad\quad\quad\quad\quad M_n\cdot + S \xrightarrow{k_s} S\cdot + M_n$ (with other molecules) $\hfill$ (11-8)

11-2.1 Initiation

Most materials which decompose spontaneously or under stimulus to form a radical can initiate a polymerization. When radiation is used as the stimulus, C can be a monomer or any other radical forming species. In chemically initiated polymerizations C, the catalyst, becomes permanently attached to the polymer chain.

11-2.2 Propagation

Propagation involves the reaction of a radical with a monomer. The reactivity of the system is governed both by the resonance stabilization of the monomer and radical, and steric effects due to substituents on the molecule and radical.

11-2.3 Termination

The rate of terminations is often proportional to the number of radicals. At high concentrations of radicals there are a comparatively large number of terminations, resulting in a comparatively lower molecular weight. In general, $n \neq m$ in Eq. (11-5), and the two n's in Eq. (11-4) are not equal.

11-2.4 Chain Transfer

This occurs without a reduction in the number of free radicals. It results in a lowering of the molecular weight, unless the chain transfer is to a dead polymer chain.

11-2.5 Inhibition

Substances which when introduced into the polymerization system slow or stop the reaction are called retarders or inhibitors. These generally function by forming stable complexes or products with reactive intermediates.

11-2.6 Autoacceleration (Gel or Trommsdorff Effect)

Autoacceleration, which occurs principally with monomers of the type $CH_2=CHX$, manifests itself by an increase in rate of polymerization at high viscosities. The high viscosity is thought to reduce diffusion and hence termination, since this depends on collision of two radicals.

11-3 IONIC POLYMERIZATION

Ionic polymerizations, which may be cationic or anionic in nature, differ from addition polymerizations in that the unstable intermediates bear positive or negative charges. An example of a cationic polymerization is the polymerization of isobutylene by boron trifluoride in the presence of water as cocatalyst, or promoter:

Initiation:
$$BF_3 + H_2O \longrightarrow F_3BOH^- + H^+ \tag{11-9}$$

$$H^+ + CH_2{=}C(CH_3)_2 \longrightarrow (CH_3)_3C^+ \tag{11-10}$$

Propagation:
$$(CH_3)_3C^+ + CH_2{=}C(CH_3)_2 \longrightarrow CH_3\underset{\underset{CH_3}{|}}{\overset{\overset{CH_3}{|}}{C}}{-}CH_2{-}\underset{\underset{CH_3}{|}}{\overset{\overset{CH_3}{|}}{C}}{}^+ \tag{11-11}$$

Termination:
$$R{-}\underset{\underset{CH_3}{|}}{\overset{\overset{CH_3}{|}}{C}}{}^+ \longrightarrow R{=}C(CH_3)_2 + H^+ \tag{11-12}$$

$$\searrow \qquad R{-}C\overset{\diagup CH_3}{\underset{\diagdown\!\!\diagdown CH_2}{}} \quad + H^+$$

Anionic polymerizations can be catalyzed by metallic sodium, sodium ethoxide, aqueous alkalis, and so forth. A plausible mechanism for the polymerization of the monomer M in the presence of base is:

Initiation:
$$K + NH_3 \longrightarrow K^+ + NH_2^- + 1/2\,H_2 \tag{11-13}$$

$$M + NH_2^- \longrightarrow RNH_2^- \tag{11-14}$$

Propagation:
$$RNH_2^- + M \longrightarrow R'NH_2^- \tag{11-15}$$

Termination:
$$R'NH_2^- \longrightarrow P + NH_2^- \tag{11-16}$$

$$R'NH_2^- + NH_3 \longrightarrow PNH_3 + NH_2^- \tag{11-17}$$

The kinetics of ionic polymerization depend on the nature of the medium. A high dielectric constant medium will induce charge separations. It thus increases the rate of initiation and decreases terminations since electrical neutrality must be maintained by counter ions.

11-4 COPOLYMERIZATION

The simultaneous polymerization of two or more monomers to yield a polymer chain which contains more than one monomer is called copolymerization. Where two monomers M_1 and M_2 are involved, four radical-monomer reactions may occur

$$M_1 \cdot + M_1 \xrightarrow{k_{11}} M_1 M_1 \cdot \qquad (11\text{-}18)$$

$$M_1 \cdot + M_2 \xrightarrow{k_{12}} M_1 M_2 \cdot \qquad (11\text{-}19)$$

$$M_2 \cdot + M_1 \xrightarrow{k_{21}} M_2 M_1 \cdot \qquad (11\text{-}20)$$

$$M_2 \cdot + M_2 \xrightarrow{k_{22}} M_2 M_2 \cdot \qquad (11\text{-}21)$$

The structure of the resulting copolymer depends on the reaction rates of the competing reactions. If, for instance, $k_{12} \approx k_{21}$ and k_{11} and k_{22} are small, an alternating structure of

$$-M_1-M_2-M_1-M_2-M_1-$$

is formed.

11-5 METHODS OF POLYMERIZATION

Bulk or *mass polymerizations* as they are often called, are carried out with the pure monomer in the gas, liquid, or solid state. In bulk polymerizations there is often a great deal of difficulty in controlling the temperature. When this occurs the polymer has a relatively wide distribution of molecular weights, and only moderately good mechanical properties.

In *solution polymerizations*, where the monomer is dissolved in a solvent, better temperature control is achieved. There are other important features: (1) traces of solvent may be incorporated in the polymer, and (2) chain transfer, with a consequent lowering of the molecular weight, may occur.

Emulsion techniques involve suspending the monomer as an emulsion, generally in an aqueous soap media. At the beginning of the polymerization the monomer is present in the form of dispersed droplets covered with soap, or is solubilized in the soap micelles. According to some of the currently held theories of emulsion polymerization, the initiation is started in the micelles by radicals formed in the aqueous phase. Monomer now diffuses in, and the monomer-polymer particles become the loci for the propagation and termination reaction. This process continues till the monomer from the droplet reservoirs has been used up.

Techniques other than bulk, solution, and emulsion polymerization are used; they are, however, of considerably less importance, and have been little studied by radiation chemists.

11-6 POLYMERIZATION KINETICS

The steady state assumption in which the transient species are characterized by an equal rate of formation and disappearance, when applied to a reaction scheme such as Eqs. (11-1)—(11-8) gives from Eqs. (11-1) and (11-4)

$$R_i = R_t = k_t [M_n\cdot]^2 \tag{11-22}$$

Equation (11-22) may be used to eliminate $[M_n\cdot]$ from the rate expression for monomer disappearance (11-3)

$$-\frac{dM}{dt} = R = k_p [M_n\cdot][M] = k_p k_t^{-1/2} R_i^{1/2} [M] \tag{11-23}$$

Equation (11-23) assumes that monomer consumption is restricted to the propagation step, and that the radical reactivity is independent of chain length, and that termination is by (11-4).

For the case of a radiation-initiated reaction, if G_r^M is the radical yield for M, ϕ the radiation flux, and μ_{en}/ρ the mass-energy absorption coefficient

$$R_i = G_r^M \phi\mu_{en}/\rho[M] \tag{11-24}$$

A very considerable number of special kinetic expressions governing radiation-induced polymerizations may be developed. Some of these are demonstrated in Example 11-1.

EXAMPLE 11-1: Develop overall kinetic expressions for the rate of disappearance of monomer for the following special conditions:

(1) For polymerization in the presence of substance S.

(2) Recombination of primary radicals.

(3) A copolymerization.

(4) Develop expressions for $\overline{DP}_n$ the degree of polymerization for a solvent polymerization, and for a bulk polymerization at low dose rates.

SOLUTION:

(1) S may also take part in the initiation, in which case, providing there is no energy transfer

$$R_i = \phi \left(G_r^M \, (\mu_{en}(M)/\rho)\,[M] + G_r^S \, (\mu_{en}(S)/\rho)\,[S] \right) \qquad (11\text{-}25)$$

S may also take part in the propagation however, unless S· is unreactive, this will not affect the rate of reaction, even though it will affect the molecular weight.

Substituting Eq. (11-25) into Eq. (11-23)

$$R = k_p k_t^{-1/2}[M]^{3/2} \quad \phi G_r^M (\mu_{en}(M)/\rho)^{1/2}$$

$$\times \left[1 + \frac{(\mu_{en}(S)/\rho)\,G_r^S\,[S]}{(\mu_{en}(M)/\rho)\,G_r^M\,[M]} \right]^{1/2} \qquad (11\text{-}26)$$

Note that Eq. (11-26) provides a way of determining G_r^S/G_r^M by carrying out polymerizations in solvents.

(2) If the primary radical concentration is very high then termination reactions (11-4a) and (11-4b) can take place

$$C\cdot + C\cdot \xrightarrow{k_{tc}'} 2C \qquad (11\text{-}4a)$$

$$C\cdot + M_m\cdot \xrightarrow{k_{tc}} CM_m \qquad (11\text{-}4b)$$

The expressions for the rate of formation and disappearance of radicals C· and M· are:

$$\frac{dC\cdot}{dt} = 0 = R_i - k_{tc}'\,[C\cdot]^2 - k_p[C\cdot][M] - k_{tc}\,[C\cdot][M_m\cdot] \qquad (11\text{-}27)$$

$$\frac{dM\cdot}{dt} = 0 = k_{pc}\,[C\cdot][M] - k_t\,[M_n\cdot]^2 - k_{tc}\,[C\cdot][M_n\cdot] \qquad (11\text{-}28)$$

the subscript c has been added to denote reactions involving the radical C·, which we now assume has a reactivity different from $M_n\cdot$. These equations are such that it is not possible to find a simple expression for the overall rate, $R = k_p[M][M_n\cdot]$ in terms of molecular concentrations. There are, however, a number of limiting conditions under which solutions are available. If, for instance, the rate of initiation is so high that $k_{tc}[C\cdot][M_n\cdot] \gg k_t[M_n\cdot]^2$, i.e., all terminations are by primary radicals, then Eq. (11-28) becomes

$$[M_n\cdot] = k_{pc}/k_{tc}\,[M] \tag{11-29}$$

and substituting for $M_n\cdot$ into Eq. (11-23), we find that the overall rate is independent of the initiation

$$R = \frac{k_p k_{pc}}{k_{tc}}\,[M]^2 \tag{11-30}$$

If the dose rate is increased still further, then an appreciable amount of monomer can disappear via

$$C\cdot + M \xrightarrow{k_{pc}} M\cdot$$

and we must write, for the overall rate, Eq. (11-23)

$$R = k_p[M][M_n\cdot] + k_{pc}[C\cdot][M] \tag{11-31}$$

Equation (11-27) at high dose rates where the last two terms on the right-hand side may be neglected, reduces to

$$[C\cdot] = R_i^{1/2}/k_{tc'}^{1/2} \tag{11-32}$$

Substituting Eqs. (11-32) and (11-29) into (11-31)

$$R = k_p k_{pc}/k_{tc} + k_{pc}R_i^{1/2}[M]/k_{tc'}^{1/2} \tag{11-33}$$

The variation of polymerization rate with increasing dose rate as expressed by Eqs. (11-23), (11-30), and (11-33) is shown graphically in Fig. 11-3.

(3) In a steady state copolymerization the rate at which $M_1\cdot$ is transformed into $M_2\cdot$ [Eq. (11-19)] must equal the rate at which $M_2\cdot$ is transformed to $M_1\cdot$ [Eq. (11-20)]. Thus, the ratio of $M_2\cdot$ to $M_1\cdot$, according to Eqs. (11-19) and (11-20), must be

$$[M_2\cdot]/[M_1\cdot] = k_{12}[M_2]/k_{21}[M_1] \tag{11-34}$$

The rate of consumption of monomers M_1 and M_2 equals their rate of appearance in the polymer

$$-dM_1/dt = k_{11}[M_1\cdot][M_1] + k_{21}[M_2\cdot][M_1] \tag{11-35}$$

$$-dM_2/dt = k_{12}[M_1\cdot][M_2] + k_{22}[M_2\cdot][M_2] \tag{11-36}$$

Dividing Eq. (11-36) into (11-35), and substituting Eq. (11-34) we obtain

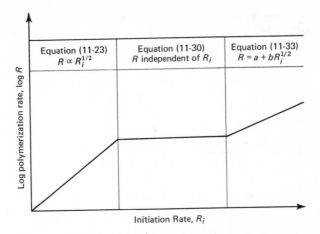

Fig. 11-3. Variation of polymerization
rate with dose rate.

$$\frac{d\mathrm{M}_1}{d\mathrm{M}_2} = \frac{[\mathrm{M}_1]}{[\mathrm{M}_2]}\frac{r_1[\mathrm{M}_1] + [\mathrm{M}_2]}{[\mathrm{M}_1] + r_2[\mathrm{M}_2]} \tag{11-37}$$

where $r_1 = k_{11}/k_{12}$ and $r_2 = k_{22}/k_{21}$ are the monomer reactivity ratios. Values of r greater than 1 indicate that a
radical prefers to react with its own monomer rather than
with the other monomer.

(4) The degree of polymerization equals the total amount of
polymer produced divided by the number of termination (or
initiation) reactions. If there is chain transfer to monomer
M, or solvent S

$\overline{DP}_n$ = (velocity of propagation)/[(velocity of termination)

+ (velocity of transfer to monomer)

+ (velocity of transfer to solvent)]. (11-38)

If we assume Eq. (11-6), transfer to monomer, to be relatively
unimportant,

$$\overline{DP}_n = \frac{k_p[\mathrm{M}_n\!\cdot\!][\mathrm{M}]}{k_t[\mathrm{M}_n\!\cdot\!]^2 + k_s[\mathrm{M}_n\!\cdot\!][\mathrm{S}]} \tag{11-39}$$

Equation (11-39) can be conveniently expressed in terms of $\overline{DP}_o$, the degree of polymerization in the absence of chain transfer

$$\frac{1}{\overline{DP}_n} = \frac{1}{\overline{DP}_o} + \frac{k_s[S]}{k_p[M]} \tag{11-40}$$

where

$$\overline{DP}_o = \frac{k_p[M_n\cdot][M]}{k_t[M_n\cdot]^2} = \frac{k_p[M]}{(k_t)^{1/2}(R_i)^{1/2}} \tag{11-41}$$

If termination is by chain combination [Eq. (11-5)] $\overline{DP}_o$ must be doubled.

11-6.1 Polymerization Kinetics — Unsteady State

For an unsteady state polymerization which follows a second order termination, the concentration of radicals is

$$d[R\cdot]/dt = R_i(t) - k_t[R\cdot]^2 \tag{11-42}$$

where $R\cdot$ is the radical concentration, and R_i the rate of initiation. Equation (11-42) has an analytical solution when R_i is zero, or constant. When R_i is a periodic function of time, as in a rotating sector experiment, it becomes convenient to render the equation dimensionless by substituting the variables

$$R'\cdot = R\cdot/R_s\cdot$$

$$R_i' = R_i(t)/R_{is} \tag{11-43}$$

$$t' = t/\tau$$

where the subscript s refers to the steady state, and τ is the radical lifetime. Equation (11-42) which can now be written as

$$d[R'\cdot]/dt = R_i'(t') - k_t[R'\cdot]^2 \tag{11-44}$$

is both dimensionalized and normalized if the initiation rate R_i is set equal to the maximum value of the periodically varying initiation rate, $R_i(t)$.

A computer solution to Eq. (11-44) for the case of square wave and sinusoidal $R_i(t)$ functions, is shown in Fig. 11-4. The ordinate, $\overline{R'}$, is the average radical concentration divided by the radical concentration at a steady state where the dose rate is the maximum value that the intermittent dose rate attains. Both curves asymptote

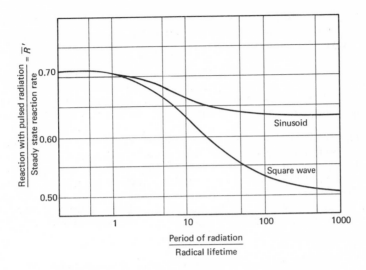

Fig. 11-4. Effect of intermittancy on reaction rate.
[N. Steinberg and E. J. Henley, *J. Phys. Chem.*, 67:
1942 (1963).]

at the same value at high frequencies, because the average values of
R_i' are the same, and the system is half order in radical concentration. At low frequencies there are appreciable differences in the
reaction rates between square wave and sinusoidal initiation rates.

11-7 SPATIAL DISTRIBUTION OF INITIATION EVENTS

Implicit in the foregoing equations and discussion is the assumption of a homogeneous distribution of reacting species. For
radiation-induced polymerizations, this homogeneity can be achieved
only if the radical concentration is randomized by diffusion. If it is
not, then the nonrandom concentration of the free radicals formed
along the particle tracks must be considered. If the spurs are highly
localized, and the reaction is very fast, then the free radicals will
remain isolated during the whole reaction period. As long as
this situation prevails, an increase in dose rate (R_i) will simply
create new radicals; the $\overline{DP}_n$ will not be changed; and the polymerization rate will be proportional to R_i rather than to $(R_i)^{1/2}$ as indicated by Eq. (11-23), which was derived on the basis of homogeneous
reaction kinetics.

11-8 LIQUID PHASE POLYMERIZATION

The liquid phase, radiation-induced polymerization of over one
hundred monomers has been reported in the literature. Although

some of the systems studied show characteristic peculiarities, the polymerization of styrene can be considered as representative of most vinyl systems.

The earliest radiation-induced bulk polymerizations of styrene were conducted at room temperatures without additives. Linear rate curves were observed up to about 60 percent conversion, and then a sudden increase in both molecular weight and rate took place.

The reaction was found to be inhibited by traces of air, benzo-quinone, and other free radical inhibitors, thus suggesting a conventional free radical mechanism, even though the very marked acceleration towards the end of the radiation induced polymerization is not observed when conventional free radical catalysts are employed. Thus the acceleration must be due to some peculiarity of the radiation polymerization, probably operating in conjunction with the gel effect.

A qualitative explanation of this phenomena lies in the fact that styrene, like benzene, is highly radiation resistant. Its vinyl bond, being conjugated with the phenyl ring, helps stabilize the excited states, the net result being that G_r (styrene) = 0.69, which is lower even than G_r (benzene). Polystyrene, on the other hand, has a structure which more nearly resembles alkyl-substituted benzenes, for which G_r values run between 1.5 and 4. Thus more radicals are created, and the rate of polymerization, the molecular weight, and the degree of branching would be expected to increase with the degree of conversion.

Additional evidence for the creation of radical sites on the polymer during polymerization can be found in the tensile properties of the polymers formed. The radiation polymerized polystyrene shows a higher tensile strength than comparable thermally polymerized specimens, a fact which one may attribute to the higher degree of branching and crosslinking.

11-8.1 Dose Rate Effects

A very exhaustive analysis of the dose rate experiments has been made by Chapiro. From Fig. 11-5, which correlates the results of eight different investigations, it is seen that the square root dependence of rate and molecular weight on initiation rate [Eqs. (11-23) and (11-41)] are followed closely over a dose rate of 2×10^{-3} to 10 rads per second.

11-8.2 Effect of Temperature

The overall activation energy, ΔE for a "simple" vinyl polymerization [Eq. (11-23)] is

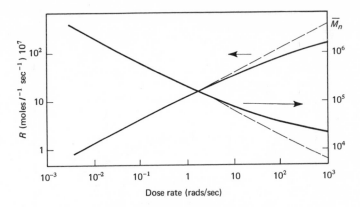

Fig. 11-5. Influence of the dose rate on the rate of polymerization of styrene and on the molecular weight of the resulting polymer. All results are normalized to a reaction temperature of $20°C$. Broken lines are extrapolations. (A. Chapiro, "Radiation Chemistry of Polymeric Systems," Interscience Publishers, New York, 1962.)

$$\Delta E = \Delta E_p - 1/2\ \Delta E_t + 1/2\ \Delta E_i \qquad (11\text{-}45)$$

Normal values for radical reactions of this type are $\Delta E_p \approx 5\text{-}8$ kcal per mole; $\Delta E_t \approx 0\text{-}3$ kcal per mole. For a radiation initiated reaction, ΔE_i would be expected to be zero, and thus $\Delta E \approx 6$.

We note also that, in accordance with Eq. (11-41) the kinetic chain length should, in the absence of chain transfer, rise with temperature with an activation energy also of $\Delta E \approx 6$.

EXAMPLE 11-2: The following data, based on that of Ballantine,[1] give the rate, dose rate, molecular weight, and temperatures for the radiation induced polymerization of styrene. Compare these data with what one would expect on the basis of Eqs. (11-45) and (11-41).

Temp., °C	Rate (moles 1^{-1} sec^{-1})$\times 10^7$	$\overline{M}_n$, $\times 10^{-3}$	Dose rate, rad/hr
-18	20	23,200	175,000
25	100	73,500	175,000
72	500	330,000	175,000

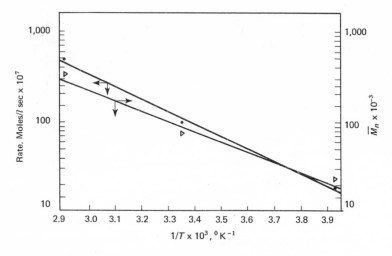

Fig. 11-6. Arrhenius plots for Example 11-2.

SOLUTION: The data is shown on a semilogarithmic plot in Fig. 11-6.

From the measured slopes of the lines, ΔE_{act} = 6.5 kcal per mole for polymerization, and 5.7 kcal per mole for $\overline{M}_n$. This result is seen to agree quite well with theory.

The measurement of the radical yield in styrene is an interesting application of the kinetic equations developed in Example 11-1. Combination of Eqs. (11-23), the rate expression for low dose rates, and (11-41) the mutual termination form of the equation for $\overline{DP}_o$ allows us to determine the value of $k_p k_t^{-1/2}$ which is the slope of a plot of $1/\overline{DP}_n$ vs R, i.e.,

$$R = k_p k_t^{-1/2} R_i^{1/2} [M] \tag{11-23}$$

$$\overline{DP}_o = 2 k_p k_t^{-1/2} [M] R_i^{-1/2} \tag{11-41}$$

$$(\overline{DP}_n)^{1/2} = \sqrt{2} k_p k_t^{-1/2} [M] R^{-1/2} \tag{11-46}$$

Thus the slope of a plot of $(\overline{DP}_n)^{1/2}$ vs $R^{-1/2}$ can be used to obtain $k_p k_t^{-1/2}$. R_i can then be calculated from either Eq. (11-23) or Eq. (11-41). At high dose rates, and in the presence of chain transfer reactions, appropriate corrections need to be made.

11-9 SOLUTION POLYMERIZATION

The presence of a diluent raises the possibility of multiple initiation steps, chain transfer, energy transfer, as well as chemical reactions other than polymerizations. Although these secondary reactions complicate the polymerization kinetics, solvent polymerizations have proven to be useful tools for studying the radiolysis of the solvents themselves. The studies involving styrene may be used as an example.

In the absence of complicating effects, one would predict that the rate of polymerization at low dose rates will follow Eq. (11-26)

$$R = k_p k_t^{-1/2}[M]^{3/2} \phi G_r^M (\mu_{en}(M)/\rho)^{1/2} \left[1 + \frac{(\mu_{en}(S)/\rho) G_r^S [S]}{(\mu_{en}(M)/\rho) G_r^M [M]} \right]^{1/2}$$

(11-26)

This is borne out by Fig. 11-7, which shows the relative rate of conversion of styrene dissolved in benzene, toluene, xylene, and ethylbenzene as a function of the mole fraction of styrene. It is seen that down to about 20 mole percent styrene the experimental points agree with the theoretical curve obtained by dividing Eq. (11-26) by Eq. (11-23), thus yielding R/R_o.

$$R/R_o = [M]^{1/2} \phi G_r^M (\mu_{en}(M)/\rho)^{1/2} \left[1 + \frac{(\mu_{en}(S)/\rho) G_r^S [S]}{(\mu_{en}(M)/\rho) G_r^M [M]} \right]^{1/2}$$

(11-26a)

Similar experiments have been carried out with ethyl chloride, butyl chloride, cyclohexyl chloride, monochlorobenzene, o-dichloro benzene, and ethyl chloride with identical results. Solutions of styrene in CCl_4, $CHCl_3$, CH_3Br, CB_4, and CH_3CHI, on the other hand, show anomalous behavior, and must be analyzed from the standpoint of excitation energy transfer.

Kinetic equations for this type of system were developed by Nikitina and Bagdasaryan, who postulated the following series of steps in a system consisting of monomer M, and diluent S. The starred compounds denote intermediary excited states.

(1) Protection — if S is highly radiation resistant and M can transfer energy to S

$$M \longrightarrow M^* \longrightarrow S^* \longrightarrow S + KE$$

(11-47)

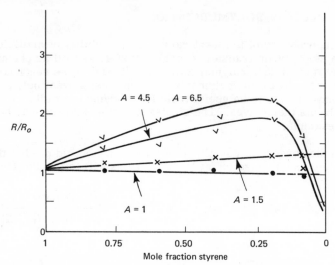

Fig. 11-7. Relative rates of conversion of styrene dissolved in benzene (A = 1), toluene (A = 1.5), xylene (A = 4.5), and ethylbenzene (A = 6.5). $G_r^S \mu_S / G_r^M \mu_M = A$. (A. Chapiro, "Radiation Chemistry of Polymeric Systems," Interscience Publishers, New York, 1962.)

(2) Sensitization — if S can transfer energy to M, producing radicals

$$S \longrightarrow S^* \longrightarrow M^* \longrightarrow M\cdot \qquad (11\text{-}48)$$

Kinetically the series of reactions may be written as

$$ (11\text{-}49) $$

If one assumes that the energy transfer between M^* and S^* is very fast, and occurs with equal rapidity, then, for the two transfer processes:

$$k_{SM}[S^*][M] = k_{MS}[M^*][S] \qquad (11\text{-}50)$$

The steady-state balances for the excited species S^* and M^* are

$$R_i[M] + k_{SM}[S^*][M] = k_M[M^*] + k_{M\cdot}[M^*] + k_{MS}[M^*][S] \tag{11-51}$$

$$R_i[S] + k_{MS}[M^*][S] = k_S[S^*] + k_{S\cdot}[S^*] + k_{SM}[S^*][M] \tag{11-52}$$

Equations (11-51) and (11-52) can now be solved in combination with Eq. (11-50) to yield expressions for $[S^*]$ and $[M^*]$. When multiplied by $k_{M\cdot}$ and $k_{S\cdot}$ respectively, we obtain expressions for the creation of monomer free radicals,

$$R_{[M\cdot]} = k_{M\cdot}[M^*] = \frac{R_i([M] + [S])k_{M\cdot}/(k_M + k_{M\cdot})}{1 + \{(k_S + k_{S\cdot})k_{MS}[S]/(k_M + k_{M\cdot})k_{SM}[M]\}} \tag{11-52a}$$

The ratio $k_{M\cdot}/(k_M + k_{M\cdot})$ is the probability of formation of free radicals $M\cdot$ from M^* in pure M, and hence equal to $\phi\mu_M G_r^M$. Likewise, $k_{S\cdot}/(k_S + k_{S\cdot}) = \phi\mu_S G_r^S$.

$$P_{rel} = \frac{\dfrac{k_{MS}}{k_M + k_{M\cdot}}}{\dfrac{k_{SM}}{k_S + k_{S\cdot}}} \approx \frac{\text{probability of energy transfer from } M^* \text{ to } S}{\text{probability of energy transfer from } S^* \text{ to } M} \tag{11-53}$$

We obtain, from (11-52a) and its analogous expression in S, expressions for the total production of radicals, and the overall polymerization rate

$$R_{[R\cdot]} = R_{[M\cdot]} + R_{[S\cdot]}$$

$$= \phi G_r^M(\mu_{en}(M)/\rho)\,([M] + [S])\,\frac{1 + \dfrac{(\mu_{en}(S)/\rho)G_r^S[S]}{(\mu_{en}(M)/\rho)G_r^M[M]}P_{rel}}{1 + P_{rel}\dfrac{[S]}{[M]}} \tag{11-54}$$

$$R = k_p k_t^{-1/2} [M]^{3/2} (\mu_{en}(M)/\rho) G_r^M \phi^{1/2} \left(1 + \frac{[S]}{[M]}\right)^{1/2}$$

$$\times \left[\frac{1 + \dfrac{(\mu_{en}(S)/\rho) G_r^S [S]}{(\mu_{en}(M)/\rho) G_r^M [M]} P_{rel}}{1 + P_{rel} \dfrac{[S]}{[M]}} \right]^{1/2} \tag{11-55}$$

Equations (11-54) and (11-55) are the energy transfer analogs of Eqs. (11-25) and (11-26) differing only insofar as they contain the factor P_{rel}. It is seen that if P_{rel} equals 1, Eqs. (11-55) and (11-54) reduce to (11-25) and (11-26). If $P_{rel} > 1$ the energy transfers are from M to S, the opposite being true if $P_{rel} < 1$.

Various investigators have obtained values of P_{rel} by measuring the rate of solution polymerization of styrene. Figure 11-8 summarizes the results obtained in three independent experiments involving styrene polymerization in chloroform. It is seen that when $G_r^S/G_r^M = 17$ and $P_{rel} = 10$, Eq. (11-55) provides a good fit for the data. The theory of energy transfer in solvent polymerization is, however, far from complete. Equation (11-54) fails to explain much of the available data, and the values of P_{rel} and G_r^S/G_r^M which have been obtained by other techniques. There is evidence to indicate that, in addition to "simple" energy transfer from a donor molecule to an acceptor molecule having a lower lying excited state, other processes are taking place.

11-10 HETEROGENEOUS POLYMERIZATION—PRECIPITATING MEDIA

Two phase polymerization systems exist if (1) the monomer or the solvent is a precipitant for the polymer, (2) an emulsion system is used, or (3) if the monomer is adsorbed on a solid surface.

Figure 11-9 shows the relative rates of conversion of styrene dissolved in various alcohols as a function of the mole fraction of the monomer in the mixture. All of the alcohols are precipitants for the polymer. Given also are the curves corresponding to the theoretical solution polymerization equation, Eq. (11-26), assuming $G_r^S/G_r^M = 80$, and 50.

Figure 11-9 may be divided into three portions, each corresponding to a different reaction mechanism:

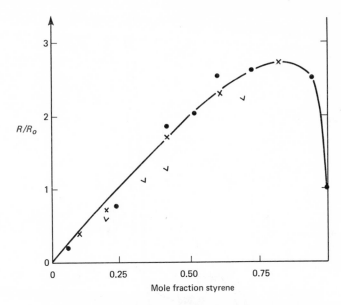

Fig. 11-8. Relative rates of polymerization of styrene in chloroform solutions as a function of the mole fraction of styrene. The solid line is the theoretical relationship based on Eq. (11-55) with $G_r^S/G_r^M = 17$ and $P_{rel} = 10$. x = gamma rays, v = beta particles, and • = mixed reactor radiation. (A. Chapiro, "Radiation Chemistry of Polymeric Systems," Interscience Publishers, New York, 1962.)

(1) *0-30 percent alcohol* — Although the general form of the curve is in accordance with Eq. (11-26), the values of G_r^S required to fit the curve (50–80) are much too high in light of the known G_r^S values for alcohol. The increased rate is due to a sensitization effect aided and abetted, perhaps, by the fact that in a precipitating media the local monomer concentration near the polymer chains may be higher than in the bulk solution.

(2) *30-70 percent alcohol* — In this range the polymer separates as a transparent fluid layer, a phenomena which apparently seriously disturbs the kinetics. In order to account for the decrease in both rate and molecular weight in this region, one must invoke a hypothesis involving either a decrease in k_p or an increase in k_t.

(3) *70-95 percent alcohol* — Here both the molecular weight and the rate rise sharply, the polymer separating out as a powder, in a skin-like film, or in tail-like structures. The reaction now also

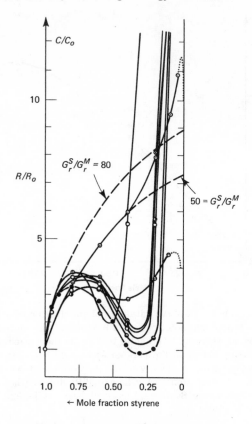

Fig. 11-9. Relative rates of conversion of styrene dissolved in various alcohols as a function of the mole fraction of monomer. The broken curves correspond to the theoretical relationship, Eq. (11-26). ● = methanol; O = 1-propanol; ◐ = 2-propanol; ⊗ = 1-butanol; ◑ = t-butanol; O = 1-octanol; O = 2-octanol; O = benzyl-alcohol. [A. Chapiro, *J. Chem. Phys.,* 47: 747 (1950).]

exhibits a strong *after-effect*, i.e., a continued reaction after the sample is removed from the radiation field. All of these phenomena are indicative of a strongly hindered termination.

Solvents other than alcohols exhibit behavior less strongly dependent on solvent concentration, the general pattern being intermediate between pure solution behavior, Eq. (11-26), and the alcohol curves shown in Fig. 11-9. The type of precipitate formed, and the adsorption of monomer by the polymer are additional phenomena which must be considered.

11-10.1 Emulsion Polymerization

In an emulsion polymerization the monomer is in a water suspension, and initiation is usually by radicals formed in the water, rather than monomer phase. Indeed, much of the early work in emulsion polymerization was directed at learning more about the primary events taking place in the radiolysis of water. The emulsion polymerization of acrylonitrile, for instance, was used to demonstrate the formation of OH and H radicals by Dainton, who found these species to be attached to the ends of the polymer chains.

The radiation induced emulsion polymerization of styrene proceeds about a hundredfold more rapidly than the bulk polymerization, the resulting polymer having ten- to thirtyfold higher molecular weights (Table 11-1). The overall activation energy was found to be 3.7 kcal per mole.

Two factors contribute to the higher molecular weight and rate: (1) the higher radical yields in water, and (2) the lower rate of chain termination, which is believed to occur only in the isolated polymer particles. This is in accord with the classic theory of catalytic emulsion polymerization, other results however are not. The rate equation, for instance, for an inorganic peroxide catalyzed emulsion polymerization in which a radical formed in the water phase enters a micelle particle and remains there until terminated by a reaction due to the entry of another radical,[2] can be shown to be

$$-dM/dt = k_p [M] \bar{N}/2 \qquad\qquad (11\text{-}56)$$

Table 11-1. BULK AND EMULSION RADIATION
POLYMERIZATION OF STYRENE[*]

Method	Intensity $r/\min$	Temperature, $^\circ$C	Conversion rate, %/hour	Molecular weight of polymer ($\times 10^3$)
Bulk	4400	-18	0.1	17—26
Bulk	3200	30	0.42	38—110
Bulk	4100	72	2.53	165—348
Emulsion	1000	25	36	800—1500
Emulsion	1000	35	45	885—1726
Emulsion	1000	45	54	1200—2060

[*]From Ballantine, et al., B.N.L. 294, 1954.

The number of particles per liter, $\overline{N}$, can be related to the area covered by the emulsifier, the rate of swelling of single particles, and to the two-fifths power of the rate of production of free radicals $(R_i)^{2/5}$. The overall rate in terms of the radiation intensity I, assuming Eq. (11-56) is also valid for radiation polymerization, and $(R_i)^{2/5} \propto I^{2/5}$ is

$$-d\mathrm{M}/dt = \text{Const } [\mathrm{M}] \, I^{2/5} \tag{11-57}$$

Acres and Dalton[3] carried out the emulsion polymerization of styrene under conditions such that Eq. (11-57) would have been expected to apply. Their results (Fig. 11-10) were not in accord with the equation thus indicating a fundamental difference between radiation catalysis and conventional catalysis. The unexpected kinetic behavior may be explained in terms of the existence of hydrogen atoms, which are not produced by conventional initiators. If these hydrogen atoms combine, or if the radicals formed by reactions with hydrogen atoms dimerize, then the intensity dependence of the reaction will have the form shown in Fig. 11-10.

Our understanding of emulsion polymerizations is, unfortunately, far from complete. As has been pointed out by Ley, Hummel, and Schneider,[4] "almost every system exhibits characteristic behavior ... it is not possible to press the various systems into one scheme. The conversion-time curves reveal so many details in the behavior of the different systems that a generalized description is no longer justified."

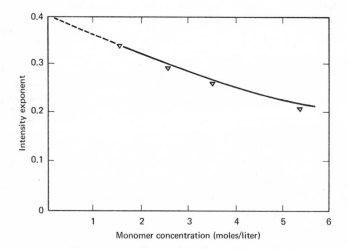

Fig. 11-10. Variation of intensity exponent with styrene concentration. [Acres and Dalton, *J. Polymer Sci.*, 1(10): 3013 (1963).]

11-11 COPOLYMERIZATIONS

The copolymerization of styrene with methyl methacrylate was studied in 1955 by Seitzer and Tobolsky, who found that both peroxides and radiation catalyzed polymerizations resulted in copolymers containing identical amounts of both species. This was interpreted as *prima facie* evidence of a radical reaction, since it is known that cationic initiators such as stannic chloride yield copolymers which are more than 99 percent styrene, while anionic initiation yields polymers containing more than 99 percent methyl methacrylate.

A major shift away from the free radical mechanisms outlook took place in 1957 when Davison, Pinner, and Worrall found that isobutene at -78°C could be polymerized by radiation. The reaction showed many characteristics which could be explained only on the basis of an ionic mechanism. Shortly thereafter copolymerization studies were again being used as a tool, this time to identify the ionic components of polymerization mechanisms.

11-12 IONIC AND PARTIALLY IONIC LIQUID-STATE POLYMERIZATIONS

The radiation induced isobutylene polymerization, which we will take as an example, has the following characteristics:

(1) At 0°C and above there is very little polymerization.

(2) At -80°C there is a relatively rapid reaction.

(3) The low temperature reaction is inhibited by di-isobutene, which is known to inhibit ionic reactions.

(4) The rate is directly proportional to the intensity at low temperatures and to $(I)^{1/2}$ at 20°C.

(5) Oxygen and benzoquinone inhibit the low temperature reaction, zinc oxide increases the rate, diphenylpicrylhydrazyl does not affect it.

(6) Positive ions from isobutene have been identified.

(7) Photopolymerization will take place at -150°C with 1470 Å (8.44 ev) light, but not with 1600 Å light. This experiment indicates not only an ionic mechanism, but also the fact that the ionization potential of the monomer is at least 0.8 ev lower in the gas phase than in the liquid phase, since 1600 Å UV catalyzes gas phase polymerizations.

(8) The copolymers formed from isobutylene/vinylchloride as well as other monomer mixtures, are a strong function of temperature (Fig. 11-11). At low temperatures, where the ionic polymerization predominates, one finds there is more isobutylene, thus indicating ionic reaction.

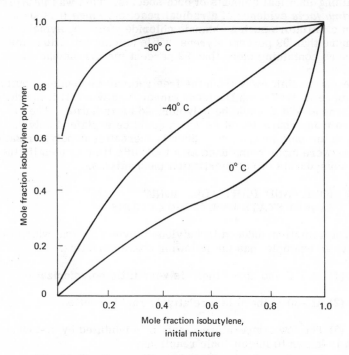

Fig. 11-11. Composition of copolymers formed as a function of the composition of the initial mixture for the isobutylene/vinylidene chloride system at various temperatures. [Sheinke, et al., Dokl. Akad. Nauk. SSR **124**:632 (1959), from R. Roberts, "Radiation-Initiated Polymerization and Graft Polymerization," IAEA Review Series 13, 1961.]

(9) The apparent activation energy at room temperature is 14 kcal per mole, and zero at -78°C.

(10) At low temperatures polar solvents such as ethylchloride change the copolymer composition such that it is enriched in the more ionic polymer.

The foregoing experiments offer proof of the dual, ionic-radical nature of the radiation catalysis. An approximate kinetic analysis of an anionic polymerization scheme, Eqs. (11-13) and (11-17), yields

$$R_i = R_t = k_t \, [\text{MNH}_2^-] \tag{11-58}$$

$$R = R_p = k_p \, [\text{MNH}_2^-] \, [\text{M}] = \frac{k_p R_i \, [\text{M}]}{k_t} \tag{11-59}$$

This confirms that, to a first approximation: (1) the rate is dependent on the first power of the dose rate, (2) the activation energy must be negative since k_t is the only rate constant which should have any appreciable activation energy, and (3) the reaction rate should be higher at lower temperatures. The third point of course, is a corollary of the second.

To explain the one anomaly, the inhibition of polymerization by some free radical scavengers, and its enhancement by zinc oxide, Collison, Dainton, and Gillies propose that the primary process is the ionization of isobutene to produce a positive ion and electron. Normally, the walls of the vessel trap the electrons, and prevent ion recombination. The addition of electron trapping agent such as ZnO would, therefore, be expected to enhance the reaction, which proceeds via positive ion catalysis. On the other hand, the charged species produced as a result of electron trapping by oxygen and benzoquinone are free to diffuse through the solution, and thus to inhibit the reaction by ion recombination. On the other hand, DPPH would not be expected to stop the reaction, since its primary reaction probably is with the methyl-substituted alkyl radicals produced.[5]

11-12.1 Effect of Dose Rate and Concentration on Ionic Polymerizations

Two other interesting variables which may affect the ratios of the ionic and radical components of a polymerization are monomer concentration and dose rate. Figure 11-12 shows the effect of monomer concentration on the polymerization rate for acrylonitrile dissolved in ethylene at $-78°$C. The rate of polymerization decreases and then increases with the mole fraction of monomer, pyrogallol being an inhibitor only at high monomer concentrations. This suggests a radical mechanism at the high concentrations and an ionic mechanism at the lower. This is borne out by the infrared spectrum of the polymer; the number of $C\equiv N$ bonds increases with monomer concentration and the number of $C=N$ bonds decreases. This result is attributable to an anionic polymerization of $C\equiv N$ in dilute solution, and a radical polymerization of $C=C$ in concentrated solution. The structures of the two polymers would, in the extreme case, be

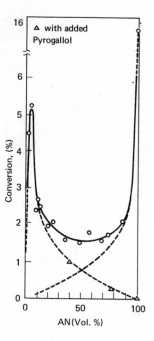

Fig. 11-12. The relation between conversion and the concentration of acrylonitrile in the monomer mixture at -78°C. Dose rate was 7×10^4 r/hr. Total dose was 6.4×10^6 r. The effect of pyrogallol on the polymerization is also shown. [Oshima and Tabata, in P. Greebler and E. Henley (eds.), "Advances in Nuclear Science and Technology," Academic Press, New York, 1965.]

$$CH_2{=}CH \xrightarrow[\text{radical}]{\sim\!\!\sim\!\!\sim} -CH_2-CH-CH_2-CH-CH_2-CH- \qquad (11\text{-}60)$$
$$\underset{CN}{|} \qquad\qquad \underset{CN}{|} \quad \underset{CN}{|} \quad \underset{CN}{|}$$

$$CH_2{=}CH \xrightarrow[\text{ionic}]{\sim\!\!\sim\!\!\sim} -C{=}N-C{=}N-C{=}N-C{=}N- \qquad (11\text{-}61)$$
$$\underset{CN}{|} \qquad\quad \underset{\underset{CH_2}{\overset{\|}{CH}}}{|} \quad \underset{\underset{CH_2}{\overset{\|}{CH}}}{|} \quad \underset{\underset{CH_2}{\overset{\|}{CH}}}{|} \quad \underset{\underset{CH_2}{\overset{\|}{CH}}}{|}$$

The dose rate effect manifests itself insofar as the radical reaction is proportional to the square root of the dose rate, whereas the ionic reaction is proportional to the first power. Hence low dose rates should favor radical reactions and high dose rates ionic reactions, a fact which has been confirmed for the styrene, acrylonitrile, and isobutylene polymerizations at low temperatures.

11-12.2 Solid State Polymerizations

Oshima and Tabata classify the solid state polymerizations into three categories.

(1) Monomers which polymerize via a radical mechanism at relatively high temperatures.

(2) Monomers which polymerize via nonionic and nonradical "excitation" mechanisms at low temperatures.

(3) Ring opening of monomers.

Examples of each type are shown in Table 11-2.

Table 11-2. POLYMERIZATION OF SOLID MONOMERS

Monomer	Melting point, °C	Temp. of irradiation	Activation energy, kcal/mole	Type
Acrylamide	83	0, 80	4	1
Acrylic acid	12		24	1
Vinyl carbazole	64	20, 60	12	1
Cetylmethylacrylate	15	−21, −78	0.7	1
Acrylonitrile	−83	−83, −196	−3 to 1	2
Styrene	−30	−51, −78	9.2	2
Butadiene		−100, −196	0.1	2
2-Methyl-5-vinyl piridine	−13	−13, −196	0.3	2
Vinyl acetate	−93	−196	0	2
Isoprene	−120	−120, −196	0.2	2
Formaldehyde	−118	−118, −160	2.2	3
β-Propiolactone	−33.4	−33, −70	−12.6	3
Hexamethylcyclotrisiloxane	64	64, 0	9.6	3
Diketene	−6.5	−6.5, −130 −130, −196	−2.4 0.11	3
Styrene oxide	−	−80, −120	0.1	3

At the present time, our knowledge of solid state polymerizations is very incomplete. There is no fully accepted unifying theory to explain many of the observed data. Important factors which are known to affect the rate of polymerization and the type of polymer include crystal size and state, additives, and the degree of conversion.

In some cases, high percentages of stereospecific polymers are obtained, indicating that the propagation is controlled by the arrangement of the monomer in the lattice. This is true for butadiene and acrylonitrile, but it is not true for acrylamide or acrylamide-related polymers. This seems to indicate that at higher temperatures [Category (1) monomers] propagation is controlled by the geometrical structure of the monomer crystal in the initial stage of the polymerization only, and that in the final stage it proceeds at the interface between crystal monomer and amorphous polymer.

Category (2) polymers respond to the addition of additives in very unusual ways. Structural differences often occur, scavengers which inhibit the liquid phase polymerizations have little effect on the solid state polymerization, whereas a number of compounds which completely inhibit polymerization in the solid state do not affect the liquid state. Isoprene, for instance, exhibits three types of kinetic mechanism, depending on the temperature and state of monomer. In the liquid state at high temperatures, a "classic" free radical reaction is observed, and at a low temperature the reaction is ionic. In the solid state, above the transition temperature $(-158°)$, dose rate and scavenging experiments indicate that the reaction may be ionic, but at temperatures below $(-158°)$ a number of unexplained effects, including a change in the polymer structure, take place. A possible explanation is that a collective excitation of the monomer crystal *as a whole* takes place. Tabata and co-workers call this "electronic polymerization" and postulate that a superexcitation by one monomer unit in a sequence of N monomers will cause a collective excitation wave in the N monomer units as a whole, and that this collectively excited group of N monomer units could change instantly to the corresponding polymer with N degree of polymerization. The time for formation of the excited wave is expected to be about 10^{-14} sec, and the polymerization could be completed in as little as 10^{-11} sec.

Less elegant, but no less plausible mechanisms involving step by step energy transfer between adjacent atoms in a crystal have been proposed.

11-13 GRAFT POLYMERIZATIONS

Graft or block polymers are generally created by polymerizing a monomer (A) in the presence of a polymer (B_m) in such a manner that the resulting polymer of A, A_n, is linked to polymer B to form a graft copolymer $(A_n B_m)$. As evidenced by Table 11-3, which lists the radiation grafted fiber systems studied up to 1967, a very large number of systems have been investigated.

To obtain a block or graft polymer using radiation the polymerization must be initiated on the polymer "backbone" a process which can be accomplished by

(1) Direct irradiation of a system composed of a monomer and a (more radiation sensitive) polymer.

(2) Bringing a monomer into contact with a preirradiated polymer which has either (a) trapped free radicals or (b) is peroxidized.

Table 11-3. RADIATION-INDUCED GRAFT COPOLYMERIZATION
ON VARIOUS FIBERS*

Fiber type	Monomer grafted	Monomer form	Radiation source
	Polyamide fibers		
Nylon-6 (Kapron)	Acetylene Acrylonitrile Acrylic acid Butadiene Ethylene Methyl methacrylic acid Phenyl acetylene Propargyl alcohol Propylene Styrene Vinyl acetate	Vapor phase	^{60}Co
Nylon-6 (Kapron)	Acrylonitrile Ethylene Methyl methacrylate Propylene	Vapor phase	X-ray source (80 kv, 200 ma)
Nylon-6	Vinyl pyrrolidone	—	
Nylon-6 (Kapron)	Styrene	Vapor phase	^{60}Co
Nylon-6	Styrene	Vapor phase	^{60}Co
Nylon-6 (Kapron)	Acrylonitrile	—	
Nylon-6	Acrylonitrile	—	^{60}Co
Nylon-66	Methacrylic acid	—	^{60}Co
Nylon-66	Acrylic acid Maleic acid	—	^{60}Co
Nylon-66	Acrylonitrile Butadiene Ethyl acrylate Methyl acrylate Vinyl acetate	Vapor phase	^{60}Co
Nylon-66	Acrylic acid Acrylonitrile Allyl acrylate Butadiene 1,3-Butylene dimethacrylate Divinyl sulfone Ethylene	—	^{60}Co

*115 references are cited by R. D. Gilbert and V. Stannett, *Isotopes Rad. Tech.* 4(4), Summer 1967.

Table 11-3. RADIATION-INDUCED GRAFT COPOLYMERIZATION
ON VARIOUS FIBERS* (Continued)

Fiber type	Monomer grafted	Monomer form	Radiation source
	Ethyl acrylate		
	Ethylene dimethacrylate		
	Methyl acrylate		
	Methyl methacrylate		
	Propylene		
	Styrene		
	Vinyl acetate		
	Vinyl chloride		
	n-Vinyl pyrrolidone		
	Ethylene dimethacrylate-methyl acrylate		
	Ethylene dimethacrylate-acrylic acid		
	1,3-Butylene dimethacrylate-acrylic acid		
	Polyester fibers		
Polyethylene Terephthalate (Terylene)	4-Vinyl pyridine	—	^{60}Co
Polyethylene Terephthalate	Methacrylic acid		^{60}Co
Polyethylene Terephthalate (Lavsan)	Styrene	—	^{60}Co
Polyester	Acrylic acid	—	^{60}Co
	Acrylonitrile		
	Butadiene		
	Divinyl sulfone		
	Ethyl acrylate		
	Ethylene		
	Methyl acrylate		
	Methyl methacrylate		
	Propylene		
	Styrene		
	Vinyl acetate		
	Vinyl chloride		
	n-Vinyl pyrrolidone		
	Cellulose fibers		
Cellulose	Methyl acrylate	—	^{60}Co
	Methyl methacrylate		
	Vinyl acetate		
Cellulose	Styrene	—	^{60}Co
Cellulose	Polyvinyl alcohol (vinyl acetate)	—	

Table 11-3. RADIATION-INDUCED GRAFT COPOLYMERIZATION
ON VARIOUS FIBERS* (Continued)

Fiber type	Monomer grafted	Monomer form	Radiation source
Cellulose	Styrene	—	^{60}Co
Cellulose	Acrylonitrile Methacrylamide	—	^{60}Co
Cellulose	Methyl acrylate	—	
Cellulose	Acrylonitrile Methyl acrylate Methyl methacrylate Styrene Vinyl acetate	—	
Cellulose	Styrene	—	^{60}Co
Cellulose	Acrylonitrile-styrene Methyl methacrylate- 　styrene Methyl methacrylate- 　acrylonitrile Methyl methacrylate-a- 　methyl styrene Acrylonitrile-α- 　methyl styrene Vinyl acetate- 　styrene	—	^{60}Co
Cellulose	Methacrylic acid		^{60}Co
Cellulose (cotton)	Acrylonitrile Butadiene Ethyl acrylate Methyl acrylate Vinyl acetate	Vapor phase	^{60}Co
Cellulose (cotton)	Acrylic acid Acrylonitrile Allyl acrylate Butadiene Divinyl sulfone Ethylene Ethyl acrylate Methyl acrylate Methyl methacrylate Propylene Methylol acrylamide Styrene Vinyl acetate Vinyl chloride n-Vinyl pyrrolidone	—	^{60}Co
Cellulose (cotton)	Acrylonitrile Styrene	—	^{60}Co

Table 11-3. RADIATION-INDUCED GRAFT COPOLYMERIZATION
ON VARIOUS FIBERS* (Continued)

Fiber type	Monomer grafted	Monomer form	Radiation source
Cellulose (cotton)	Styrene	Solution	^{60}Co
Cellulose (cotton)	Styrene	—	^{60}Co
Cellulose (cotton)	Acrylonitrile Methyl methacrylate Vinyl acetate	—	
Cellulose (cotton)	Styrene	—	

Cellulose (cotton)	Acrylonitrile
	Styrene
	Methyl methacrylate
	Styrene-acrylic acid
	Styrene-methyl
	  methacrylate
	Acrylonitrile-methyl
	  methacrylate
		—	^{60}Co

Cellulose (cotton)	Styrene	—	^{60}Co
Cellulose (cotton)	Styrene	—	
Cellulose (cotton)	Methacrylic acid	—	^{60}Co
Cellulose (cotton)	Methacrylamide Methyl acrylate	—	^{60}Co
Cellulose (cotton)	Butadiene-styrene Butadiene-acrylonitrile Styrene-acrylonitrile Butadiene-styrene- acrylonitrile	—	^{60}Co
Cellulose (cotton)	Styrene	—	
Cellulose (cotton)	Butadiene Butadiene-styrene Butadiene-acrylonitrile	—	
Cellulose (cotton)	Acrylonitrile a-Methyl styrene Vinylidene chloride Vinyl toluene	—	^{60}Co
Cellulose (cotton)	Acrylonitrile Methacrylamide Methacrylic acid	—	^{60}Co

Table 11-3. RADIATION-INDUCED GRAFT COPOLYMERIZATION
ON VARIOUS FIBERS* (Continued)

Fiber type	Monomer grafted	Monomer form	Radiation source
Cellulose (cotton)	Methyl methacrylate Styrene Acrylonitrile Butadiene Ethyl acrylate Methyl acrylate	—	^{60}Co
Cellulose (rayon)	Styrene	—	Atomic reactor
Cellulose (rayon)	Styrene	—	^{60}Co
Cellulose (rayon)	Styrene Acrylonitrile	—	^{60}Co
Cellulose (rayon)	Styrene	—	^{60}Co
Cellulose (rayon)	Styrene	—	^{60}Co
Cellulose (rayon)	Styrene	—	
Cellulose (rayon)	Styrene	—	
Cellulose (rayon)	Styrene	—	^{60}Co
Cellulose (rayon)	Vinyl pyrrolidone	—	^{60}Co
Cellulose (rayon)	Butadiene Butadiene-styrene Butadiene-acrylonitrile	—	
Cellulose (rayon)	Acrylic acid Acrylamide Allyl acrylate Butadiene 1,3-Butylene dimethacrylate Divinyl sulfone Ethylene Ethyl acrylate Ethylene dimethacrylate 2-Ethyl hexyl acrylate Methyl acrylate Methyl methacrylate Propylene Styrene Vinyl acetate	—	^{60}Co

Table 11-3. RADIATION-INDUCED GRAFT COPOLYMERIZATION
ON VARIOUS FIBERS* (Continued)

Fiber type	Monomer grafted	Monomer form	Radiation source
	Vinyl chloride		
	n-Vinyl pyrrolidone		
	Allyl acrylate-acrylic acid		
	1,3-Butylene dimethacrylate-acrylic acid		
	Ethylene dimethacrylate-acrylic acid		
	Ethylene dimethacrylate-methyl acrylate		
Cellulose acetate	Acrylonitrile Butadiene	—	^{60}Co
Cellulose acetate	Styrene	—	^{60}Co
Cellulose acetate	Acrylic esters	—	
Cellulose acetate	Styrene	—	
Cellulose acetate	Acrylonitrile-styrene Methyl methacrylate-acrylonitrile Methyl methacrylate-styrene Vinyl acetate-styrene a-Methyl styrene-acrylonitrile a-Methyl styrene-methyl methacrylate	—	^{60}Co
Cellulose acetate	Styrene	—	^{60}Co
Cellulose acetate	Styrene	—	^{60}Co
Cellulose acetate	Styrene	—	^{60}Co
Cellulose acetate	Methyl methacrylate	—	^{60}Co
Cellulose acetate	Acrylic acid Acrylonitrile Allyl acrylate Butadiene 1,3-Butylene dimethacrylate Divinyl sulfone Ethylene Ethyl acrylate	—	^{60}Co

Table 11–3. RADIATION-INDUCED GRAFT COPOLYMERIZATION
ON VARIOUS FIBERS* (Continued)

Fiber type	Monomer grafted	Monomer form	Radiation source
	Ethylene dimethacrylate		
	Methyl acrylate		
	Methyl methacrylate		
	Propylene		
	Styrene		
	Vinyl acetate		
	Vinyl chloride		
	n-Vinyl pyrrolidone		
	Allyl acrylate- acrylic acid		
	Ethylene dimethacrylate- acrylic acid		
	1,3-Butylene dimethacrylate- acrylic acid		

Polyolefin fibers

Fiber type	Monomer grafted	Monomer form	Radiation source
Polyethylene	Styrene	—	^{60}Co
Polyethylene	Butadiene	—	^{60}Co
Polyethylene	Vinyl chloride	—	^{60}Co
Polyethylene	Methyl methacrylate Styrene Vinylidene chloride Dichloroethylene Trichloroethylene Tetrachloroethylene	—	^{60}Co
Polyethylene	Acrylonitrile Ethylene Methyl methacrylate Propylene	—	^{60}Co
Polyethylene	Methacrylic acid	—	^{60}Co
Polyethylene	Acrylic acid Acrylonitrile Acetylene Butadiene Ethylene Methyl methacrylate Phenyl acetylene Propylene Propargyl alcohol Propylene Styrene Vinyl acetate	—	^{60}Co

Table 11-3. RADIATION-INDUCED GRAFT COPOLYMERIZATION
ON VARIOUS FIBERS* (Continued)

Fiber type	Monomer grafted	Monomer form	Radiation source
Polyethylene	Acrylic acid Acrylonitrile 2-Methyl-5-vinyl pyridine	—	^{60}Co
Polypropylene	Acrylonitrile Butadiene Ethyl acrylate	—	^{60}Co
Polypropylene	Butadiene	—	^{60}Co
Polypropylene	Acrylic acid Methyl methacrylate	—	^{60}Co
Polypropylene	Glycidyl methacrylate	—	^{60}Co
Polypropylene	Styrene	—	^{60}Co
Polypropylene	Acrylic acid	—	^{60}Co
Polypropylene		—	^{60}Co
Propylene	Vinyl pyrrolidone Vinyl acetate	—	^{60}Co
Polypropylene	Acrylonitrile Ethylene Methyl methacrylate Propylene	—	^{60}Co
Polypropylene		—	Atomic reactor $(n, a$ reaction used to produce a particles)
Polypropylene	Styrene-maleic acid Styrene-fumaric acid Styrene-diethyl fumarate Styrene-itaconic anhydride Styrene-maleic anhydride Vinyl acetate-maleic anhydride Acrylonitrile-maleic anhydride 2-Methyl-5-vinyl pyridine- maleic anhydride	—	Atomic reactor $(n, a$ reaction used to produce a particles)
Polypropylene	Acetylene Acrylic acid Acrylonitrile Butadiene Ethylene Methyl methacrylate Phenylacetylene Propargyl alcohol	—	^{60}Co

Table 11-3. RADIATION-INDUCED GRAFT COPOLYMERIZATION
ON VARIOUS FIBERS* (Continued)

Fiber type	Monomer grafted	Monomer form	Radiation source
Polypropylene	Propylene Styrene Vinyl acetate Acrylic acid Acrylonitrile 2-Methyl-5-vinyl pyridine	—	^{60}Co
Polypropylene	Acrylic acid Allyl acrylate Butadiene 1,3-Butylene dimethacrylate Divinyl sulfone Ethylene Ethyl acrylate Ethylene dimethacrylate Methyl acrylate Methyl methacrylate Propylene Styrene Vinyl acetate Vinyl chloride n-Vinyl pyrrolidone	—	^{60}Co
Wool fibers			
Wool	Acrylonitrile Butadiene	—	^{60}Co
Wool	Acrylonitrile Methyl methacrylate Styrene	—	^{60}Co
Wool	Acrylonitrile Allyl acetate Allyl benzoate Allyl stearate Styrene	—	^{60}Co
Wool	Acrylic acid Acrylonitrile Butadiene Divinyl sulfone Ethyl acrylate Ethylene Methyl acrylate Methyl methacrylate Propylene Vinyl acetate Vinyl chloride n-Vinyl pyrrolidone	—	^{60}Co

Table 11-3. RADIATION-INDUCED GRAFT COPOLYMERIZATION
ON VARIOUS FIBERS* (Continued)

Fiber type	Monomer grafted	Monomer form	Radiation source
	Miscellaneous fibers		
Polyvinyl chloride	Glycidyl methacrylate	—	^{60}Co
Polyvinyl chloride	4-Vinyl pyridine	—	^{60}Co
Jute	Styrene	—	^{60}Co
Cyanoethylated cotton	Acrylonitrile	—	^{60}Co
Acrylic	Methacrylic acid	—	^{60}Co
Acrylic	Acrylic acid Acrylonitrile Butadiene Divinyl sulfone Ethyl acrylate Ethylene Methyl acrylate Methyl methacrylate Propylene Vinyl acetate Vinyl chloride n-Vinyl pyrrolidone	—	^{60}Co

Process (1) consists of

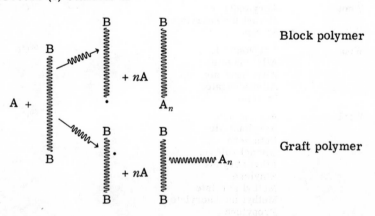

Process (2a) is schematically identical to Process (1), the only difference being that the monomer A is introduced after the polymer has been irradiated (in the absence of air). In the one-step, direct-graft procedure, where mixtures of monomer and polymer are ir-radiated, homopolymer may also be formed, the ratio of homopolymer to copolymer depending, to a first approximation, on the ratio of G_r^A to G_r^B. Other factors influencing the ratio of graft/homopolymer are the diffusion, solubility, and degree of equilibration between monomer and polymer, the presence of inhibitors or solvents, as well as the dose rate, and ambient conditions. Graft polymerization kinetics, as will be demonstrated, are more complicated than homogeneous system kinetics insofar as the system is exceedingly viscous, and the reaction may become diffusion controlled. Furthermore, depending on the degree of solubility, dose rate, and diffusivities, the graft may be on the surface only, or volumetric (homogeneous).

Peroxidized polymers are created by preirradiating the polymer in the presence of oxygen, in which case either diperoxides or hydroperoxides may be created. In either case, the peroxides are decomposed by heat in the presence of monomer to form the grafted polymer

Relatively few grafting experiments involving preirradiation initiation (trapped free radical or peroxide) have been carried out. The trapped free radical technique is, of necessity, difficult and complicated since free radical scavengers (oxygen in particular) must be carefully removed, and the monomer must be added very soon after the irradiation. Peroxide initiation, on the other hand, leads to considerable homopolymerizations, since small free radicals diffuse into the monomers during the heating step.

The individual rate constants for graft polymerization kinetics vary considerably from those obtained in radiation induced solution polymerizations, the main difference being in the termination rate constant, k_t. This is most clearly demonstrated by the work of Steinberg, who measured the rate of grafting to a polyethylene sample immersed in styrene under both constant and intermittent ^{60}Co gamma radiation.

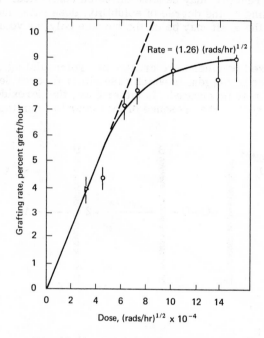

Fig. 11-13. Rate of grafting as a function of dose rate. [Steinberg, Henley, and Daugherty, CEP Symposium Series 68, 62:28 (1966).]

Figure 11-13 shows the rate of grafting as a function of dose rate. It is seen that "conventional" square root kinetics [Eq. (11-23)] are followed at dose rates up to about 200,000 rads per hour, above which the reaction rate levels off with dose rate, the reaction, as will be shown later, becoming diffusion controlled.

To obtain the individual rate constants k_p and k_t, unsteady state sector techniques were employed. Figure 11-14 shows the characteristic plot obtained by substituting the experimental $R_i(t)$ function used by Steinberg into Eq. (11-44) and solving the resulting equation numerically. The radical lifetimes and rate constants can then be calculated, as will be demonstrated in Example 11-3.

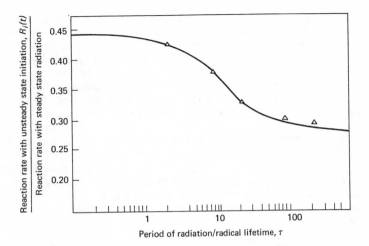

Fig. 11-14. Ratio of intermittent to steady state reaction rates as a function of period and radical lifetime. [Steinberg, Henley, and Daugherty, *CEP Symposium Series* 68, **62**:28 (1966).]

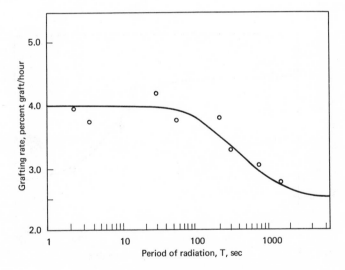

Fig. 11-15. Grafting rate as a function of radiation period. [Steinberg, Henley, and Daugherty, *CEP Symposium Series* 68, **62**:28 (1966).]

EXAMPLE 11-3: Figure 11-15 is a plot of rates of grafting as a function of the period of the unsteady state radiation for the system styrene-polyethylene, steady state grafting rates for which were shown in Fig. 11-13. A solution to Eq. (11-44) for the particular $R_i(t)$ function used was shown in Fig. 11-14. If the maximum dose rate of the intermittent radiation is 49.8 krads per hour, determine the radical lifetimes and the rate constants k_p and k_t assuming Eq. (11-42) applies.

SOLUTION: Referring to Fig. 11-13 we see that at the maximum dose rate the extrapolated steady state rate would be 8.7 percent graft per hour. According to Fig. 11-15 the reaction rate at high frequencies should be 44 percent of the steady state dose rate or 3.8 percent weight gain per hour. The actual value is ~4 percent weight gain per hour, showing good agreement between theory and data.

The radical lifetime can be obtained by calculating the average horizontal displacement between curves 11-15 and 11-14, after the ordinates of both curves are normalized. The point where the period and radical lifetimes are the same can be marked on the theoretical curve, and the value of the period, where this point falls on the experimental graph, is the radical lifetime (34 sec).

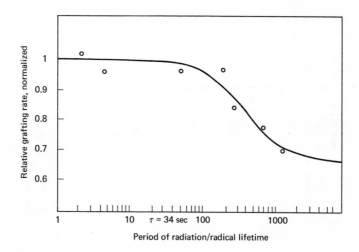

Fig. 11-16. Solution to Example 11-3.

The value of the individual rate constants may now be obtained. According to Eqs. (11-23) and (11-25)

$$k_p k_t^{-1/2} = \frac{d\mathrm{M}}{dt} \left[\frac{1}{[\mathrm{M}]\,R_i^{1/2}} \right] \tag{1}$$

$$R_i = \phi G_r^M \,(\mu_{en}(\mathrm{M})/\rho)\,[\mathrm{M}] \tag{2}$$

The only unknown in Eqs. (1) and (2) is $k_p k_t^{-1/2}$ which, after the appropriate rates and concentrations are inserted, was calculated to be $(2700 \text{ moles}/1\text{ hr})^{-1/2}$. The radical lifetime is the number of radicals present divided by their rate of creation (or removal) thus

$$\tau = (k_t R_i)^{-1/2} \tag{3}$$

As calculated from Eq. (3), k_t is 1.1×10^4.

The relative rate constants for homopolymerization and graft polymerization are shown below for comparison:

	k_p (moles/1)$^{-1}$(sec)$^{-1}$	k_t (moles/1)$^{-1}$(sec)$^{-1}$
Homo- polymerization	55	2.5×10^7
Graft copolymerization	91	1.1×10^4

The propagation constants are approximately equal. The termination constant for the grafting reaction, however, is one-thousandth the size of the termination constant for homopolymerization. This is strong evidence in favor of a graft mechanism involving immobile radicals that terminate in a slow bimolecular termination reaction.

11-13.1 Graft Polymerizations — Effect of Monomer Diffusion

Figure 11-13 clearly shows that at high dose rates the rate of graft polymerization no longer depends on the square root of the radiation intensity. This plus experiments conducted with varying film thickness lends credence to the idea that, under certain conditions, grafting reactions become diffusion controlled. If this be the case, one can write a relation defining the concentration of monomer within the polymer, C, in terms of the diffusion coefficient $\bar{D}$, and the reaction rate [Eq. (11-23)].

$$\frac{\partial C}{\partial t} = \bar{D} \frac{\partial^2 C}{\partial x^2} - k_p (R_i/k_t)^{1/2} C \tag{11-62}$$

In Eq. (11-62) the first term on the right-hand side represents the rate of diffusion of the monomer into the polymer, and the second term the rate of grafting. The solution to this equation, as given by Chandler, Henley, and Tractenberg,[6] is

$$Q = \frac{8 \bar{K} C_1 t}{\pi^2} \sum_{\substack{n=1,3, \\ 5, \ldots}}^{\infty} n^{-2} \left[\frac{a}{a + \bar{K}} \right]$$

$$- \frac{8 \bar{K} C_1}{2} \sum_{\substack{n=1,3, \\ 5, \ldots}}^{\infty} n^{-2} \frac{\bar{K}}{(a + \bar{K})^2} [\exp\{-(a + \bar{K})t\} - 1] \tag{11-63}$$

where Q = amount of graft per unit volume

$a = \pi^2 n^2 \bar{D}/l^2$

l = thickness of polymer film

$\bar{K} = k_p (R_i/k_t)^{1/2}$.

Equation (11-63) contains a transient term as well as a steady-state term, and predicts a dependence of the grafting rate on:

(1) thickness of polymer sample

(2) diffusivity of monomer in polymer

(3) saturation concentration of monomer in polymer

(4) radiation dose rate

(5) reaction rate constants in the polymerization

(6) temperature insofar as it affects rate constants and diffusivity.

Although Eq. (11-63) has been applied with some success, a complete description of radiation grafting must take into account such factors as the physical and chemical structure of the monomer and polymer.

11-14 IMPURITY EFFECTS

A primary difficulty in studying chain reactions in general, and polymerizations in particular, is the problem of impurities. It is not uncommon to find that ultrapure systems give extremely variable results; styrene being no exception. Metz[7] reviews the work that has been done. In general, it is found that the removal of trace water may greatly enhance the reaction rate. Since the sensitivity towards water in many organic reactions lies in the order: carbanion > carbonium ion > free radical, it is postulated that as water is progressively removed from vinyl monomers the free radical propagation is augmented or supplanted by a carbonium ion mechanism. This in turn is further enhanced at low water content by carbanion mechanism. It must be emphasized that these conclusions are speculative.

PROBLEMS

11-1 The monomer reactivity ratios, r_1 and r_2, are 2 and 0.5 respectively. Plot the initial copolymer composition as a function of the ratio of monomers.

11-2 Develop an equation for the degree of polymerization at high dose rates.

11-3 From the following data on the bulk polymerization of methyl methylacrylate, determine the form of the kinetic rate equation. Calculate the radical yield, $k_p k_t^{-1/2}$, and the overall activation energy. In calculating the radical yield, assume that both disproportionation and combination occur.

Dose Rate Dependence

R, (moles/l sec)$\times 10^6$	$\overline{M}_n$, $\times 10^5$	Dose rate, rads/sec
3	20	5×10^{-3}
8	12	5×10^{-2}
20	8	5×10^{-1}
70	4	5
150	2	50
250	1.5	300

Dose rate, rads/sec	Temp., °C	R, (moles/l sec)$\times 10^6$	$\overline{M}_n$, $\times 10^3$
68.5	-18	72.5	70
64.5	25	211	162
63.4	70	499	260
0.77	30	44.5	340
0.77	50	64	510
0.77	70	104	670

11-4 Derive the forms of Eq. (11-43) suitable for calculating radical yields for the cases of

(a) A solvent polymerization

(b) Combination and disproportionation

(c) High dose rates

(d) Transfer to monomer

(e) Transfer to polymer.

11-5 From the data of Fig. 11-11 confirm the following monomer reactivity ratios, r_1 = isobutylene; r_2 = vinyl chloride.

Temp., °C	r_1	r_2
-78	25	0
-40	1.27	0.21
0	0.03	1.3

11-6 Calculate the radical yields for methyl methylacrylate using the following data and assumptions.

Dose rate, rad/ sec $\times 10^{-5}$	R, (moles/ l sec) 10^2	Assuming 100% Combination	Assuming 50% Combination and 50% Disproportionation	
0.2	2.9	$k_t/k_p^2 = 180$	$\left(k_{tc} + k_{td}\right)$	$k_p^2 = 120$
1.1	5.9	$k_t/k_p^2 = 180$	$\left(k_{tc} + k_{td}\right)$	$k_p^2 = 120$
4.0	6.6	$k_t/k_p^2 = 180$	$\left(k_{tc} + k_{td}\right)$	$k_p^2 = 120$

11-7 Write a mechanism for the ionic and free radical polymerization of acrylonitrile dissolved in ethylene at -78°C.

REFERENCES

1. D. Ballantine, *Chem. Eng. Prog.*, **50**:267 (1954).

2. W. V. Smith and R. P. Ewart, *J. Chem. Phys.*, **16**:592 (1948).

3. G. J. Acres and F. L. Dalton, *J. Polymer Sci.*, Part A, **1**(10): 3013 (1963).

4. G. Ley, D. Hummel, and C. Schneider, "Gamma-Radiation-Induced Polymerization of Some Vinyl Monomers in Emulsion Systems," Advances in Chemistry Series, **66**, p. 184, ACS, 1967.

5. F. Lampe, *J. Chem. Phys.*, **63**:1986 (1959).

6. H.Chandler, E. Henley, and E. Trachtenberg, *Int. J. Appl. Rad. Isotopes*, **13**:239 (1962).

7. D. Metz, "Radiation-Induced Polymerization of Pure Liquid α-Methylstyrene," Advances in Chemistry Series 66, p. 170 ACS, 1967.

BIBLIOGRAPHY

F. A. Bovey, "Effects of Ionizing Radiation on Natural and Synthetic High Polymers," Interscience Publishers, New York, 1958.

A. Chapiro, "Atomic Radiation and Polymers," Pergamon Press, London, 1960.

R. F. Gould, (ed.), "Irradiation of Polymers," Advances in Chemistry Series, **66**, ACS, 1967.

12

EFFECT OF RADIATION
ON POLYMERS

Polymers, because of their high molecular weights, undergo substantial physical changes with relatively low doses of radiation. If the G value for a radiation induced reaction is 5, a dose of a million rads causes about 3.2×10^{18} chemical changes per gram in a material of unit density. If the molecular weight (MW) of the substrate is 100, this involves $3.2 \times 10^{18} / 6 \times 10^{21}$, or about 0.5×10^{-3} of the molecules present; if the MW is 10^6, then *each* molecule suffers an average of five chemical reactions. If the chemical change in question is a bond rupture the polymer will suffer a 6-fold decrease in molecular weight, an occurrence which results in a measurable deterioration of physical properties. If the chemical change results in a coupling (crosslinking) reaction the molecular weight increases by a factor of 6, as a result of which the polymer begins to assume a three-dimensional structure.

The two examples cited, that of a polymer whose molecular weight increases under irradiation, and that of a polymer whose molecular weight decreases, form the basis for dividing all polymers into two categories; those which primarily crosslink under irradiation, and those which degrade. Table 12-1 is a listing of polymers in each of these two categories. The empirical rule which can be used with reasonable accuracy as a predictive tool is that polymers of the type $(-CH_2-CHR-)_n$ crosslink, whereas in polymers of the type $(-CH_2-CCH_3R-)_n$, degradation reactions predominate. Polyvinyl alcohol, however, is an example of a polymer for which the rule does not hold. The basis of the rule, most likely, is that the polymers which degrade have tetrasubstituted carbons under large steric strains. In general, the polymers which degrade give large yields of monomers upon pyrolysis in vacuo, and have low enthalpies of formation.

Chemical changes occurring when polymers are irradiated closely follow those of their low molecular weight analogs; crosslinking and degradation are simply synonyms for condensation and scission. Other effects, such as gas evolution, double-bond formation, oxidation, color formation, and so forth can also be predicted with reasonable assurance. The radiolysis products of polyethylene can, for instance, be predicted from the behavior of cyclohexane. Differences in products and yields, where they occur, can be traced

Table 12-1.   EFFECT OF RADIATION POLYMERS*

Predominant crosslinking	Predominant degradation
Polythene Polypropylene	Poly(isobutylene)
Poly(vinyl chloride) Chlorinated polythene Chlorosulphonated polythene	Poly(vinylidine chloride) Polymonochlorotrifluorethylene Polytetrafluorethylene
Poly(acrylonitrile) Poly(acrylic acid) -Poly(acrylates) Poly(acrylamide) Poly(vinylpyrrolidone) Poly(vinyl alkyl ethers) Poly(vinyl methyl ketone)	Poly(a-methacrylonitrile) Poly(methacrylic acid) Poly(methacrylates) Poly(methacrylamide)
Polystyrene Sulphonated polystyrene	Poly(a-methyl styrene)
Natural rubber Synthetic rubber [except poly(isobutylene)] Polysiloxanes	
Polyamides Poly(ethylene oxide) Polyesters	Poly(ethylene terephthalate) Cellulose plastics

*Swallow, "Radiation Chemistry of Organic Compounds," Pergamon Press, New York, 1960.

to cage and solid-state effects. It must also be recognized that polymers in general, and commercial polymers in particular, are at best impure, and at worst, mixtures of polymer molecules of various chain lengths mixed with plasticizers, antioxidants, mold release agents, catalyst fragments, and the like. Indeed, most of the data available on the effect of radiation on commercial polymers is of little scientific import.

In this chapter we will consider the effect of radiation on polyethylene and polymethylmethacrylate, polymers which, respectively, crosslink and degrade when irradiated. In many respects their behavior is typical insofar as the results obtained can be generalized and applied to other polymers of their type.

12-1 EFFECT OF RADIATION ON POLYETHYLENE

Polyethylene (PE), which could be thought of as consisting simply of CH_2 groups, has, in fact, a complicated structure. It can be primarily crystalline or primarily amorphous; branched and unbranched, the size and type of the crystal regions being influenced by the extent of branching. The more crystalline polymers have higher densities and fewer branches, and are produced in a low pressure, catalytic, Ziegler-type process. Low density polyethylene on the other hand, is a result of a high pressure, gas phase polymerization. It is more highly branched, less crystalline and has a melting point of about $115°C$, in contrast to the high density PE which melts at about $135°C$.

A. Charlesby, who was the first to characterize radiation crosslinking effects, reports the following major effects when polyethylene is irradiated:

(1) The evolution of gases and low molecular weight hydrocarbons

(2) The formation of $C-C$ bonds between molecules (dimerizing and crosslinking)

(3) An increase in unsaturation

(4) Destruction of crystallinity

(5) Color changes. In common with many other polymers, polyethylene acquires a yellow tinge on irradiation.

(6) Oxidative reactions, particularly near the surface, when the irradiation is carried out in the presence of oxygen.

These changes result in the physical and chemical transformation of polyethylene into what has been recognized by the Patent Office to be a new and novel material; irradiated polyethylene. The transformation is not an abrupt one, the material passing through various stages as the number of crosslinks per molecules increase. Charlesby calls these stages, successively, rubberlike, cheeselike, and glasslike, in accordance with the mechanical behavior of the polymer.

12-1.1   Effect of Radiation on Polyethylene- Chemical Changes

12-1.1a   Gas Evolution

The behavior of polyethylene parallels that of the lower molecular weight alkanes. Hydrogen is a major radiolysis product, the amount and types of other gases being a function of the branching, and total radiation dose. Although some of the experimental data is conflicting, a number of general observations can be made.

(1) The yield of hydrogen gas from polyethylene is independent of crystallinity and chain length. The G value for H_2 formation, which is about 4, shows the same value for polyethylenes having from 50 to 85 percent crystallinity (Table 12-2). This value is about the same as that for normal alkanes.

Table 12-2. RADIATION-CHEMICAL YIELDS FOR THE EVOLUTION OF HYDROGEN AND HYDROCARBON GASES IN THE RADIOLYSIS OF POLYETHYLENE[*]

Type of polymer	Type of radiation and irradiation temperature	$G(H_2)$	$G(RH)$	G $-(CH{=}CH)-$
High pressure PE	Reactor (70°C)	4.0	0.08	—
High pressure PE	800 kev electrons	5.0[a]	0.9[a]	1.9
Polymethylene	800 kev electrons	4.7[a]	0	1.2
High pressure PE	Reactor	5.0[b]	—	—
High pressure PE	^{60}Co gamma	3.75	—	—
High and low pressure	2 Mev electrons (-196°C to +80°C)	3.1	—	1.3
High (and low) pressure PE	^{60}Co gamma	4.0	—	1.7-2.4
High (or low) pressure PE	Reactor (80°C)	7.0	—	—
Low pressure PE	800 kev electrons			
Marlex-50	(-170° to 34°)	3.75[a]	0.07[a]	⎫
Marlex-50	136°	5.5[a]	0.13[a]	⎬ 2.0
Marlex-50	240°	5.8[a]	0.17[a]	⎭
High pressure PE	50 kv X-rays, 13°C	2.5	0.15	⎫
High pressure PE	50 kv X-rays, 80°C	3.0	0.36	⎬ 1.15-1.35
Low pressure PE	50 kv X-rays, 10°C	2.8	0.03	
Low Pressure PE	50 kv X-rays, 80°C	3.0	0.09	⎭

[a]Corrected values assuming that the energy released per roentgen in polyethylene is 6×10^{13} ev/g.
[b]G (total gas).
[*]From Chapiro, "Radiation Chemistry of Polymeric Systems," Interscience Publishers, New York, 1962.

(2) Serious differences exist with respect to the exact composition and yield of the gaseous products other than hydrogen, which account for between 7 and 0.4 percent of the total gases. The gases have been characterized by various investigators as containing: (a)

traces of C_2H_6 and C_2H_4 only, (b) saturates only, (c) unsaturates only, (d) no methane, and (e) mostly methane.

One of the most comprehensive studies conducted to date is that of Harlan,[1] whose data is given in Table 12-3. The gaseous products of the polymethylene series, which were prepared from the corresponding diazoalkanes, are strongly dependent on the side chain composition, i.e., butane is the major hydrocarbon gas evolved by the butyl branched polymethylene, etc. Indeed, Harlan suggests radiation as an analytical tool for determining the presence and composition of side chain branches. The presence of unsaturated gases implies hydrogen transfer reactions to the main chain.

The differences in the amount of gases evolved by polymethylene and the high pressure PE also indicates a propensity for side chain fracture. It is to be noted that in the case of octasone, which is shown for comparison, the high ratio of hydrocarbon to hydrogen evolution is due to the low ratio of chain ends to main chain carbons.

(3) The ratio of hydrogen/hydrocarbon gases is not a constant, but drops with increasing dose, due either to crosslinking or unsaturation.

(4) Production of H_2 is essentially constant with temperatures between about $-200°C$ and room temperature. At higher temperatures the yield increases; ΔE activation is about 0.8 kcal per mole. The yield of hydrocarbon gases also increases with temperature; activation energies as high as 2.5 kcal per mole have been reported between $10°$ and $80°C$.

12-1.1b Unsaturation

Unsaturation in polyethylene may be determined by bromine or iodine titration, or by infrared analysis. The former method gives total unsaturation only whereas infrared can distinguish between the various forms of unsaturation; vinyl ($-CH=CH_2$), vinylidene ($-CR=CH_2$), and *trans*-vinylene ($-CH=CH-$), *cis*-vinylene is not favored because of the zig-zag nature of the hydrocarbon chain. In theory spectral measurements are easily made, in practice a great deal of care is required to achieve unambiguous interpretations of results.

Commercial polyethylenes contain an average of one double bond per molecule. All types of unsaturation are found, the ratios are approximately one vinyl and *trans*-vinylene to three vinylidenes. Upon irradiation these "pendant" double bonds disappear with very high initial G values, -10, giving rise to some interesting albeit speculative energy transfer mechanism since the results can be ascribed to hydrogenations or random interactions.

Table 12-3. GAS EVOLUTION FROM IRRADIATED POLYETHYLENES*

Polymer	H_2	CH_4	C_2H_6	C_3H_8	C_4H_{10}	C_5H_{12}	C_6H_{14}	C_7H_{16}	Unsaturated					
									C_2	C_3	C_4	C_5	C_6	C_7
Polyethylene	99.38%	0.12	0.05	0.01	0.02	0.01	0.01	0	0.30	0.09	0.01	—	—	—
Methyl-branched polymethylene	98.46	0.72	0.20	0.09	0.11	0.06	0.03	—	0.20	0.03	0.08	0.02	—	—
n-Butyl-branched	92.93	0.90	0.23	0.20	2.5	0.20	0.17	0.17	0.70	0.75	1.2	0.05	—	—
n-Amyl-branched	98.07	0.50	0.09	0.08	0.08	0.50	0.05	—	0.26	0.15	0.10	0.09	0.03	—
British High pressure polythene	96.9	0.22	0.82	0.21	0.59	0.16	0.07	0.05	0.68	0.04	0.09	0.02	0.07	0.08
American High pressure polythene	96.91	0.17	0.84	0.04	0.75	0.17	0.21	0.05	0.41	0.12	0.20	0.09	0.04	—
Octasone†	91	0.5	2.1	1.3	0.9	1.1	0.7	0.6						

*P. Harlan, et al., J. Polym. Sci., 18:589 (1955).
†A. A. Miller, E. J. Lawton, and J. S. Balwit, J. Phys. Chem., 60:599 (1956).

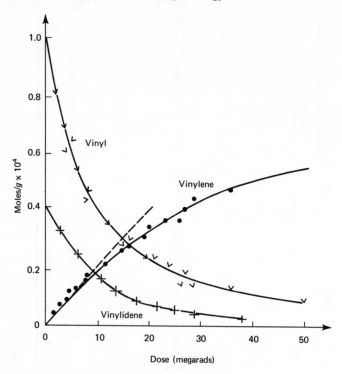

Fig. 12-1. Changes of unsaturation in irradiated polyethylene as a function of dose. [M. Dole, D. C. Milner, and T. F. Williams, *J. Am. Chem. Soc.*, 80:1580 (1958).]

As seen from Fig. 12-1, the vinylene formation is linear with dose up to about 10^6 rads, then the yield begins to drop.

An equilibrium between double bond formation and destruction appears to be reached at about one double bond per 18 carbon atoms; a similar behavior has been observed for lower molecular weight alkanes. The mechanism of the destruction of unsaturation is not understood, since there is no accompanying decrease in hydrogen yield such as one would expect if the reaction were

$$-CH=CH- + H_2 \longrightarrow -CH_2-CH_2- \qquad (12\text{-}1)$$

nor is there an increase in crosslinking such as one would have if the disappearance were due to a radical reaction like

$$-CH=CH- + R \longrightarrow \overset{\displaystyle R}{\underset{\displaystyle |}{-CH}}-\overset{\displaystyle \cdot}{CH}- \qquad (12\text{-}2)$$

The formation of *trans*-vinylene is almost completely independent of temperature from -200°C to 150°C. This, plus the fact that free radical scavengers do not affect the reaction and that it is independent of the type of PE is strong evidence that the formation of *trans*-vinylene bonds involves a molecular detachment of hydrogen from the main chain, or possibly an ionic mechanism. In this connection, it is interesting to note that UV irradiation of benzophenone-sensitized PE does not induce *trans*-type unsaturation, whereas both UV and ionizing radiation produce conjugated unsaturation.

12-1.1c Main-Chain Scission and Crosslinking

The good correlation between the amount of branching and the release of hydrocarbon gases (Table 12-3) strongly suggest that a minimum of main-chain scissions occurs. This is a difficult point to verify, the only experimental technique available is to dissolve the polymer after irradiation, and separate the low molecular weight, soluble fraction (sol) from the crosslinked fraction (gel).

To obtain a quantitative relationship between the number of scissions, crosslinks, and molecular weight we must first develop the requisite statistical theory.

To develop the quantitative relationships, we must assume an initial molecular weight distribution for the polymer. Let us first examine the type of distribution we would obtain if an infinitely long polymer chain were subject to random scissions. Let

$$N(x) = \text{number of fragments of length } x \text{ where}$$
$$x = \text{monomer units (mers)}$$

$$N = \text{total number of fragments}$$

$$P_o = \text{probability of a scission}$$

$$(1 - P_o) = \text{probability of no scission}$$

$$(x - 1) = \text{total number of bonds between monomer units in a}$$
$$\text{fragment of length } x$$

The probability that a sequence of bonds joining x monomer units will not be cut at any point is $(1 - P_o)^{x-1}$, and the probability that the unit of x monomers will be cut is $P_o(1 - P_o)^{x-1}$ hence

$$N(x)/N = P_o(1 - P_o)^{x-1} \qquad (12\text{-}3)$$

which, for $P_o \ll 1$, and $x \gg 1$ can be approximated by

$$N(x) = NP_o e^{-P_o x} \qquad (12\text{-}4)$$

This corresponds to a "most probable," "exponential," or "ran-dom" distribution of weights.

The average value of the function would be the number average degree of polymerization $\overline{DP}_n$:

$$\overline{DP}_n = \frac{N \int_0^{\infty} xP_o \, e^{-P_o x}}{N} = \frac{1}{P_o} \qquad (12\text{-}5)$$

To obtain the corresponding weight average degree of polymerization $\overline{DP}_w$, we must use the more general formula [Eq. (12-6)]. If $n = 2$

$$\frac{N \int_0^{\infty} P_o^n x^n \, e^{-P_o x} \, dx}{N} = \frac{2}{P_o} = 2\overline{DP}_w \qquad (12\text{-}6)$$

For molecular weight distributions other than the most probable $2\overline{M}_n \neq \overline{M}_w$, and a different set of relationships applies.

The argument whereby Eq. (12-6) and (12-5) evolved, may be reversed. We can, for instance, start with the most probable distribution of molecular weights and crosslink the molecules. If we crosslink each to another, one large molecule would result, i.e., the process whereby Eqs. (12-6) and (12-5) were evolved would be reversed. For the case of crosslinking, it is convenient to define two new parameters.

δ = crosslinking coefficient, the number of crosslinked units per weight averaged primary molecules. At gelation $\delta = \delta_c = 1$

γ = crosslinking index, the number of crosslinked units per number average primary molecule.

The following relationships hold for the most probable distribution

$$\delta = P_o \overline{M}_w, \qquad \gamma = P_o \overline{M}_n, \qquad \delta = 2\gamma \qquad (12\text{-}7)$$

At the gel point

$$\delta_c = P_{oc} \overline{M}_w = 1, \qquad \gamma_c = P_{oc} \overline{M}_n, \qquad \gamma_c = \overline{M}_n / \overline{M}_w \qquad (12\text{-}8)$$

For the most probable distribution, $\gamma_c = 0.5$, i.e., there is one crosslinked unit for every two primary number average molecules, and $\delta = 2\gamma$. If the molecular weight distribution is still broader, $\delta = n\gamma$, where

$$\overline{M}_n = n\overline{M}_w \tag{12-9}$$

EXAMPLE 12-1: Bovey[2] shows that if we start with a monodisperse assembly of finite chains, and break them at random, one obtains for the weight and number average molecular weights

$$\overline{M}_w = \frac{f^2\overline{DP}_o + 2(1-f)\,[(1-f)^{\overline{DP}_o} + f\overline{DP}_o - 1]}{f^2\overline{DP}_o} \tag{12-10}$$

$$\overline{M}_n = \frac{\overline{DP}_o}{1 + f(\overline{DP}_o - 1)} \tag{12-11}$$

where $\overline{DP}_o$ = degree of polymerization of the original molecule,

f = fraction of linkages severed

(1) Show that the ratio of $\overline{M}_w/\overline{M}_n$ approaches that of a most probable distribution after only a few scissions per original molecule, s.

(2) Derive the relationship between γ, the crosslinking index and δ, the crosslinking coefficient, and compare the result with Eq. (12-9).

SOLUTION: For a high molecular weight polymer, $\overline{DP}_o \approx \overline{DP}_o - 1$ and $f = s/(\overline{DP}_o - 1) \approx s/\overline{DP}_o$ thus

$$(1-f)^{\overline{DP}_o} \approx (1 - s/\overline{DP}_o)^{\overline{DP}_o} \approx e^{-s} \tag{12-12}$$

Substituting Eq. (12-12) into (12-10) and assuming $s/\overline{DP}_o \ll 1$ we obtain

$$\overline{M}_w/\overline{DP}_o = (2/s^2)\,(e^{-s} + s - 1) \tag{12-13}$$

while

$$\overline{M}_n/\overline{DP}_o = 1/(1 + s) \tag{12-14}$$

and

$$\overline{M}_w/\overline{M}_n = [2(1 + s)/s^2]\,(e^{-s} + s - 1)$$

Values of $(\overline{M}_w/\overline{M}_n)$ for various values of s are

$(\overline{M}_w/\overline{M}_n)$	1.5	1.7	1.8	1.9	1.95
s	1	2	3	5	7

Comparing with Eq. (12-6) we note that after three scissions per original chain, the distribution approaches 90 percent of the most probable.

If the molecular weight distribution is uniform then, in accordance with Eq. (12-9)

$$\delta = \gamma, \text{ and at gelation, } \delta_c - \gamma_c = 1$$

and we have one crosslink per primary molecule.

When scission and crosslinking both occur simultaneously we can no longer use the same symbol (P_o) for probability, and it becomes convenient to define two new parameters, $\underline{\alpha}$ and $\underline{\beta}$

$$\text{probability of crosslinking} = \underline{\alpha} D$$

$$\text{probability of scission} = \underline{\beta} D$$

where D = radiation dose.

If these probabilities remain constant with dose, then $\underline{\beta}/\underline{\alpha}$ determines the ratio of soluble to gel fraction. If, at gelation, there is one crosslinked unit per weight averaged molecules (two per number average), then gel formation will not occur if

$$\underline{\beta}/\underline{\alpha} > 2$$

It is now necessary to derive a relationship between the soluble fraction s and $\underline{\beta}$ and $\underline{\alpha}$. The derivation, which was formulated by Charlesby,[3] leads to a result which is shown in Fig. 12-2. The solid curves are for an initially random distribution, the dotted curve is for the monodisperse molecular weight distribution, discussed in Example 12-1. Thus, by measuring gel content as a function of dose it is possible to establish relative values of $\underline{\beta}/\underline{\alpha}$.

Work carried out in the early and mid 1950s suggested simultaneous fracture and crosslinking in polyethylene. The data of Charlesby, which was plotted in Fig. 12-2 yields an α/β ratio of about 0.35. Similar results were obtained by Basckett and Miller who extracted the gel fraction from irradiated PE, and reirradiated it. Both sets of results have been questioned; it is suspected that either oxidative- or solvent-induced degradation took place.

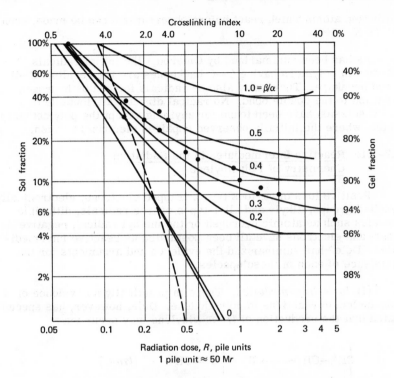

Fig. 12-2. Sol and gel fraction of irradiated polyethylene. The black dots indicate observed values, solid lines indicate theoretical curve assuming a random probability initially (numbers represent ratio of chain fracture to crosslinking), and broken lines indicate theoretical curve assuming uniform initial distribution (no chain fracture). (A. Charlesby, "Atomic Radiation and Polymers," Pergamon Press, London, 1960.)

The currently held theory is that in vacuo, no main-chain scission occurs except at branch points, or near chain ends (the second or third carbon).

12-1.1d Free Radical Production

ESR has been a very valuable tool in identifying and detecting free radicals in irradiated polymers. Its success is due largely to the fact that the radicals, which are relatively immobile in the solid matrix, have relatively long lives. In general, to assure that all the primary radicals are trapped, measurements are made at liquid nitrogen temperatures, where it is assumed that radical reactions do not occur. This has been shown to be true for all species except hydrogen atoms which react before observations can be made, even at $77°K$.

As has been summarized by Omerod,[4] the initial radicals formed in polymers having C—C backbones are the result of C—H bond breakage. There may also be radicals formed by hydrogen addition to the double bond. No radical directly attributable to a C—C scission have been found for anything except the polymethacrylates, where the initially observed unpaired electron is an ion.

12-1.1e Reactive Intermediates in the Radiation Chemistry of Polyethylene

Positive ions of various types, trapped electrons, electronically excited groups, alkyl- and allyl-types of free radicals, diffusible species such as atomic hydrogen or the methyl radical, negative ions, and electrons have all been postulated as reactive intermediates. Dole[5] has summarized the evidence and arguments for the existence of each of these species.

(1) *Ionic Intermediates.* There is practically no evidence of ion-molecule reactions in polyethylene. Dole, however, has speculated that the production of *trans*-vinylene may occur via

$$\overset{|}{\underset{|}{CH_2^+}}-CH_2- \longrightarrow H_2 + \overset{|}{\underset{|}{CH^+}}=CH- \qquad (trans)$$

(2) *Negative Ions and Trapped Electrons.* At present there is no direct evidence that carbanions R^- or trapped electrons enter into any chemical reactions. (The carbanions are presumably formed from the electron trapping of the free radicals.) Thermoluminescence due to trapped electrons has, however, been observed.

(3) *Diffusible Intermediates.* Although there is considerable secondary evidence that hydrogen atoms exist, they have never been observed directly, even at temperatures as low as $-195°C$. The same is true of alkyl free radicals, methylene radicals, and methyl radicals, even though methyl radicals have been observed in polypropylene.

Allyl free radicals and polyenyl free radicals have, however, been observed by ESR and ultraviolet spectroscopy respectively.

12-1.1f Mechanism of Radiation Effects in Polyethylene

ESR studies as well as gas evolution indicate that the initial radiation induced reaction is a C—H bond scission

$$-CH_2-CH_2-CH_2 \xrightarrow{\;\wedge\wedge\;} -CH_2-\overset{\bullet}{C}H-CH_2 + H \qquad (12\text{-}15)$$

Another initial reaction is the formation of vinylene unsaturation

$$-CH_2-CH_2-CH_2-CH_2- \xrightarrow{\hspace{0.5cm}} -CH_2-CH=CH-CH_2- + H_2 \tag{12-16}$$

To account for the alkyl radical, which has been shown to appear when polymers are irradiated at 77°K and allowed to warm to room temperature, Reaction (12-17) is thought to occur

$$-CH_2-\dot{C}H-CH_2- + -CH_2-CH=CH- \longrightarrow$$

$$-CH_2-CH_2-CH_2- + -\dot{C}H-CH=CH- \tag{12-17}$$

The role of the hydrogen atom formed by Reaction (12-15) is not known quantitatively; however, there is general agreement that the following reactions take place

$$H\cdot + -CH_2-CH_2-CH_2- \longrightarrow -CH_2-\dot{C}H-CH_2- + H_2 \tag{12-18}$$

$$H\cdot + \text{unsaturation} \longrightarrow \text{a radical} \tag{12-19}$$

$$2H\cdot \longrightarrow H_2 \tag{12-20}$$

$$H\cdot + -CH_2-\dot{C}H-CH_2- \longrightarrow -CH_2-CH_2-CH_2- \tag{12-21}$$

Crosslinking is thought to occur primarily via

$$2(-CH_2-\dot{C}H-CH_2-) \longrightarrow \text{crosslink} \tag{12-22}$$

and by

$$-CH_2-\dot{C}H-CH_2- + -\dot{C}H-CH=CH \longrightarrow \text{crosslink} \tag{12-23}$$

A number of minor reactions, such as the destruction of vinyl and vinylydene unsaturation, and main-chain breakage have not been taken into account. The material balance, however, is moderately well satisfied insofar as

$$G_{H_2} = G_{(\text{crosslinking})} + G_{(\text{unsaturation})},$$

as evidenced by Table 12-2.

A serious objection to the above sequence of reactions is the high activation energy, 8 kcal per mole, required by Reaction (12-18), which is the precursor for (12-22). The facility with which crosslinking takes place at room temperature suggests that perhaps the hydrogen atom formed in Eq. (12-15) is "hot," i.e., carries excess kinetic energy. If this be the case, Eq. (12-18) may be thought of as occurring at every collision. If this be true, Eq. (12-16) could then be thought of as proceeding via

$$-CH_2-\overset{\overset{\boxed{H}}{|}}{CH}-\overset{\overset{H}{|}}{CH}-CH_2- \longrightarrow CH_2-CH=CH-CH_2 + H_2 \quad (12\text{-}17a)$$

where the box denotes a hot atom.

Weiss, Dorfman, Chapiro, and other authors have invoked ionic mechanisms to explain the radiation effects. Although less convincing than the radical mechanism, they are supported to some extent at least by the fact that radiation increases the conductivity of polyethylene (Sec. 12-1.2d).

The ionic crosslinking process is thought to either be analogous to the methane condensation observed in the mass spectrometer

$$CH_3^+ + CH_4 \longrightarrow C_2H_5^+ + H_2 \quad (12\text{-}24)$$

that is

$$\overset{|}{\underset{|}{CH^+}} + \overset{|}{\underset{|}{CH_2}} \longrightarrow -\overset{|}{\underset{|}{{}^+C}}-\overset{|}{\underset{|}{CH}} + H_2 \quad (12\text{-}24a)$$

or, to the well-known proton transfer process:

$$CH_4^+ + CH_4 \longrightarrow CH_5^+ + CH_3\cdot \quad (12\text{-}25)$$

A crosslinking sequence based on Reaction (12-24a) would be[6]

Proton transfer

$$\overset{|}{\underset{|}{CH_2^+}} + \overset{|}{\underset{|}{CH_2}} \longrightarrow \overset{|}{\underset{|}{CH\cdot}} + \overset{|}{\underset{|}{CH_3^+}} \quad (12\text{-}26)$$

Neutralization

$$\overset{|}{\underset{|}{CH\cdot}} + \overset{|}{\underset{|}{CH_3^+}} + e^- \longrightarrow \overset{|}{\underset{|}{CH\cdot}} + \overset{|}{\underset{|}{CH\cdot}} + H_2 \quad (12\text{-}27)$$

The two polymer radicals would be in close proximity and thus could combine to form a crosslink.

12-1.1g Oxidation Reactions

Oxygen reacts rapidly with polymer radicals to form peroxide radicals, approximately five oxygen molecules chain reacting per radical. The initial reaction is

$$-CH_2-\overset{\bullet}{C}H-CH_2 + O_2 \longrightarrow -CH_2-\overset{\overset{\displaystyle \overset{\bullet}{O}_2}{|}}{C}-CH_2 \qquad (12\text{-}28)$$

possibly followed by

$$RO_2\cdot + RH \longrightarrow R\cdot + RO_2H \qquad (12\text{-}29)$$

$$R\cdot + O_2 \longrightarrow RO_2 \qquad (12\text{-}30)$$

or by intra- rather than intermolecular reactions

$$-CH_2-\overset{\bullet}{C}H-CH=CH-CH_2- \qquad (12\text{-}31)$$
$$\downarrow O_2$$
$$-CH_2-CH(O_2\cdot)-CH=CH-CH_2- \qquad (12\text{-}31a)$$

$$-CH_2-CH(O_2H)-\overset{\bullet}{C}=CH-CH_2- \qquad -CH_2-\overset{\bullet}{H}C-O_2-CH=CH-CH_2-$$
$$(12\text{-}31b)$$

$$-CH_2-CH(OH)-C(O)-\overset{\bullet}{C}H-CH_2- \qquad -CH_2-HC=O$$
$$+ O=CH-\overset{\bullet}{C}H-CH_2- \quad (12\text{-}31c)$$
$$\downarrow O_2 \qquad\qquad\qquad\qquad\qquad \downarrow O_2$$
$$CH_2-CH(OH)-C(O)-CH(O_2\cdot)-CH_2- \quad O=CH-CH(O_2\cdot)-CH_2-$$
$$(12\text{-}31d)$$

In both the inter- and intramolecular schemes termination is generally thought to occur via

$$R\cdot + R\cdot \longrightarrow R-R \qquad (12\text{-}32)$$

$$RO_2\cdot + R \longrightarrow ROOR \qquad (12\text{-}33)$$

**12-1.2   Effect of Radiation on Polyethylene —
Physical Changes**

12-1.2a Crystallinity and Specific Volume

The crystal regions in polyethylene give rise to electron diffraction patterns consisting of a sharp ring superimposed on diffuse halos. The pattern arises due to the presence of small individual crystallites dispersed in the amorphous polymer. X-ray diffraction patterns of irradiated PE show only a gradual weakening of the sharp ring structure with increasing dose. The lack of ring broadening, or changes in spacing indicates that radiation destroys crystallinity but does not change the size or structure of the crystals. 500×10^6 rads is required to destroy all traces of crystallinity.

The specific volume of PE is a function of temperature, crystallinity, and crosslinks. Radiation affects the specific volume insofar as it influences the latter two parameters, assuming the nature of the major changes are predictable.

(1) at high temperatures (T $>$ 115°C) where all crystallinity has been destroyed, irradiation crosslinked PE has a lower increase in specific volume with temperature than at low temperatures.

(2) At low temperatures, and low to moderate radiation doses, the density of polyethylene decreases with radiation because of the destruction of the more dense, crystal phase.

(3) At low temperatures, and for doses of radiation large enough to have destroyed a major portion of the crystallinity, and to have created many crosslinks per molecule, the density increases because the distance between two crosslinked carbon atoms is about 1.5 Å, in contrast to 4 Å for uncrosslinked carbons.

12-1.2b Mechanical Property Changes

Figure 12-3 shows the stress-strain behavior of low density, irradiated polyethylene. In addition to showing the effect of radiation, the three 15 Mr curves at 150°C, 25°C, and -81°C demonstrate the temperature dependence of the elastic modulus, the slope of the stress-strain curve. The elastic modulus drops sharply as the test temperature is raised, due largely to the destruction of crystallinity at the higher temperatures.

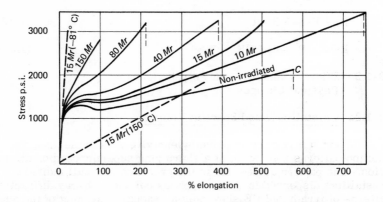

Fig. 12-3. Tensile strength of low density polyethylene. Unless indicated, the temperature is 25°C. Mr is the dose of electron radiation in megaroentgens. [Data from Lawton, Balwit, and Bouche, *Ind. Eng. Chem.*, **46**:1703 (1954).]

The general behavior demonstrated by the nonirradiated sample is that of a plastic. The initial Hook's law region is superseded by a region of increasing cold flow and orientation. Point C is the ultimate break point.

The effect of initial irradiation is an increase in both tensile strength and ultimate elongation. As irradiation is increased, both the tensile strength and elongation rise to a maximum and then decrease, indicating a decrease in plastic flow and an improvement in elastic recovery. There is a decided shift from a plasticlike to an elasticlike behavior. At both high temperatures (15 Mr curve at 150°C), and at high doses (150 Mr) where the crystallinity has been largely destroyed, the shape of the stress-strain curves are similar, and characteristic of rubberlike materials.

The most dramatic change in behavior between irradiated and unirradiated material occurs at temperatures above 110°C. Here, polyethylene irradiated to 10-20 Mr behaves as an elastic material, it can be stretched as much as 270 to 450 percent without tension set, and has a tensile strength of over 100 psi. The unirradiated material has essentially no tensile strength and behaves like a viscous liquid.

12-1.2c Memory Effects

Radiation has been used to impart a striking and useful property to polyethylene and other polymers which can be crosslinked. The effect depends on the network formed on irradiation being an equilibrium network. Thus the polymer, if induced to undergo a cyclic change, will always assume the equilibrium dimensions it possessed while being crosslinked.

Polyethylene in the form of a 1 in. tube, for example, can be irradiation crosslinked to impart a "memory." The tube can then be heated above the crystal melting point, stretched to form a 2 in. diameter tube and cooled in the stretched state. The 2 in. diameter would be retained *until* the tube was reheated to a temperature exceeding the melting point of the crystals. At that time, the tube will "remember" that its equilibrium diameter was 1 in. and contract to its original 1 in. dimension. This effect has given rise to important industrial applications (Chap. 13).

12-1.2d Electrical Properties

The electrical conductance σ of polyethylene increases markedly with irradiation; polyethylene sheets, for instance, show a thousandfold increase with doses of only a few hundred to a few thousand rads. The conductivity rises very rapidly, reaches a saturation value, and remains constant. At the end of the irradiation, the conductivity drops to its original value (providing the total dose was not high).

The current induced by the radiation is a strong function of the radiation intensity, the value of the exponent n in Eq. (12-34) varies between 0.5 and 1.0.

$$\underline{\sigma} = k' \, \phi^n \tag{12-34}$$

where ϕ = radiation intensity

The value of n provides an insight into the behavior of the Compton and primary electrons. If:

(1) $n = 1$, the electrons move freely to the anode, or are permanently trapped after a short distance.

(2) $n = 0.5$, the electrons recombine rapidly with the positive ions formed in the ionization process.

(3) $n = 0.5-1$, the electrons are in shallow traps; the probability of escape depends on the depth of the trap and ambient conditions.

The value of n for polyethylene, which is between 0.6 and 0.8, has given rise to a number of theoretical treatments aimed at determining the lifetimes of ions produced by irradiation.

12-2 EFFECT OF RADIATION ON METHYLMETHACRYLATE

Methylmethacrylate, which has the repeating structure

$$-CH_2-C(CH_3) \, (COOCH_3)-CH_2-$$

is a clear, amorphous polymer which softens at about 80-120°C. The principal changes produced by radiation, main chain fracture and side chain decomposition, exemplify the changes induced in polymers which degrade under irradiation.

12-2.1 Effect of Radiation of Polymethylmethacrylate — Chemical Changes

12-2.1a Gas Evolution

Methylmethacrylate, upon irradiation, releases copious quantities of gas. The amount of gas liberated at 75-100 Mrad and trapped in the polymer is sufficient to cause the polymer to bubble or "foam" upon heating. The gases, which originate primarily with the ester side chain, consist of hydrogen, carbon monoxide, carbon dioxide, and methane. Although there is general agreement with respect to the qualitative nature of the gas evolution, the quantitative results vary considerably. Table 12-4 presents the results of Wall and

Brown;[7] the numbers in parentheses represent the spread of the data reported in the literature.

Some of this spread is due to experimental conditions; Wall and Brown irradiated with gamma rays in vacuo to 6.5 Mrad, while the other data were taken in air, with mixed-pile irradiation, at higher temperatures and doses.

Table 12-4. COMPOSITION OF GASEOUS PRODUCTS
FROM POLYMETHYL METHACRYLATE

	Composition of Gases, (%)					G (total)
	H_2	CH_4	CO	CO_2	Monomer	
Wall and Brown	13	34	28	20	0	1.6
Others	(44–13)	(6–34)	(23–36)	(19–25)	0	(1.5–1.1)

Although there is major disagreement with respect to the hydrogen/CH_4 ratio, all results show about half the gases to be ($H_2 + CH_4$) while the products CO plus CO_2 make up the rest of the gas in the ratio 3/2. There is no way of establishing a material balance for the gases based on the destruction of the formate side chain.

12-2.1b Unsaturation

There is strong evidence that one of the UV absorption bonds developed when PMMA is irradiated is due to conjugated unsaturation.

12-2.1c Main-Chain Scission and Crosslinking

Since PMMA degrades upon irradiation, no gel fraction is formed, the polymer can be dissolved, and the molecular weight can be established unambiguously by classical techniques such as light scattering and viscosity. Charlesby[3] has summarized the G values for chain scission obtained by four different groups of workers. All but the last three results in Table 12-5 are due to Wall and Brown, who used ^{60}Co gammas. The last three results were obtained at much higher dose rates with mixed-reactor or electron radiation. No effect of radiation intensity or biaxial orientation of the polymer is observed. Oxygen, however, reduces the amount of degradation by about one third.

Although it is clear that the *net* result of the irradiation is to degrade the polymer, the validity of the assumption that there is no accompanying crosslinking or chain branching needed to be established unambiguously. This was done by using various techniques for determining molecular weights.

Table 12-5. G VALUES FOR MAIN CHAIN FRACTURE OF
POLYMETHYL METHACRYLATE AT ABOUT 25°C*

Sample	Vacuum treatment before radiation		G values irradiation	
	(°C)	(hr)	(Vacuum)	(Air)
Film	100	20	1.23	0.645
FB-1	100	20	1.70	0.894
FB-1	120	20	2.00	1.25
FB-2	100	20	1.99	1.37
FB-2	120	20	2.48	1.52
Commercial sample (oriented)	—	—	2.28	
	100	20	2.31	
	120	20	2.23	
Commercial sample (unoriented)	—	—	2.23	
	100	20	2.16	
	120	20	2.16	
1/2 in. rod shavings			1.6	1.6
Thin sheet				1.5
Film				1.7

*Charlesby, "Atomic Radiation and Polymers," Pergamon Press, New York, 1960.

12-2.1d Free Radical Production

At room temperature all methacrylate polymers give the same
ESR spectrum after electron, gamma, or ultraviolet radiation. It is
widely agreed that, among other things, the radical

$$-CH_2-\dot{C}(CH_3)(COOR)$$

is present.

12-2.1e Mechanism of Radiation Effects in PMMA

In view of the available evidence, a 1-4 diradical mechanism
of decomposition is indicated.

$$-CH_2-\underset{\underset{CH_3}{|}}{\overset{\overset{O}{\|}}{\underset{|}{C}}-OCH_3}-CH_2-\underset{\underset{CH_3}{|}}{\overset{\overset{O}{\|}}{\underset{|}{C}}-OCH_3}-\!\!\!\text{-\!w\!\!\rightarrow} \;\; -CH\underset{\underset{CH_3}{|}}{\overset{\overset{O}{\|}}{\underset{|}{C}}-OCH_3}-CH_2-\underset{\underset{\cdot CH_2}{|}}{\overset{\overset{O}{\|}}{\underset{|}{C}}-OCH_3} \;\; + \; H\overset{\overset{O}{\|}}{C}OCH_3 \qquad (12\text{-}35)$$

gases

$$-CH_2\underset{\underset{CH_3}{|}}{C}=CH_2 \quad + \quad CH_2=\underset{\underset{COCH_3}{|}}{\overset{\overset{O}{\|}}{C}}-$$

This mechanism is in accord with most of the facts. It explains the presence of the type of free radical found and indicates scission to take place at the quaternary carbon.

Table 12-6. PROTECTIVE EFFECT OF ADDITIVES IN RADIOLYSIS (OF POLYMETHYL METHACRYLATE)*

Additive	Concentration, wt %	Protection, %
Benzoic acid	1.0	76
Naphthalene	2	32
Anthracene	2.1	37
Phenanthrene	2.2	51
Biphenyl	2.5	56
Phenol	2.7	52
a-naphthylamine	2.5	78
8-hydroxyquinoline	2	52
Diphenylthiourea	3.6	69
a-naphthol	5.5	82
β-naphthol	5.3	24
Ethylurea	10.0	12
Paraffin	~10	3

*From P. Alexander and D. J. Toms, *Rad. Res.*, 9(5):509 (1958).

The effect of various additives on the rate of scission is an interesting though not fully explained phenomena. As indicated in Table 12-6 almost every substance added to PMMA reduces the number of chain scissions, the percent protection, P, being defined as % $P = 100\,(E_p - E)/E_p)$, E and E_p being the energy per bond scission with and without additives respectively. Three possible protective mechanisms exist: (1) the protective agent is sacrificially destroyed, (2) the protective agent enters the chain and repairs the breaks, (3) there is excitation energy transfer over long distances. From curves of concentration versus protective action, and tracer experiments, one may conclude that all three mechanisms are operative; their relative importance varies with the type of additive. Naphthalene, for instance, protects primarily by a combination of mechanisms (2) and (3), and 8-hydroxyquinoline by a combination of (1) and (2).

12-2.2 Effect of Radiation on PMMA — Physical Changes

12-2.2a Mechanical Properties

Changes in mechanical properties associated with main chain fracture become evident at doses above 10 Mrad. Figure 12-4 shows the changes in tensile strength and elongation at break, for PMMA exposed to mixed-pile radiation. The decrease in molecular weight with radiation dose can be calculated from the relationship between molecular weight and tensile strength.

12-2.2b Static Discharges

When a block of polymer is irradiated, electrons collect in the solid, and a negative space charge builds up. In many polymers, and in glass, the space charge can be discharged by a grounded, point electrode. Beautiful Lichtenberg patterns can thus be built up in PMMA and other polymers.

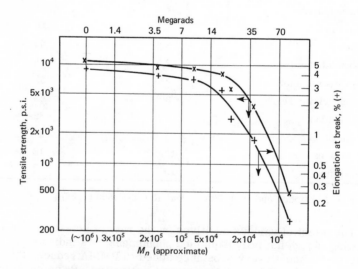

Fig. 12-4. Decrease in tensile strength and elongation at break of irradiated polymethyl methacrylate. [Data of C. D. Bopp and O. Sisman, *Nucleonics*, **13**(7):28 (1955).]

PROBLEMS

12-1 How many crosslinks per weight average and number average polymer molecule are required to reach the gel point?

12-2 Assuming a G value for hydrogen formation of 4.1, calculate the G values for the formation of the other gases reported in Table 12-1.

12-3 Derive the equations for the molecular weight distribution obtained when a series of chains of finite size are broken at random, the original molecular weight distribution being characterized by $\overline{M}_n/\overline{M}_w = 0.25$. How would this initial distribution affect the values shown in Fig. 12-2?

12-4 Discuss the possibility that the ionic reactions below are involved in the crosslinking and formation of unsaturation in PE.

$$2-CH_2-\overset{+}{C}H-CH_2- \longrightarrow -CH_2-C-CH_2- + H_2 +$$

$$-CH_2-CH-CH_2-$$

$$-CH_2-CH_2-\overset{+}{C}H-CH_2- \longrightarrow -CH_2-CH=CH-CH_2- + H_2^+$$

Complete the reaction sequence (Weiss, *J. Polymer Sci.*, **29**: 425 (1958).

REFERENCES

1. P. Harlan, et al., *J. Polym. Sci.*, **18**:589 (1955).

2. F. Bovey, "Effect of Ionizing Radiation on Natural and Synthetic Polymers," Interscience Publishers, New York, 1958.

3. A. Charlesby, "Atomic Radiation and Polymers," Pergamon Press, London, 1960.

4. M. Omerod, in E. Henley and H. Kouts (eds.), "Advance in Nuclear Science and Engineering," vol. 2, Academic Press, New York, 1964.

5. M. Dole, "Reactive Intermediates in the Radiation Chemistry of Polyethylene," Advances in Chemistry Series **66**, 31, ACS, 1967.

6. A. Chapiro, "Chemical Nature of the Reactive Species Produced in Polymers by Ionizing Radiation," Advances in Chemistry Series **66**, 25, ACS, 1967.

7. L. Wall and D. W. Brown, *J. Res. Natl. Bu. Stds.*, **57**:131 (1956).

13

INDUSTRIAL APPLICATIONS

Experimental work leading to commercial processes did not begin until the late 1940s since it was not until then that radiation sources for industrial purposes began to be available. Much of the initial work carried out in the 1940 to 1960 period was centered about the ability of radiation to stimulate chemical reactions at low temperatures, and without catalyst. This generated worldwide optimism about the potential industrial future of radiation. Unfortunately, the one surviving project, out of the hundreds carried out on a process development basis in the 1940s and 1950s, has been the crosslinking of polymers to improve melt index, and to make them heat-shrinkable.

After the years of nearly fruitless work, new processes put into operation after 1960 now offer hope for the future. These include the Dow Chemical method for producing ethyl bromide, ESSO's radiation process for synthesis of biodegradable detergents, RAI's radiation-graft-produced membranes and battery separators, the Ford Motor Company's process for curing paint, a process for making wood-polymer laminates and the finishing and curing of fabrics. An excellent review by Jefferson, Roberts, Ley and Rogers summarizes the status of the commercial applications.

13-1 CROSSLINKED PLASTICS — WIRE, TUBING, AND TAPE

Irradiated polyethylene, under the trade name Irrathane was introduced in 1954 by the General Electric Company. The material was available in film and tape form, as an electrical insulator; it is no longer available commercially.

The next product to be developed was highly filled, polyethylene insulated, wire and cable (IPO) for the aerospace industry. The product was developed in about 1960, and is manufactured by the Raychem Corporation, the Sequoia Division of Anaconda Wire and Cable, and Suprenant, among others. Irradiated polyethylene insulation not only possesses all the excellent properties of polyethylene, but also retains those properties at elevated temperatures where unirradiated materials will fail. The commercial product will not melt or flow up to its thermal decomposition temperature of 325° C, in contrast to the best high density material which melts at 135° C. Moreover, irradiated polyethylene has no tendency towards environmental stress cracking.

The basic ingredients of the IPO wire insulation are: a resin, an antioxidant, and a flame-retarding compound. For some applications, a minor proportion of a bridging agent such as sulfur, sulfur-containing compounds, selenium, selenium-containing compounds, tellerium and tellerium-containing compounds are added (Australian Patent 217912, Sept., 1956, Paul M. Cook, etc. to Sequoia Process Corp). In that case, an additional heat treatment must be used following the radiation. In general, the exact composition varies with the end use, extrusion conditions, and anticipated service.

Table 13-1 lists the properties of some typical IPO wire and cable products. Table 13-2 provides a comparison between No. 22 AWG IPO and competing wire products. The high cost of the irradiated product is to be particularly noted. A reasonable fraction of this cost is due to special compounding and handling, but the major cost increment accrues to the irradiation. The only appreciable market for IPO wire has been the aerospace industry where the low weight and chemical inertness of the IPO are more important than the high cost.

13-1a   Crosslinked Plastics — Shrinkable Tubing and Film

Irradiation to doses of greater than 20 million rads imparts a "memory" to polymers. Thus, if the polymer is stretched after being irradiated, it will, when heated (usually to temperatures in excess of 235° F) shrink back to its original size and shape. This type of material is finding extensive applications as harness jackets, preformed insulators, and as a terminator and joint cover. Well over $20,000,000 per year of shrinkable tubing is being sold.

Table 13-3 lists the types of heat shrinkable tubing available from Raychem. In addition to polyethylene, fluorocarbon, polyvinylchloride, and neoprene tubings are being made. Expanded dimensions are roughly 50 to 100% greater than recovered dimensions.

Irradiated, shrinkable polyethylene bags for food packaging are manufactured by the Cryovac Division of the W. R. Grace Co. The irradiated film, which is five times stronger than its non-irradiated counterpart, is stretched to about twice its original size and then control-shrunk by a hot-water-dip process at the food processing plant. A dose of about 15 to 20 megarads is used. About 1,500 tons per year of the film are said to be produced.[2]

13-2 RADIATION GRAFTED PRODUCTS — WOOD-PLASTIC MATERIAL

The concept of grafting a monomer A onto a polymer B to impart additional desirable properties to the polymer is attractive,

Table 13-1. TYPICAL IPO WIRE AND CABLE*

Hook-Up Wire Multi-Conductor Cable

Voltage Ratings:	Type "R" 300 Volt rms, 1600 Volt rms test
	Type "L" 600 Volt rms, 2200 Volt rms test
	Type "LL" 1000 Volt rms, 3000 Volt rms test
Temperature Rating:	−55°C to +135°C continuous duty
Conductor:	No. 30 through No. 1/0 AWG
	Concentric strandings as well as ultra-flexible tinned copper is standard, but also available with silver, nickle or special platings.
	High-strength copper alloys are also available.
Insulation:	ELECTROSET S/E, ELECTROSET
	ELECTROSET LT/or special polyolefin insulation to meet specific operating conditions.
Shields:	Standard basket-weave, spiral wrap or metallic faced tapes.
Jackets:	Same as primary insulation as well as vinyls, nylon, Glass braid and other suitable materials.
Colors:	Available in standard NEMA colors in accordance with MIL-STD-104 and also with permanent contrasting spiral strips.

High Voltage Cable

Voltage Ratings:	dc from 1.0 to 50 kv
	ac from 2.5 to 25 kv
Temperature Rating:	−55°C to +135°C continuous duty.
Conductor:	No. 24 through No. 14 AWG; materials, strandings and platings same as specified for hook-up wire.
Insulation:	Either flexible or semi-rigid.

*E. J., Henley, The Irradiated Polyolefin Wire, Cable, and Tubing Industry, Proceedings of the Fifth Annual Isotopes in Industry Conference (Tokyo), 1963.

Table 13-2. COMPARISONS OF INSULATED WIRE (No. 22 AWG)*

	IPO (Lockheed)	TFE	FEP	Silicone rubber	PVC	Hi D PE
Cost/1000'	18.00	20.00	26.00	24.00	3.00	5.00
Density	1.1	2.2	2.2	1.3	1.3–1.6	.95
Max. cont. temp.	135°C	250	200	200	105	100
Flammability	ext	none	none	burns	ext	burns
Abrasion res.	fair	fair	fair	poor	good	fair
Radiation res.	good	very poor	poor	good	poor	good
R.T. cut through	good	poor	poor	good	good	fair
Solder iron res.						
500–600°F	60+ sec	60+	60+	good	melts	melts
600–650°F	40 sec	60+	10 sec			
700–750°F	15 sec	60+	8 sec			
800+ °F	2 sec	60+	2 sec			
Electricals (LF)	exc	exc	exc	good	good	exc
Electricals (HF)	exc	exc	exc	fair	poor	exc
Diel. const.	2.4	2.1	2.1	2.9	3–9	2.3
Diel. strength (vpm)	800	1200	1200	500	800	1050
Pottability	fair	poor	poor	good	good	fair
Power factor (60 C)	.002	.0003	.0003	.0006	.04–.15	.0002
Water abs. (%)	nil	nil	nil	.25–1.00	.15–.75	less .01
Solubility	none	none	none	steam, oils	ketones, esters, swells in arom. hyd.	Hot arom. Hyd.
Tensile strength (psi)	3000	3000	3000	895	2300	3800
Elongation (%)	120	300	300	150	280	150
Hi T corrosiveness	little	much	much	none	much	none
Toxicity on decomp.	slight	high	high	none	high	none
Printability	fair	poor	poor	good	good	fair

*Henley, (1963).

Table 13-3. THERMOFIT* SHRINKABLE TUBING†

Description	Designation
Flexible—flame retarded—heat shrinkable—irradiated modified polyolefin tubing. Available in recovered sizes AWG 24 through 2". Expanded dimensions approximately 50% to 100% more than recovered dimensions.	RNF
Flexible—clear—heat shrinkable—irradiated modified polyolefin tubing. Available in recovered sized AWG 24 through 1". Expanded dimensions approximately 50% to 100% more than recovered dimensions.	RF
High strength—semi-rigid—flame retarded—heat shrinkable—irradiated modified polyolefin tubing. Available in expanded sizes 3/64" through 1". Recovered dimensions 50% of expanded dimensions.	CRN
High strength—semi-rigid—clear—heat shrinkable—irradiated modified polyolefin tubing. Available in expanded sizes 3/64" through 1". Recovered dimensions 50% of expanded dimensions.	CR
High strength—nonflammable—clear—heat shrinkable—modified fluorocarbon tubing. Available in recovered sizes AWG 30 through 0. Expanded dimensions 50% to 60% more than recovered dimensions.	TFE
Flexible—radiation crosslinked—heat shrinkable—modified polyvinylchloride tubing. Available in expanded sizes 3/64" through 4". Recovered dimensions approximately 50% of expanded dimensions.	PVC
Flexible—thermally stabilized—crosslinked—heat shrinkable—modified neoprene rubber tubing. Available in recovered sizes 1/8" through 1". Expanded dimensions approximately twice that of recovered dimensions.	NT

*Registered trademark, Raychem Corp.
†Henley, op. cit., 1963.

particularly if B is inexpensive and A, which is expensive, can be used in small amounts. In nearly all of the proposed processes, B is an inexpensive, natural, high molecular weight compound such as wood or cellulose, or a hydrocarbon such as polyethylene or polypropylene, while B is a hydrophilic monomer which will impart desirable surface properties such as dye receptivity, ion-permeability, or charge dissipation (antistatic properties).

The notable exception to this general rule is a wood-impregnation product which is now being produced on a commercial scale in which a monomer is grafted to the wood to improve the bulk properties of the base material. The wood is impregnated with liquid monomers such as methyl methacrylate and then polymerization is induced by radiation. Numerous combinations of polymer and wood have been evaluated. In general, the resulting product:[3]

Can be made fire resistant,

Is up to 900% harder than natural wood and therefore is more resistant to blows, scratches, or marring,

Has a considerably higher compression strength,

Has much improved static bending strength,

Absorbs moisture more slowly and therefore has more dimensional stability (resistance to warping and swelling),

Highlights the natural-wood grain and color

Can be sawed, drilled, turned, and sanded to a hard, beautiful, satin-smooth finish.

Typical applications include:

Furniture (indoor and outdoor)	Decorative trim
	Structural beams
Floors	Sporting goods
Window frames, sills, and doors	Boat decks and fittings
	Shoe lasts
Tool handles	Dies and jigs

Radiation doses required to induce the polymerization have been reduced by as much as 75% (to 0.5 megarad) in development work. Gamma energy from ^{60}Co is being used because of its deep penetration and independence of target shape. The processing of panels or veneers, however, may be better adapted to machine irradiation. (Veneer applications and wood-block flooring represent the most promising areas of commercial interest.)

The process flowsheet is shown in Fig. 13-1. The first step is to vacuum-evacuate the wood, because oxygen inhibits the polymerization. Then the wood is flooded with monomer, under pressure, in an inert-gas blanket. Next, excess monomer is removed.

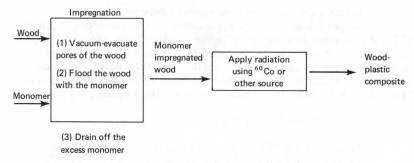

Fig. 13-1. Processing sequence for wood plastic laminates.*

---

*Chemical Engineering, p. 64, August, 1965.

Although the monomer could be used in liquid or vapor form, a liquid phase impregnation at about 200 psi is preferred. High loading of monomer, approximately 55% of the plastic, by weight, is required.

The economics of the process have been studied. For a typical 2,500 lb/hr plant, the total investment would be about $1,560,000 and $0.0338 per lb of processing costs (ex-monomer) are involved. Of this cost, $0.0226 would be irradiation costs, according to an AEC-sponsored study carried out by the Vitro Corporation.

An example of how irradiation costs can be computed for a process of this type is now given:

EXAMPLE 13-1:

L. E. Kukacka and B. Manowitz[4] report the installation costs of Co-60 radiation facilities as shown in Fig. 13-2.* Using this figure, and the following information, calculate the cost of irradiating 2×10^6 lb/year of polyethylene film to a dose of 20×10^6 rad.

Source utilization efficiency	21.5%
Co-60 ¢/curie	30
Transportation ¢/curie	1
Operating cost (% of initial cost)	1.5

---

*The 10% discrepancy between some of the results of Example 13-1 and the Kukacka-Manowitz article arose because of a 90% "use factor" which the authors used, but which was not referred to in the (edited) journal article.

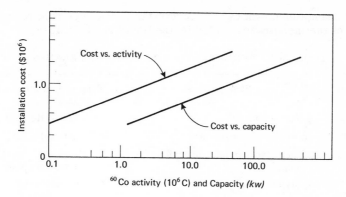

Fig. 13-2. Installation cost of a ^{60}Co or ^{137}Cs irradiator, the cost of the nuclide is excluded. (Kukacka and Manowitz, 1965.)

Insurance and taxes (% of initial cost)	3.5
Return on investment	25%
Operating time	7000 hr/yr

SOLUTION: The total amount of power required is

$$\frac{12.60 \times 10^{-4} \text{ Kw-hr}}{\text{Megarad-lb}} \left| \frac{2 \times 10^{-6} \text{lb}}{\text{yr}} \right| \frac{\text{yr}}{7000 \text{ hr}} \left| \frac{0.20 \text{ M rad}}{0.215} \right. = 34 \text{ Kw}$$

34 Kw = (curies)(2.5)(5.92 × 10^{-6}) ⇒ 2,300,000 curies

(1)	Installation cost, Fig. 13-2 =	$1,000,000
(2)	Cost of nuclide = (0.30)(2,300,000) =	690,000
(3)	Transportation cost = (0.01)(2,300,000) =	23,000
(4)	Operating cost = (0.015)((1) + (2)) =	25,000
(5)	Insurance and taxes (0.035)((1) + (2)) =	59,000
(6)	Isotope decay charges (0.125)(690,000) =	86,000
(7)	Profit 0.25 [(1) + (2) + (3)] =	430,000
(8)	Total cost [(4) + (5) + (6) + (7)] =	600,500

Unit cost, ¢/lb ≅ 60 × 10^6/2 × 10^6 = 30 ¢/lb

13-2a   Radiation Grafted Products — Ion Exchange Membranes

Radiation grafted membranes for dialysis, electrolysis, batteries, and fuel cells are manufactured by RAI Research Incorporated. The Permion membranes are homogeneous grafted copolymer ion-exchange membranes with pore sizes in the angstrom range. Some of the membranes available are listed in Table 13-4.

Table 13-4. PERMION* ION EXCHANGE MEMBRANES

Permion	Base polymer	Type of functional groups
300	polyethylene	carboxylic acid
1000	(poly)tetrafluorethylene	carboxylic acid
3000	fluorinated ethylene-propylene copolymer	carboxylic acid
1010	(poly)tetrafluorethylene	sulfonic acid
200	polyethylene	tertiary amine
1200	(poly)tetrafluoroethylene	tertiary amine
210	polyethylene	quarternary amine
1210	(poly)tetrafluoroethylene	quarternary amine

*Registered trademark, RAI Research, Inc.

The membranes, which feature high strength, and extreme chemical resistance, have enjoyed their greatest success as battery separators for the vented Ni-Cd cells, the Permion 300 series being widely used for this purpose.

13-2b Radiation Grafted Products — Textiles

The one apparently successful graft polymerization process is the electron irradiation of a cotton-polyester blend to provide a durable press finish and soil-releasing properties. This process was announced by the Deering Milliken Company in 1966.

13-3 BIOGRADABLE DETERGENTS

A major amount of work has been done on the gamma-ray initiated sulfoxidation of hydrocarbons by the ESSO Research Company in the United States and by the Hoechst Company in Germany. The process developed by the ESSO Company involves the passing of SO_2 and O_2 through straight chain hydrocarbons in the presence of gamma radiation. The SO_2 adds to the alkyl radical formed to yield an alkyl sulfonyl radical

$$R \cdot + SO_2 \longrightarrow RSO_2 \cdot \qquad\qquad (13\text{-}1)$$

which adds oxygen to form a persulfonyl radical.

$$RSO_2 \cdot + O_2 \longrightarrow RSO_2O_2 \cdot \qquad\qquad (13\text{-}2)$$

This is followed by a hydrogen abstraction, with the resulting formation of a new alkyl radical

$$RSO_2O_2 \cdot + RH \longrightarrow RSO_2O_2H + R \cdot \qquad (13\text{-}3)$$

The persulfonic acid then decomposes into persulfonyl and hydroxyl radicals both of which can abstract hydrogen from hydrocarbons to give further alkyl radicals. The result is a branching chain reaction which when started proceeds even after the source is withdrawn. Eventually, however, water formed in the reaction limits the branching.

The ESSO Company has constructed a pilot plant; however, full-scale development has not yet taken place.

13-4 THE DOW ETHYL-BROMIDE PROCESS

In March of 1963 the Dow Chemical Company began operating the world's first commercial chemical plant using radiation catalysis. The plant, which has a capacity of over one million pounds per year of ethyl bromide, uses a process based in patents issued to Pumpelly and Wilkinson (Canadian, No. 649718 Oct. 1962). Contributing strongly to the success of the venture was the research of Armstrong and Spinks[5] and the engineering development work of Harmer and Beale.[6]

Ethyl bromide is formed by the overall reaction

$$CH_2 = CH_2 + HBr \longrightarrow CH_3CH_2Br \qquad (13\text{-}4)$$

The reaction proceeds by a radical-initiated chain mechanism, the propagation steps being

$$Br \cdot + CH_2 = CH_2 \rightleftharpoons \cdot CH_2 - CH_2Br \qquad (13\text{-}5)$$

$$HBr + \cdot CH_2 - CH_2Br \longrightarrow Br \cdot + CH_3 - CH_2Br \qquad (13\text{-}6)$$

Reaction (13-5) is initiated by bromine radicals formed from hydrogen bromide, the alternate scheme involving hydrogen radicals being energetically less favorable.

The process development was carried out over a five-year period, the laboratory and pilot plant operations providing an interesting insight into the care, and level of effort involved in the commercialization of a radiation process.

13-4a Laboratory and Pilot Development of the Process

(1) As a first step, batchwise experiments in which hydrogen bromide and ethylene in stoichiometric ratios were sparged into a

500 ml vessel containing 175 ml of various solvents were carried out to find the optimum solvent and reaction conditions. Of the solvents studied — ethylene dibromide, carbon tetrachloride, perchloroethylene, and ethyl bromide — the product, ethyl bromide, gave the highest yield, and the highest G values.

(2) Next, a continuous reaction vessel was constructed from a 60-ml Pyrex bulb, the ethylene and HBr being fed at various rates, and in various weight ratios. The reaction was allowed to proceed until equilibrium conditions were established, at which time the yield was measured. Those data were adequate for making crude design estimates.

(3) A larger, 550-ml glass vessel fitted with a cooling coil was used in the next series of experiments which were carried out under conditions very similar to those in the 60-ml vessel. The gas feeding equipment, however, proved inadequate, and essentially complete conversions were obtained over the entire range of feed rates (30-140 grams C_2H_4 per hour).

The 550-ml reactor was used to establish other process variables, in particular the effect of premixing the feed, which proved beneficial, and of iron impurities, which were found to completely poison the reaction.

(4) As an alternative to carrying out a two-phase reaction in a solvent, a single-phase liquid reaction was investigated. The reactor used was a 185-cc stainless steel coil through which liquified gases were passed at 1000 psi and -5°C. For reasons that are not readily apparent, a limiting conversion was reached; above this the reaction rates are considerably reduced. This, in addition to the fact that the construction of a plant utilizing a one-phase system would involve a higher cost because of the gas compressors, rendered this system commercially unattractive.

(5) A complete, one-tenth scale prototype of the production plant was then constructed in the laboratory. Since the configuration of the production reactor had already been decided, a novel prototype reactor was built. This was pie-shaped, having a 36° sector, of the same height as the production reactor, the radiation geometry being the same as in the final plant.

The reaction system proved operable, 98 to 100% conversion being obtained at feed rates of 8.2 lb/hr of reactants at 19°C. Inhibition and poisoning of the reaction by solvent and gas impurities and corrosion products was again noted.

(6) The plant reaction system is shown in Fig. 13-3. The reactor is constructed of nickel and has a capacity of 40 gallons.

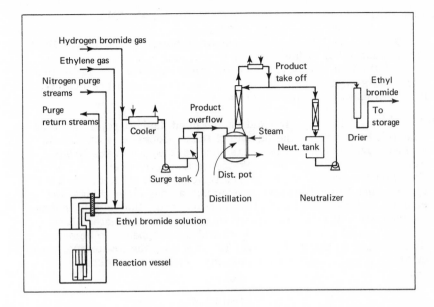

Fig. 13-3. Flow sheet for the Dow ethyl bromide radiation process.
Harmer and Beale, Chem. Eng. Prog., 60, No. 4, 33 (1964).

It is located 4 feet underground in a steel-lined, concrete-cased pit;
the 1800 curie Co-60 source in the form of aluminum clad slugs are
located in a well in the center of the reaction vessel.

In operation, a pump continuously circulates the ethyl bromide
at a rate of approximately 28 gallons per minute, the recycle ratio
being 179/1, i.e. 0.5% of the recirculating material overflows as
product.

13-5 CURING OF PAINT FILMS

This process had its origins in the early work of Ballantine,
Charlesby, and Mesrobian who found that polyesters irradiated in
the presence of a monomer cross-linked rapidly with the production
of firm gels. The process was further developed by Burlant and
his group at the Ford Motor Company. Working with paint films
composed of polyesters containing up to 35% of added monomers,
they demonstrated intensity independent polymerizations at dose
rates up to 100 rad/min with 300-kev electrons.

This method of paint curing is achieving good commercial acceptance and promises to be one of the most successful of the
radiation applications.

13-6 RADIATION POLYMERIZATION OF ETHYLENE

The polymerization of ethylene by radiation is conventionally carried out either at high pressures and temperatures (1000 atm and ~ 150° C), or catalytically at low temperatures. The latter process results in high-density material, the former in a low-density, branched material of lower softening point.

An extensive experimentation and plant design project with the objective of replacing one or both of these processes with a radiation catalyzed polymerization has been carried out at the Brookhaven National Laboratory by Steinberg and collaborators. The radiation process, which is currently being pilot planted, has been beset by mechanical problems involving, among other things, the removal of the product from the reaction zone. Unless this is done, the polymer will be contaminated with cross-linked material. If the mechanical problems can be solved there appears to be some financial and technical incentives for replacing the low temperature catalytic polymerization by a radiation catalyzed process.

PROBLEMS

13-1 Using Fig. 13-2, calculate the cost of irradiating 2,500 lb/hour of monomer impregnated wood using a Co-60 irradiator.

13-2 Compare the irradiation cost calculated in Example 13-1 with the cost of using an electron accelerator at $10,000/Kw.

13-3 Shown below (with slight modification) are the data reported by Harmer et al. for the continuous hydrobromination of ethylene in a 60 ml vessel at -10° C in ethyl bromide. From this data make an estimate of the size of the Co-60 source and reaction vessel required to produce a million pounds of ethyl bromide per year. What is the G value for the reaction?

Radiation close rate (krad/hr)	HBr feed rate (g/hr)	Ethylene feed rate (g/hr)	Yield (%)
254	72	24	86
254	116	38	61
254	180	60	75
100	64	22	94
100	84	28	68
100	138	44	14
100	180	62	3.5

REFERENCES

1. S. Jefferson, R. Roberts, F. J. Ley, and F. Rogers, "Advances in Nuclear Science and Technology," Greebler and E. Henley (ed.), Academic Press, Inc., New York, 1968.

2. R. Timmerman, *Plastics World*, August, 1963, p. 468.

3. *Isotopes and Radiation Technology*, U.S. Dept. of Commerce, Spring, 1965, p. 263.

4. L. E. Kuckacka and B. Manowitz, *Nucleonics*, **74**:85, Jan (1965).

5. W. A. Armstrong and J. W. T. Spinks, *Can. J. Chem.*, **37**:1002 (1959).

6. D. E. Harmer and J. S. Beale, *Chemical Eng. Prog.*, **60**(No. 4): 33 (1964).

Author Index

Subject Index